db391 $60

A Very Elegant Animal
The Dingo

A Very Elegant Animal
The Dingo

Roland Breckwoldt

ANGUS & ROBERTSON PUBLISHERS

ANGUS & ROBERTSON PUBLISHERS

*Unit 4, Eden Park, 31 Waterloo Road,
North Ryde, NSW, Australia 2113;
94 Newton Road, Auckland 1,
New Zealand; and
16 Golden Square, London W1R 4BN,
United Kingdom*

*First published in Australia
by Angus & Robertson Publishers in 1988
First published in New Zealand
by Angus & Robertson NZ Ltd in 1988*

*National Library of Australia
Cataloguing-in-publication data.*

*Breckwoldt, Roland, 1944–
A very elegant animal: the dingo.*

*Includes index.
ISBN 0 207 15811 8.*

1. Dingo. I. Title.

599.74'442

*Typeset in 13 pt Bembo
Printed in Singapore*

But if I have been exactly and strictly careful to give only True Relations and Descriptions of things (as I am sure I have); and if my Descriptions be such as may be of use not only to myself (which I have already in good measure experienced) but also to others in future Voyages; and likewise to such Readers at home as are more desirous of a Plain and Just Account of the true Nature and State of the Things described, than of Polite and Rhetorical Narrative: I hope all the Defects of my stile, will be met with an easy and ready Pardon.

William Dampier,
Preface to A voyage to New Holland,
in the year 1699. Volume 111.

ACKNOWLEDGEMENTS

Many people helped produce this book. Friends gave me good company and accommodation in places a long way from home. They sent copies of vital material to save me yet another trip away and let me get on with writing. People gave me access to their unpublished research and generously shared their experience. I cannot name everyone, for to do so would fill another book, but please see your name between the lines and accept my appreciation and thanks.

The Literature Board and the National Parks and Wildlife Service of New South Wales awarded me one of the 1983 Park Writers Awards and this grant contributed towards the cost of travel. The Service also gave both Gary Steer and myself the fullest co-operation and assistance while we made a film on the dingo and I wrote this book. I also thank Ronald Strahan of the Australian Museum, Sydney, for his help in delving into the taxonomy of the dingo. Likewise, I thank Alan Newsome of the CSIRO Division of Wildlife and Rangeland Research for the help that ranged over his great knowledge of the dingo.

Other organisations of particular assistance were the NSW Department of Agriculture, the Stock Routes and Rural Lands Protection Board of Queensland, the Northern Territory Conservation Commission, the Bega Pastures Protection Board, the former Southern Tablelands Wild Dog Destruction Board, and Santos Limited at the Moomba gas and oil field.

I asked people with specialised knowledge and experience to review most chapters before they went to print. This was a safeguard against errors creeping into my interpretation of material. All responded with extraordinary generosity, making helpful suggestions and supplying additional information. My thanks go to the following people: Chapter Two: Laurie Corbett, Klim Gollan, Jack Golson; Chapter Three: Leslie Maynard, Margaret Howe, Josephine Flood; Chapter Four: Max Kelly; Chapter Five: Peter Catling, John Robertshaw; Chapter Six: Alan Newsome, John Robertshaw, Peter Thomson; Chapter Seven: Peter Catling, John Robertshaw, Peter Thomson; Chapter Eight: Alan Newsome, John Robertshaw; Chapter Nine: Henry Collins, Margaret Sabine, Laki Kumaratilake, George Wilson; Chapter Twelve: Bryan Locke; Chapters Thirteen, Fourteen and Fifteen: Terry Korn, Bob Harden, Peter Thomson.

Carol and Warren Balfour gave us a base in Alice Springs and made us and Maliki, our dingo travelling companion, welcome regardless of how unkempt we were and the amount of mess we created in their home with dog and gear. Property owners helped us observe dingoes in the wild and provided logistical support along with vast amounts of hospitality. I particularly thank Andrew and Livia Smith of Allambi Station and Peter Sevron of Curtin Springs Station, Alice Springs. Rick and Annie Hain of Moles Station at Kybean, on the Monaro, always made me welcome and I thank them for many a yarn about dingoes. Not so far away, at Delegate, John Coman the dogger was always ready to share his experience with me.

My neighbours in the Tantawangalo Valley deserve special mention because they accepted a compound of 14 dingoes in their midst for over two years. Polite tolerance turned into an interest in the entire project that had them ringing me up to offer any livestock that had died as food for the dingoes. Two Valley residents made possible my extended trips away — Mike Peterson and Hans Theile fed and cared for the dingoes whenever I had to travel. They did this with such dedication that I could relax and sleep at night in an outback camp, knowing that the dingoes would be well fed and that every step of the compound fence would be paced each day and maintained against potential escapees.

I'm deeply grateful to Mary Coleman and Neil Carlyle of Angus & Robertson Publishers for the personal interest they took during the production of this book.

Gary Steer, friend and colleague, accompanied me on the dingo travels. He was always calm and supportive, even under all the tired and cramped circumstances we found ourselves in, and that is bountiful evidence of his patience and serenity that I admire so much.

None of the travel would have been possible had Anne Breckwoldt not managed the farm and cared for our son Dan while I was away on the track of the dingo. Even at home my thoughts were away during the five years that dingoes dominated my life. As if that were not enough, Anne drew the illustrations for this book. I thank Anne and Dan dearly for their understanding and support during all the times I was "away" with the dingo.

FOREWORD

My first contact with a dingo occurred when I was sixteen and working as a stockman on Augustus Downs Station in the Gulf of Carpentaria. We had been mustering all day and were driving a mob of about three hundred cattle alongside a dry creek on our way back to camp. The head stockman and an Aborigine named Percy and I were riding the wing nearest the creek when we heard whimpering and whining coming from its dry bed. We cantered over to find three little dingo puppies which had been out of the den with their mother when she ran off, frightened by the noise we made pushing the cattle along.

Each of us grabbed a pup. I was delighted to be holding such a beautiful little animal and was affectionately caressing it while planning to keep it as a pet. That lasted only a moment because the head stockman and Percy had already killed their pups. The head stockman took the pup from me with a gruff "give it here" and smashed it against a tree. He and I rode back to the cattle which were still being driven along by the other men. Percy remained for a few minutes to scalp the pups. He would buy tobacco with the meagre bonus when we got back to the homestead in a month or so.

Such was the relationship with the dingo on those big stations and I became part of it. Twenty-four years passed before I held another live dingo. My interest in animals had remained unchanged and I now owned a cattle property which also gave me the flexibility to work on an occasional wildlife or adventure film with a film-maker mate. His invitation to help on a film about the dingo resulted in us keeping dingoes and travelling the Australian outback to observe dingoes in the wild.

I was given a second chance to take a dingo into my life and the opportunity to look behind the myths about them. One of the most rewarding aspects of the entire project was discussing the dingo with people in most parts of Australia who are involved in its management — sheep and cattle graziers, wildlife researchers, dingo trappers, national park rangers, pest control authorities, wildlife conservationists. It became obvious that the story of the dingo is about people as much as it is about the animal. That is what makes it such a good story to tell.

There are other animals that give rise to strong argument; the dingo is not alone in the controversy it raises. Agriculture makes enemies of other species but they rarely attain the mystique of the dingo. The dingo is a large, powerful, clever and beautiful carnivore that arouses strong feelings. It may be the enemy of a grazier whose livelihood depends on the sheep, while to someone else it is the symbol of everything that is wild and magnificent about the Australian bush.

Myth and folklore are created to help explain the unknown, and the shadowy ways of the dingo grow easily into heroic feats or villainous treachery. The dingo carries more than its fair share of myths and it is difficult to see through them to reach the understanding necessary to resolve its future. Our expectations and demands upon the Australian environment are also symbolised by the dingo — its relationship with us has never been comfortable. Perhaps knowing and accepting the dingo is but part of reaching a much larger understanding of our place in the Australian environment.

ROLAND BRECKWOLDT
"Hilltop"
Candelo
New South Wales

Contents

Gary Steer

PART ONE

Dingo Watching

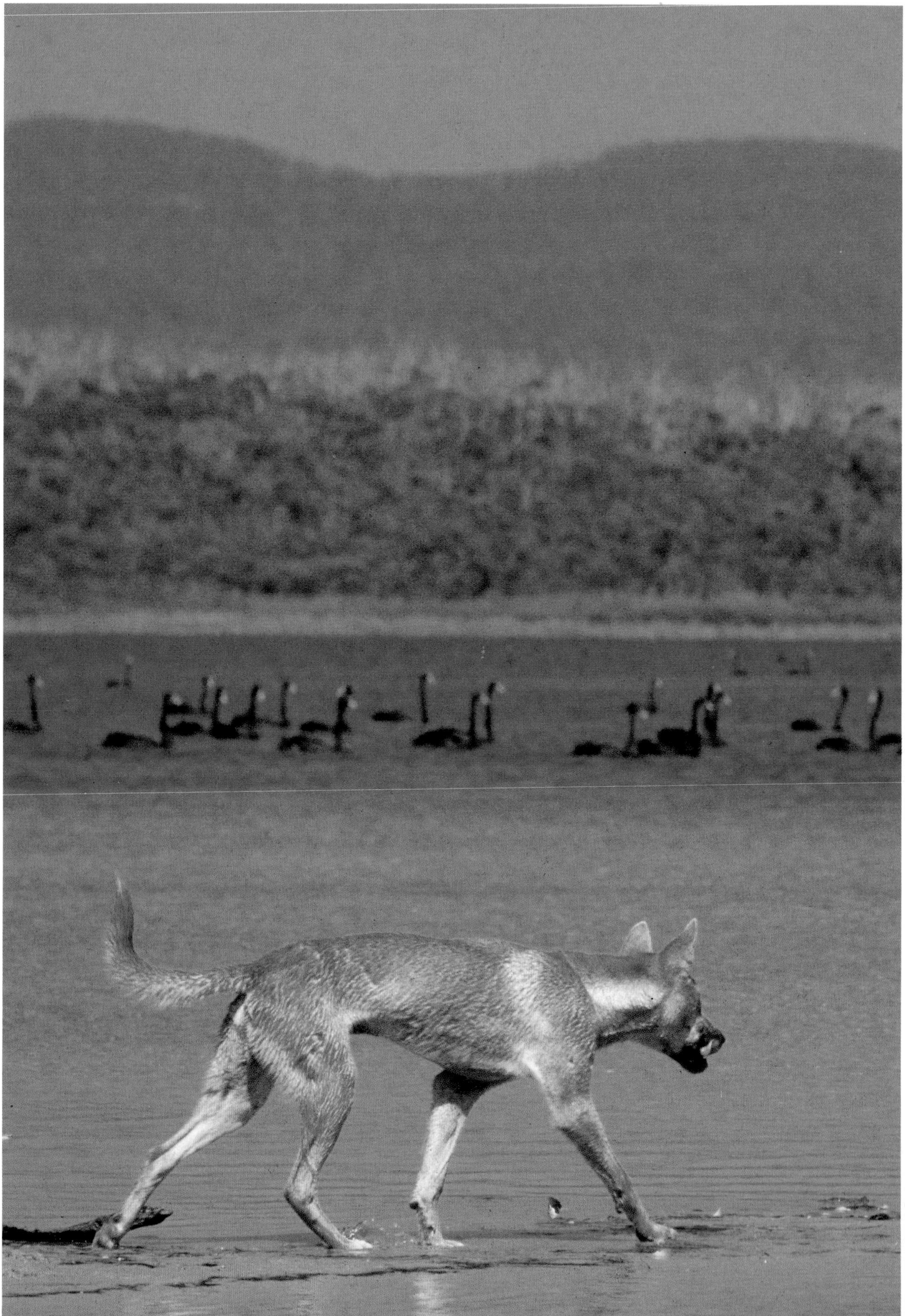

Dingo watching

The dingo that once made tracks all over the Australian mainland has been edged into remoter haunts by town and city, sheep and cattle. Many Australians have never seen a dingo in the wild . For me, the opportunity to work on a film and a book on the dingo suddenly made watching dingoes a two-year obsession. Friend and film-maker Gary Steer and I wanted to film dingoes for a television documentary. Enthusiastic and idealistic, we wanted to film the impossible—dingoes hunting, fighting, breeding, rearing pups.

We had 14 dingoes in a large semi-natural compound on my farm but we needed to observe dingoes in the wild that had not been affected by human intervention to the same extent. We travelled to wild places across the continent to search out and film dingoes. On the long trip to central Australia one of the 14 dingoes from the compound on my farm accompanied me. Maliki had become a pet and was a great ice-breaker as we travelled about and got to know the people who could help us. *Maliki* is the word the Walbiri Aboriginal people who live near the Tanami Desert in the Northern Territory use to describe their camp dingoes. They refer to the wild dingoes as *Wantibirri.*

I took Maliki with me because I did not want to leave him at home for two months without the constant attention required to keep him quiet and responsive. He was a great traveller and proved more help than hindrance. People gravitated towards him and poured forth their prejudices and opinions about dingoes. It also gave us an opportunity for some fun.

Once, in a roadside supermarket on the road to Port Augusta, the storekeeper came up and ordered me out with a stern, "No dogs allowed in here, son!"

To which I replied in equally serious manner and with great biological licence, "That's not a dog, it's a dingo!"

I expected to be thrown out, but to my great surprise, he thought for half a moment and said, "That's okay then."

The other pastime which perhaps I can justify as a primitive form of research, was to deny Maliki any dingo ancestry at all. We would be approached by a hard-bitten bushman at a roadside pub or a stockman at a store who would say, "Where did you get the dingo from, mate?"

Perfectly straightfaced, I would say, "It's not a dingo, it's a red heeler I bought from a bloke who breeds them near Wagga."

Now this is where the research comes in. Just about everyone in central Australia, where there are still enough dingoes for people to have first-hand experience with them, would reply something to this effect: "He sure saw you coming, that's a bloody dingo if ever I saw one. Wait until it gets among the chooks."

This reaction adds a nice balance to the occasional so-called expert down south where I come from who will walk up, ask the breed of dog you have with you, then proceed to tell you that it's not a dingo, perhaps a part-bred but, "Didn't you know there are no purebred dingoes left any more?"

The reaction to Maliki was one of the major considerations in our decision to take him on the trip. We even carried a cage in case it was necessary to keep him under wraps. But as so many pastoralists have kept a dingo at some time, Maliki became a good talking point. Sadly, the story was unfailingly the same — at adulthood their dingo was shot because it was a nuisance and an incorrigible hunter of anything that moved. Clearly, the dingo has been well tried as a working dog or station pet, but even the many dog lovers in the bush find a wildness in the dingo that is difficult to remove or focus into a useful talent.

Dingoes can be very efficient at avoiding people if they want to. Their tendency to be most active in the evening, during the night and early morning is guaranteed to make the task of finding them even more difficult. And when they are seen, by far the greatest number of sightings are of solitary animals. There were sufficient dingoes for us not to have any trouble locating wild populations, but choosing particular places to film was another matter. Nearly all of eastern Australia was ruled out because dingoes there are now confined to the heavily timbered rugged ranges and valleys where they easily remain unseen. There are a few places where dingoes live right on the coast and here, if one is lucky, they can sometimes be seen combing the open sandy beaches and estuaries. Despite the fact that there are more dingoes and fewer trees in the outback, choosing locations is still extremely difficult.

Not all our problems in filming were caused by the dingoes' reticence. We

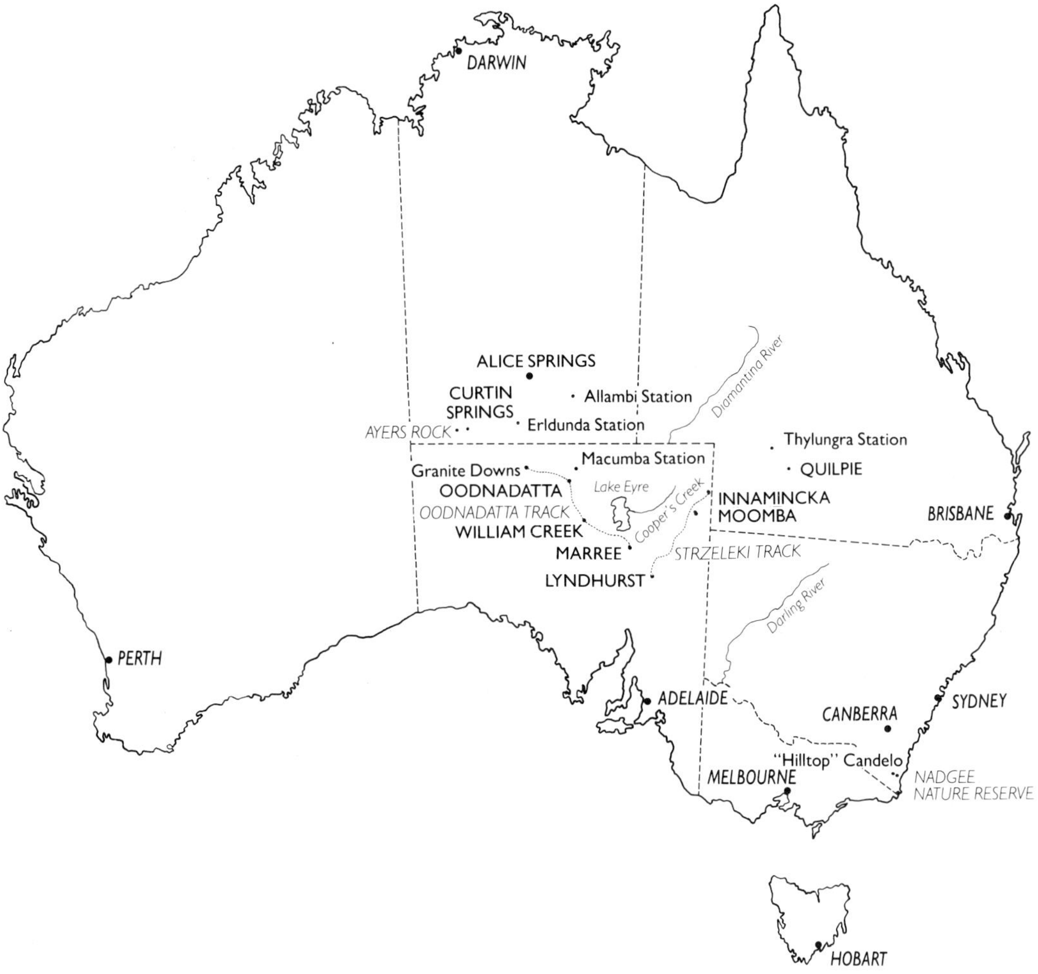

Places visited in my travels while dingo watching.

also had to deal with pastoralists' wariness of film-makers who may give them a bad name. There was an aerial baiting of dingoes on some sheep stations in southwest Queensland in April 1984. The Rural Lands and Stock Routes Protection Board gave us approval to film this; we hoped also to film some dingoes in the area. On arriving at Quilpie, the town nearest the baiting area, Gary rang the manager of Thylungra Station where the aerial baiting was to be centred, explaining that both sides of the story — conservation and control — would be presented. Ray Green, the manager, agreed to let us film but when we arrived next morning the other station managers sought our assurance that it would not misrepresent them.

There is a deep suspicion in the bush about city conservationists. The pastoralists claim to be the real conservationists themselves. Many times, I heard the sheepmen's case for killing dingoes — as well as protecting their sheep, they were protecting the native wildlife eaten by dingoes. I stifled my response, so the interviews could be spontaneous and reflect their views without being influenced by my opinions.

The high cost of travel meant that we could not afford a hit or miss approach. There was never any shortage of advice and comment. We were told, "Dingoes? There's heaps of them out on the Strzelecki Track. They will just sit there and look at you." A good lead, but we wanted to film dingoes behaving as dingoes do when not spoilt by handouts from passing tourists. Or, "Pity you weren't with me last week, came across three dogs with a big roo baled up in a dam. Every time one of them went in after it, the old man roo would hold it under." Or, "There were dozens of them on the Ten Mile Bore last month but they've scattered after the rain." We soon came to realise that whenever we chose to start our trip it would always be "last week" or "last month" when we should have been there.

The sheer difficulty of seeing dingoes in the wild while carrying all the paraphernalia that film-making requires was almost overwhelming. It was not, however, without rewards.

A COASTAL WILDERNESS

Nadgee Nature Reserve lies on the far south coast of New South Wales, right against the Victorian border. It is a glorious, unspoilt stretch of white beaches, salt lakes and estuaries that lie between headlands linked by long moors of low olive-coloured heath.

Once, years ago, I saw a yellow dingo carrying a kangaroo joey along Nadgee beach. Also on that visit, my wife Anne and I were quietly rowing down the estuary when we noticed something that looked like a stump sticking out of the water. It was right in the middle about 50 m from the shore, down near the sea, where the water spreads out across the sand flats. This object immediately caught our attention because it had not been there the day before. It was not until we got closer that we could see that it was a big grey kangaroo.

Amazed at the sight of this "bathing

The Nadgee River on the south coast of New South Wales where the dingo pups fed on a dead seal that had been washed up on the beach. Gary Steer

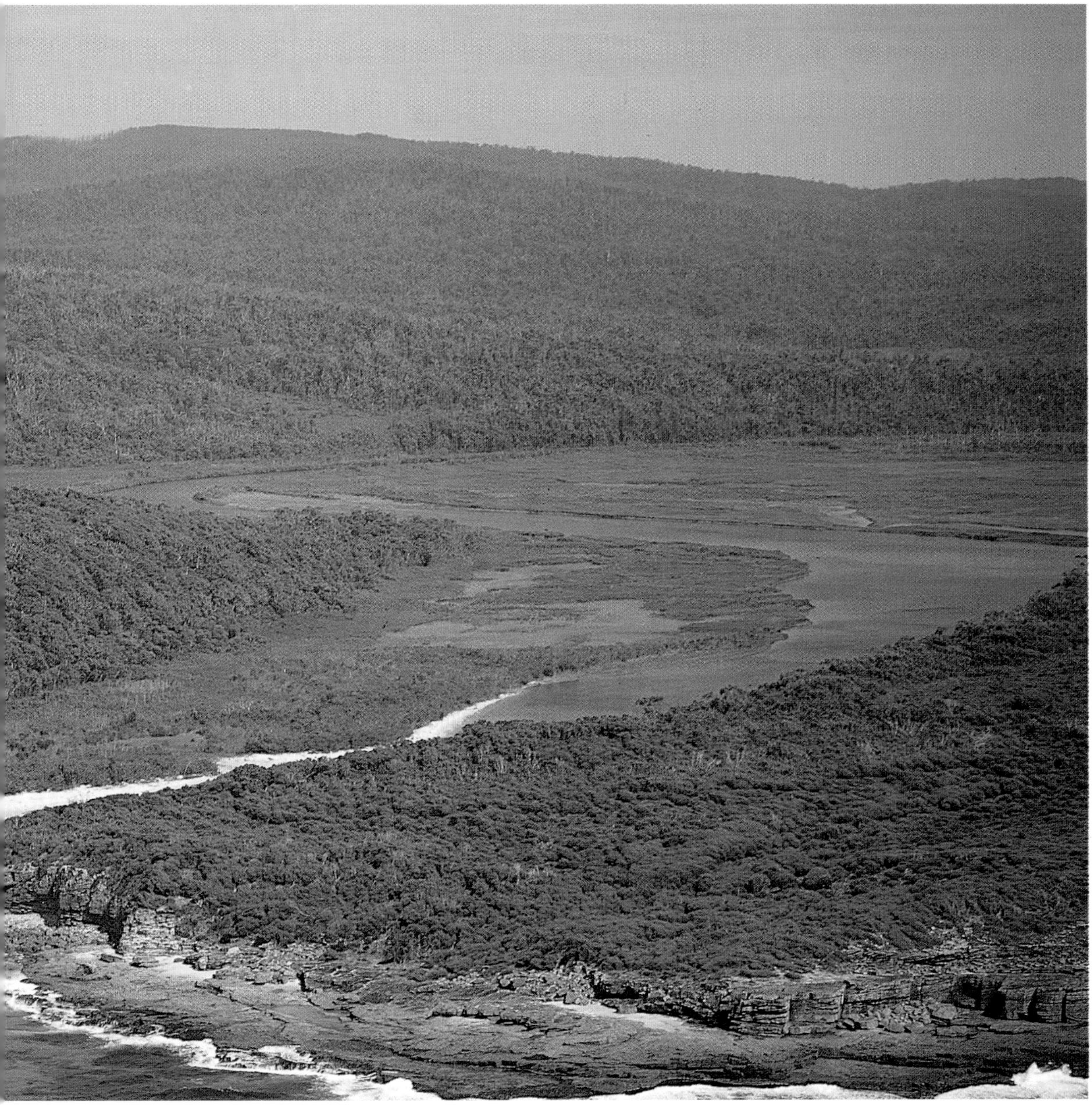

roo", we scanned the shore to try and make sense of the situation. There, in the shade of a branch overhanging the sandy shore, lay the answer. Three large dingoes. Unfortunately, they saw us at the same time as we saw them and they were off. Apparently, we had interrupted their hunt. They had baled up the kangaroo but would not go into the water after it because there it could easily hold and drown a swimming dingo. The dingoes must have been prepared to wait for their quarry to tire and emerge. Upon our arrival the kangaroo waded to shore. No doubt we gave it a welcome reprieve but he was a big old fellow and it was probably his time to go to the dogs. If only we could capture something like that on film!

The first trip Gary and I made together to Nadgee was in April 1983 for a reconnaissance trip with Commonwealth Scientific and Industrial Research Organisation (CSIRO) research workers who had been studying the Nadgee dingoes. They were interested in the level of dingo activity and had pegged out two sheep carcases to see if they would be eaten. They also monitored numerous raked plots on the roads and pads used by dingoes. The plots were checked daily for tracks then raked smooth again. Careful counting of tracks over a period of time can give an accurate picture of dingo activity.

Even at Nadgee, where the dingoes are largely undisturbed, they are hard to see. Research on the size of their home range could be achieved only by trapping them in padded traps and fitting them with a radio transmitter on a collar. Once released they were rarely seen again and were only known by a radio signal. Researcher Peter Catling tells of the time they tried to locate the lair of a bitch with pups. They could radio-track her to within a few metres but she always eluded them in the thick banksia and melaleuca coastal scrub.

We did not expect to see dingoes on that first visit, having joined the CSIRO team to explore the chances of filming in the future. Of course there was a camera handy — every wildlife filmmaker has learnt the painful lesson of not having a camera when the stars suddenly appear and perform.

We inspected a sheep carcase to find it almost eaten and the sand around it churned with tracks. Fresh tracks dotted off up the hind dune and along the beach. Walking onto Salt Lake we rounded a dune to see two dingoes just ahead on the lake's edge — a black and tan dog and a yellow bitch. We spotted them almost simultaneously and dropped for cover as if a bomb had exploded next to us, then watched from behind a dense melaleuca and agonised over whether it was worth the kilometre run back to the car to get camera and tripod. The big dog convinced us not to make the run by coming to within 15 m, picking up our smell and racing for cover. The yellow bitch lay down for a rest about 100 m away and seemed set to stay a while. Gary and I looked at each other for confirmation of what each of us had already decided.

It took at least 15 minutes to get the gear but the bitch was still there and we were able to film her over the next hour. At first she went in the opposite direction with short bursts of activity such as half-hearted attempts to chase coots in the shallows. Perhaps the chases were not as nonchalant as they appeared to us and she was actually testing the coots for moulting or slow individuals. These coastal dingoes prey heavily on coots and black swans during the moult. Eventually the yellow bitch jogged up the shore of the lake towards us. Before long she was directly in front, filling the frame. She caught our scent merely ten paces away but did not believe her senses. Almost upon us, she saw our shadowy outline and, like her mate, darted for cover. Buoyed by this good fortune, we decided to return as soon as possible for some serious filming.

Almost a year passed before we were able to return to Nadgee. In that time pups would have been born and have reached weaning age. The drought had broken with record rainfall, the tracks were washed out and the creeks brimming. The car connected with a bone-shaking rut and a thick, treackly streak of pinkish blood snaked down the windscreen. On the roof was a grey kangaroo carcase — a load of herbivore flesh to attract our carnivorous quarry. The kangaroo was a road kill that I had been saving in the freezer especially for this occasion. A matter of concern to us was whether we should be bringing in food to a wild population of dingoes? We explained our motives to the ranger and he agreed that this was such an isolated event as to be inconsequential. Subsequent events were to endorse this in no uncertain manner.

At Salt Lake we were reminded of the dynamic changes that occur in coastal systems. The long, wide lake shore where the yellow bitch ran after coots had disappeared under water. The lake had filled, but not sufficiently to break out across the barrier dune to the sea. The once sandy shoreline had been drowned and water lapped the melaleuca scrub. It was impossible to film here so we took a kangaroo carcase around to the ocean beach. The sandy beaches were the only places that provided the opportunity to hide ourselves far enough away yet still obtain good film. Elsewhere it was dense forest where it is impossible to film.

Our aim was to attract the dingoes living around Salt Lake to the kangaroo carcase so that we could film them feeding and perhaps record other aspects of their behaviour. I was reminded of the story told to me by Harry Wakefield when he worked for the CSIRO Division of Wildlife Research. He observed the rivalry between two groups of dingoes from adjoining home ranges in deciding the ownership of a bullock carcase on a waterhole at the edge of the Simpson Desert. Harry related how one group would be feeding as the other group came over the bank "on the march like a row of gladiators" and intimidated the subordinate group until they left. We were anxious to film the same type of behaviour.

Dawn lit the moor as we set out early next morning. Green Cape lighthouse kept winking at us from away to the north until the sun changed the sea from black to emerald. A few container

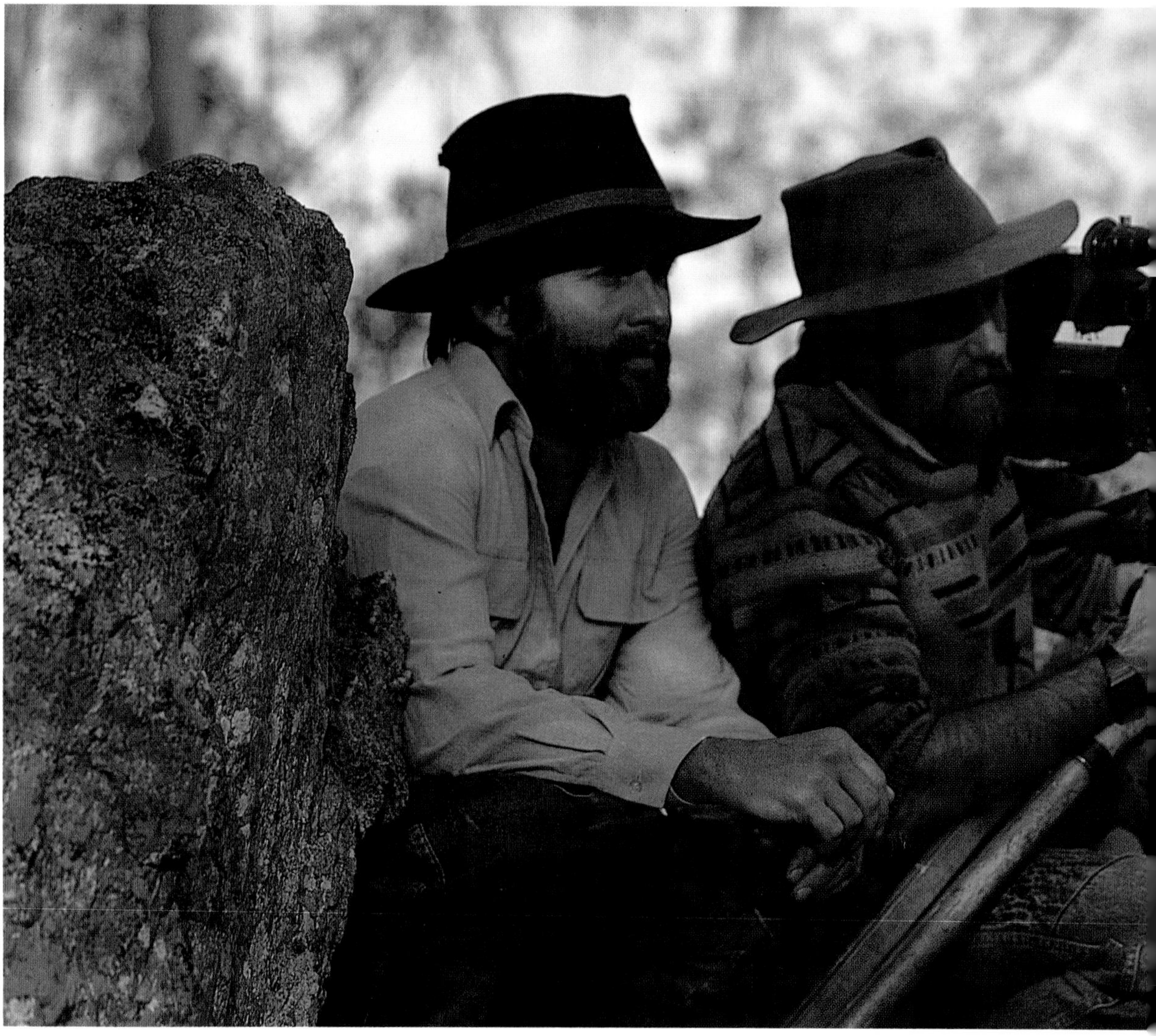

My friend Gary Steer behind the camera, with me in my usual position as 'spotter'. This combination was necessary because the action could change so quickly that Gary needed to know what was happening beyond the scene on which he was focused. Joeliska Lipps

ships occupied the sea but otherwise there was no reminder of cluttered humanity. We approached the beach as a pair of white-breasted sea eagles were holding the cool morning air in their wings as they combed the night's flotsam. The tides had been kind and the beach was littered with dead short-tailed shearwaters that did not make the arduous migration from the north Pacific to Bass Strait.

We crept to our hide about 50 m from the carcase. Even from there we could see dingo tracks everywhere; up the dunes, down the beach and sand churned around the carcase. But not a morsel of our kangaroo was touched even though the dingoes probably knew about it within hours of it being put

out. And so it continued for two days without a sign of the dingoes except their tracks. The roo remained untouched but began to look bad and smell worse. Nevertheless, it should still have been attractive to our carnivore friends, used to the ways of scavenging a meal from carrion.

It would have been easy to become despondent but serendipity was literally around the corner. Sharing base camp was a team from the Australian Museum in Sydney which was studying the honeyeaters of the heathlands. They told us of two dingo pups seen feeding off a dead seal on the beach at Nadgee Estuary.

Gary reached the beach first but came back only moments later whispering "there's a dingo down on the beach". Out with the camera gear and a rapid tiptoe down the track to where a part in the banksias gave a view of a half-grown pup tugging at the leathery remains of a seal. Finding a spot that both concealed us and allowed the camera to pan the scene, erecting the tripod, screwing on the camera, selecting the correct lens, taking a light reading, focusing and switching on the camera seemed to take forever. But at last, the friendly whir of the rolling camera; I hoped the pup would stay.

The black pup had a tug of war with the seal skin and ambled over to the very brackish water for a drink before retreating into the scrub behind the foredune. Within the minute, a yellow pup the same age came out and repeated the performance. The camera rolled, stopping only when Gary changed lenses. He and I exchanged self-congratulatory smiles.

Both pups were obviously litter mates and were in very poor condition. The yellow one chewed at a dried flipper and curled up against the seal for a rest. It seemed to be taking comfort from its dead host. Perhaps that observation is not too anthropomorphic, because these pups were so thin that it is not hard to imagine that this good fortune, in the way of a dead seal cast up by the tide, made the difference between surviving the critical weaning period or perishing. Since there were only two pups and the average litter size is five, the chances were that some of their siblings had already died. The seal was not yet at its end, and providing it had been washed up while it was still reasonably fresh, it could have fed them for a couple of weeks.

By this stage they had a well-established feeding pattern. The yellow pup rose from its siesta by the cadaver and also took a drink of the saline water before returning to the shelter of the dune, whereupon the black pup came out once again to eat. They were to repeat this on many occasions but never did the two pups leave the dune together or eat together. Only once during the five days that we watched them did they remain briefly in the open together and then the black pup was most circumspect in its relationship with the yellow one.

The fickle nature of our target became only too apparent when we spent all the next day in the hide and did not even sight the pups, or any other dingoes. The first day or two in the hide were not intolerably boring as the sea drowned our whispers and we could communicate freely, but even the best of mates run out of conversation. Luckily, the view from the hide was incredibly lovely, and we were able to enjoy the beauty of this idyllic place as we waited for our dingoes to reappear.

At last, away down the beach a black and tan adult dingo emerged from the dunes. I crawled over to Gary who was reading, nudged him and whispered, "Black dingo down the beach". The camera rolled, I felt reassured, then it was all over in a moment. The dingo sniffed out a dead short-tailed shearwater, picked it up and carried it to the seclusion of the dunes.

A couple of trips with short stays in the hide at Salt Lake ascertained that the dingoes did not fancy our kangaroo. While there was an abundance of fresh tracks, there was no sign of the dingoes so much as touching the carcase. We resolved that the next day I should watch the dead kangaroo all day just to make certain that we were not missing anything.

The dawn drive to Salt Lake next morning was worth remembering. There were tender soft-grey clouds over the sea with the rising sun reddening their bellies. To landward the moon was still up and backlighting the hills as I crept to my hide. After the sun had warmed the morning air I was startled by a sudden movement at my foot. It was a water skink catching flies that swarmed around the cuts on my feet. Going barefoot earns a few scratches but it also gives a good feel for country. I had seen these water skinks a thousand times yet not taken time to notice the rich yellow under their forelegs blending to a creamy belly. Down its side was a black strip coloured with tiny yellow lights that ran into a bright copper back.

Past noon and I was dozing. There was a rustle at my elbow but I took no notice, thinking it was my mate the skink back for more flies. The rustling seemed louder and there was a different quality to it. I rose on my left elbow and turned around to stare a one-metre tiger snake in the eye.

It was only a few centimetres from my head. My leap from the groundsheet was adrenalin in motion. The snake was unperturbed and took in the air on its forked tongue before continuing its glide over the leaf litter. I wished that it had been as startled as I and taken off in fright, thus preventing a quick return. I found myself contemplating death in the event of being bitten: should I sit and write sentimental last words or make a heroic dash for help?

Waiting until the shadows of the tall dune overtook the hideous, lonely, moribund kangaroo, I packed in my first day as a lone wildlife film-maker without a millimetre of film. I was tempted to look at the carcase but decided to avoid it until next day in case it was our scent that was still discouraging the dingoes. Even from the hide I could see that none of it had been eaten. Was it because the roo was pegged down with wire to prevent it being dragged away? But the CSIRO sheep was eaten and it was tied down. Perhaps these dingoes carry memories of being trapped by the CSIRO researchers? But not all of them would have been caught, so did the others learn from those that were? I began to convince myself that this must be the case, then realised that this is how dingo myths are born.

Gary had a more productive day. The black pup came to the seal again. This time Gary was able to position himself in a closer hide and obtained better film. The incredibly sensitive hearing of the dingo was demonstrated when, having enough film, Gary took some stills. Even at 30 m with a stiff offshore wind the pup started as the shutter clicked. It looked straight at the hide every time a photograph was taken. Had Gary made an untoward movement, the pup's eyes would have confirmed the aural message and it would have disappeared behind the dune.

The big black dog had also come out but remained far down the beach, searching for dead birds. Whenever it found one it retreated behind the dunes to eat, often followed by a retinue of crows. As the days of dingo watching went by we noticed that a dingo's appearance is frequently preceded by the flurry of noisy crows. A trapper had told us of "them dawg crows" and we had been sceptical. But "dawg crows" there are, and they regularly gave us advance notice of our quarry.

The next morning we took a close look at the kangaroo. There were many tracks, and a few pieces we had cut from a second carcase had all been taken. This convinced me that we should untie the roo and see what happened. I cut it loose and dragged it 30 m down the beach, well away from the peg driven into the sand. We would wait another day.

Back at Nadgee beach the seal was rapidly sinking into the sand. It was late morning before the black pup came out and wrestled with a dry flipper. Then, for the first time, the yellow pup came out at the same time as its litter mate. The black pup left the seal and lay down a couple of metres away while the yellow pup ate. The black pup rose, approached the seal but was quickly chased off by the yellow one. This occurred a

Above: *The two dingo pups on the beach near the mouth of the Nadgee River. The yellow pup, seen here feeding on the last remnants of the seal, was dominant and always ate first. When it had finished it would leave, allowing its black littermate to eat.* Gary Steer

Left: *Writing up notes on our observations was one way of getting through some of the long hours spent in the hide when no dingoes appeared.* Gary Steer

second time a few moments later and it became clear that the yellow pup was dominant. That there was any need to express this dominance surprised us but later in my research I learnt that this is typical. The instinct to assert dominance and maintain a hierarchy is quite evident as early as three weeks of age.

The yellow pup retreated to the side of a dune that faced the sea, the sun, and us, while the black one went off down the beach where it spent time in the same place where we had seen the adult. The black pup even climbed the dune at the same place as the adult. It reappeared half an hour later and collected a dead shearwater before returning behind the dune. Perhaps the adult dingo was one of the parents and the pups still spent some time with it. And perhaps the birds that the big dog was collecting and taking up the dune were being shared by the pups?

Later in the day the black pup returned to the seal and as there was enough film of it eating we decided to record its reaction to a human. I crept out of the hide, crawled on my belly across the sand, taking cover among the rocks whenever the pup pricked its ears to a foreign noise. I made it to the water edge with only 15 m separating us. Here, I slowly stood up and gave myself away. The pup did not waste a moment and fled to the safety of the dunes.

Watching these pups and the adult for six days from dawn to dusk we rarely saw them for more than a total of one hour on any one day. What did they do the rest of the time? Where did they go and how far? These questions plagued us as we sat in the hide with too much time to think. We had also become quite attached to the pups and wondered whether they would survive this critical weaning period. And again the questions: Will this beach and estuary support both of them as well as the adult and perhaps other unseen adults that are using it? Will one, or both, have to disperse and find new territory and how far would that be? With the constant demand for living space, only very few of the fittest pups can survive to adulthood and become breeders themselves.

We started our last day at Nadgee with a dawn watch at Salt Lake, sitting under the melaleucas with the rising sun and rolling sea providing the only action. The dingoes were probably curled up out of the cool wind, so we gave up and walked over to the kangaroo.

There were fresh tracks everywhere, even along the ocean edge, in the wet sand not yet obliterated by the waves that came in on the high tide. The dogs may well have been there as we arrived. More interestingly, the untied carcase had been dragged down the beach a good 50 m during the night but not eaten. We could only assume that, had they got it to the cover of the dunes, it would have been eaten in the same way as the other smaller pieces of kangaroo we put out. We realised that, in all our dingo watching at Nadgee, we had not seen an adult dog eating in the open during daylight. But we could not explain why they would not eat our kangaroo at night when they ate the

CSIRO sheep at the same spot only 12 months earlier.

The difficulty of filming dingoes in the wild makes a mockery of the often expressed romantic notions that they have some instinctive affinity with humans. These Nadgee dingoes had never been shot at or harmed in any way, yet they avoided all human contact. Certainly, there are dingoes that become camp hangers-on, waiting around for a free handout, but this change in behaviour comes slowly and need not imply love of man. There are a multitude of species, all over the world, that learn to feed on campers' sentiments.

We returned to Nadgee Beach and treated ourselves to the first swim in the six days we had sat next to these tempting waters. My body looked pale and unnatural in the claret and lime shandy of the estuary water at a rising tide. By breast-stroking slowly up the wide estuary I was, however, able to override the feeling of being an alien. From this duck's-eye view, the swamp thickets start at water level and lie flat until they come against a low hill clothed in eucalypts. To the left are more thickets but they run into old dunes, built when the sea rose last ice age and now covered in banksia. Ahead there is wide water that eventually becomes narrower and turns into a set of low, rolling hills that frame the west of my present universe.

Those hills are outside the nature reserve and lie within Nadgee State Forest. Those trees will be cut down, flayed into chips and sent to Japan. This use of our native forest disturbs me but did not occupy my thoughts too long on that occasion because the positive aspects of having reserves such as Nadgee surrounded by state forests become obvious when contemplating the future of the dingo pups we had been watching. Since the reserve is not girded by farms there are no strident calls for dingo control within it. Moreover, dingoes can disperse from the reserve into the state forest where they are compatible with forest management. Further out cattle predominate on fairly intensive holdings and dingoes are not a problem given occasional and modest control.

There are still a few old diehards who believe that Nadgee is a harbour and breeding ground for dingoes that "migrate" between it and the tableland country around the Monaro region where they kill sheep. No amount of research on dingo movements will convince them otherwise — but more about that in other chapters. For the time being, the scene before me and what I knew about the land beyond, spoke in favour of land use planning and rationalisation as a means of conserving the dingo in national parks and equivalent reserves.

DESERT DOGS AND GAS

Moomba appears on the horizon like any other human settlement in the bush — dwarfed by oceans of space. As you get closer it seems to be an apparition. This must be Saudi Arabia, the Persian Gulf, Texas. Oil and gas rigs are only in their infancy in Australia's national psyche and are hard to relate to. The Moomba gas and oil plant sits in a flat grey desert valley between red dunes. It is a huge wedding cake of pipes with tall cracking towers for candles; it is bizarre, surreal and, in a perverse way, beautiful.

Two huge flares shoot flame high into the air where the west wind whips them to a frenzy. Below, the same wind is yellow with dust. The flares mate with the sunset; then the lights are turned on and the giant cake twinkles like the stars. The plant runs day and night, worked by men using the most sophisticated technology. Yet out here, so far from the world that spawned them and their machines, they seem driven by some alien atavistic instinct. Here, human desires and dreams are made of gas.

There were dingoes at Moomba dump, plenty of them judging from the fresh tracks in abundance, but they only came in at night because many had been poisoned and shot two months earlier and others had scattered with the rain. It was the same old story — "You should have been here last week." The desert blooms after rain but such times are anathema to those in search of dingoes. Plentiful water means that animals no longer rely on traditional watering holes but can spread their territories to inaccessible reaches.

On this trip Gary and I were joined by Damon Smith who, as pilot and sound recordist, proved an invaluable addition to the team. Gary made camp on a dune overlooking the dump, hoping to film in the early morning light some interaction between the dingoes that gather there at night but vanish during the day. We found a dead dingo near the dump that could have died only that day. Did it pick up an old bait, a piece of deadly foreign material or perhaps botulism from discarded food? We took the dead dingo and placed it in sight of Gary's tent. It was after dark when from down the valley came the primeval howl of a pack of dingoes, as the eternal flame from the plant burners waved insanely to the night with an imperative no less primitive than the howling dogs.

It seemed certain that Gary would have got some film. There were howling dogs all around during the night which left tracks right up to the tent. But no film was shot. The dogs had vanished before first light, leaving only the furry skull and forelegs of the dead dingo. All else had been eaten. It *must* have been eaten by the other dingoes, as there were no crows or eagles to devour it at night. We regretted the lack of a light intensifier which would have enabled us to film dog eating dog during the night.

Gary stayed another night looking out over the dump while Damon and I returned to Moomba camp. We rose before dawn to try some independent filming and drove out near the dump to pick up a red dingo making its way to wherever home was. It bolted when it saw us but we decided to pursue him at a distance to see what happened. After 3 km of driving over saltbush plains and around gullies and alluvial fans, the dingo got used to us.

I kept the vehicle between him and the high dunes where following is impossible. Then we gradually drove in closer and closer. Damon shot film for the next half hour while I tried to avoid putting him through the roof and the car in a bog. The dingo was "good talent" and we soon ran out of film.

That afternoon we flew over Lake Eyre, which was almost full after being empty for ten years. It had been known to fill only once before in the last 200 years. We flew in a tiny cocoon over infinite desert — though I have come to dislike the word "desert". Every time I have been to the centre of Australia it has held varied plants and abundant wildlife — "desert" does not ring true. Perhaps this label is another symbol of our discomfort in the land that was desperately inhospitable to the early explorers and the pastoralists who followed them.

Dingo on the shore of Lake Eyre. The lake was full of water for only the second time in 200 years. Gary Steer

What lay below was certainly not a desert, even with the endless rolling sand dunes that run parallel away into the horizon. The dunes were hidden beneath green clumps of spinifex and the broad valleys between were yellow with grass and blue with saltbush. And everywhere there was water. Every claypan, each depression, and the watercourses that start and finish as veins between dunes, had water in them. Where we flew over it, the mighty Coopers Creek was a braided, twisting bed of sand broken with waterholes. Looking north you could see it coming down. There, near the horizon, it was spilling out into every channel, every ancient oxbow and meander, created as it drained western

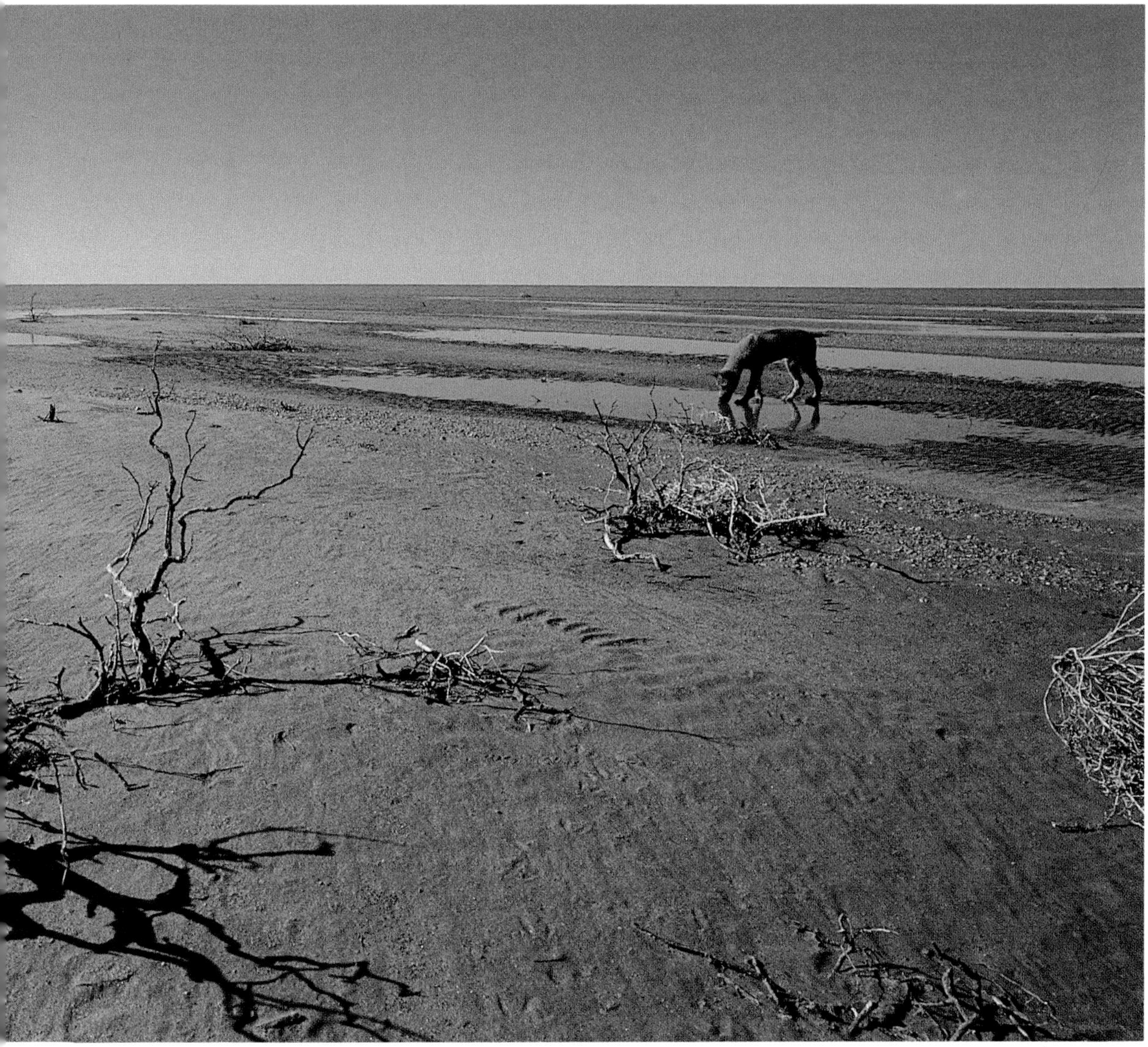

Queensland for millennia. The waters we could see would not reach Lake Eyre until August. It was then only April. Here was territory often featured in Australian history books and I thought how, as a schoolchild, I had been sold short with dates and facts when it was the emotions, the guts, the feel of the places where events occurred that stirred the imagination.

During the day Gary had some spotlights made up and we used them that night to film dingoes around the dump. They scattered when we shone the spotlight but we used the system Damon and I had found successful — pick out one dingo and stick with it until it gets used to you. The driving was nerve-racking but after following a dingo for two hours it became so accustomed to us that he even sat down within 20 m and howled mournfully or melodiously, depending on how you feel about dingoes, to his mates.

The next day our system paid off again, this time with footage of the prettiest little dingo bitch I had ever seen. She was almost the rich red colour of a fox and had a shiny, luxuriant coat with a big white chest patch and the typical white points on pads and tail. An added bonus was that she was mates with a black and tan dingo so we had the two colour types together. Both ran like dogs possessed when they spotted the Toyota but we followed at a respectable distance. Five km of saltbush and sandy gully later, they settled down and we began to film.

They became so accustomed to us that the vehicle was of no consequence at all and the red bitch began to catch grasshoppers in the spinifex. It was less dramatic than the kill of large game, but this is how desert dingoes live, scavenging and catching whatever is most abundant. There were grasshoppers and lizards aplenty following the rain.

Eventually we were able to keep within 20 m of the bitch while the dog stayed out a bit wider. On two occasions we filmed them together. This was important to us because there are still many people who believe that all pure bred dingoes are yellow-ginger and that black is a sign of crossbreeding with domestic dogs.

We left our dingoes at the foot of a large dune where they would probably spend the day resting in the shade. We returned to Moomba, packed, loaded the plane and flew with light wings and heavy hearts back "inside". The last of the Corner Country dunes passed beneath us. Then came the timber and scrub of western New South Wales, but it was the ploughed paddocks further towards the coast that jarred the most. Planes get you to your destination quicky but they bring you back too fast.

YELLOW DINGOES — RED COUNTRY

It takes nearly a day to drive from Adelaide to Marree, where one crosses the dingo fence into the unprotected cattle country. The long drive emphasises the large proportion of South Australia from which dingoes are excluded.

Dust, bone-rattling corrugations, flat tyres up the Oodnadatta Track. Constant enquiries about dingoes to Aborigines, publicans, stockmen and drinkers, missionaries saving souls with the help of Toyota.

"No dogs about for a while now mate. There's been a four-year drought. Should've seen 'em before the dry — used to shoot them from the pub window," volunteered a now idle dogger in the bar at the William Creek Hotel up near Lake Eyre.

On to Oodnadatta, where the people from the outlying stations were coming in to see the Slim Dusty movie being shown around the inland to adoring audiences who compensated for the icy reception the film received in the eastern cities. The Oodnadatta open-air theatre is an experience not to be missed. It looks like any vacant lot on a corner block in a tiny spread-out inland town except for the tattered, discoloured screen. Cars go to the rear and there are a few benches and space to sit on the dust down the front. The audience mostly consisted of Aborigines; their "Saturday best" cowboy clothes and dark faces in the half light were far more interesting than anything on the screen. They sat quietly talking through the film except for Moses who insisted on singing old Tom Jones hits. The young white policeman came and quietened Moses with the threat of "yarding" him for the night. Yarding is the cattleman's euphemism for being put in gaol. Everyone sang along when Slim broke into tune, which he did most of the time.

The Macumba Station vehicle was pointed out to us during interval and we introduced ourselves to the wife of the manager. He couldn't make it to town as there was a muster out in one of the cattle camps on this vast 15,000 sq km property. The manager's wife was very helpful and we would be welcome to visit but it was the same story — there hadn't been many dogs about since the drought. We knew that the drought did not extend up as far as Alice Springs so we decided to drive on to "the Alice".

While we were in Oodnadatta a couple of tourists asked whether they could take photos of Maliki and while doing so, told us that they saw a number of dingoes at a roadside camp at Curtin Springs Station near Ayers Rock. They told us that the dingoes would come right into the camping ground at night and lick water from a leaking tap. Of course we made a sharp mental note of this and said we would have a look if our search took us in that direction. A camping ground beside a road did not rate highly as a good filming location. Had we simply packed up there and then and gone on to Curtin Springs we would have saved many weeks' work.

On the way north towards the Alice, we called in at Granite Downs homestead. A knock at the door while keeping a watchful eye on an intimidating blue heeler brought the manager to the door. His greeting of "What's your problem?" showed his impatience at tourists requesting petrol and mechanical aid after a breakdown on the Oodnadatta Track. On hearing that we were filming dingoes he invited us in for a cool drink and became a friendly fund of local knowledge. Our best chance, he believed, was around the camp of a quarry gang who were crushing gravel for the Stuart Highway. They had a garbage dump frequented by dingoes. We were becoming nauseated at the news that the only dingoes that seemed possible to film were always around garbage dumps, but we had to follow this lead since we were so close.

On the drive out to the camp we checked all the watering points for tracks but there were few traces of dingoes. It was Sunday afternoon as we turned into the quarry camp. It was a large camp, housing about 40 people, mostly men but there were one or two family groups in caravans. The rest consisted of the prefabricated demountable units that now make up nearly every mining settlement in central Australia.

A blue metal quarry in the centre of Australia is an uninspiring scene. Worse, it was impossible to film around the dump because there was rubbish scattered all through the limited field of vision given by the surrounding scrub. We did learn that there was a fairly tame bitch hanging around the camp and that she had been seen with pups in tow about three weeks previously. To film a bitch with pups would be marvellous so we asked to meet the person who saw her with the pups. Together we drove to the location. Searching the rocky outcrops for the den proved like the proverbial search for a needle in a haystack but we gave it a try. After an hour or two we realised the hopelessness of the task and set up camp.

The foreman of the camp wanted us to explain our presence. He was both tough and friendly and had me contemplating the particular skills required to run a camp like this. My curiosity was well placed because while talking with him one of the workmen came in with an arrow deeply embedded in his hand between thumb and forefinger. It couldn't be pulled out because of its barbed head. In great pain and with an arrow dangling from his hand, the poor fellow explained that he had been out hunting and shot the arrow into his own hand while drawing the bow. There was no doctor this side of Alice Springs, six hours' drive away, so the foreman cut the arrow off at skin level and bandaged the whole hand with the arrow head in it. In this condition he had to sit up all night until a truckie who was returning to the Alice took him in next morning.

After a welcome hot shower in one of the demountables I tended to be less critical of their ugliness. And there, shining in the headlights of the car as we drove to our camp, were the unmistakable eyes of a dingo. It turned side on to run across the road and melt into the night. At least there were some dogs about.

The dawn light showed what a dismal location we were in for filming. Between a few low hills was thick scrub that was no good for either sighting dingoes or following them with a camera. We took a look around in the soft morning light before the camp stirred and the machinery started. There were no dingoes abroad and everything told us to move on. But not before taking some photos of Maliki in a paddock full of the rich, red flowers of Sturt's desert pea.

Moving further north, we stopped at a roadhouse near the border between South Australia and the Northern Territory. There the waitress told us about her father-in-law, a rabbiter who had recently taken in a dingo pup. We asked directions to his camp; who better to tell us the whereabouts of dingoes than a rabbiter? He was out on Erldunda Station, the next large pastoral holding towards Alice Springs. We decided the lead was worth investigating and headed off along the "highway".

The rabbiter's camp was signposted

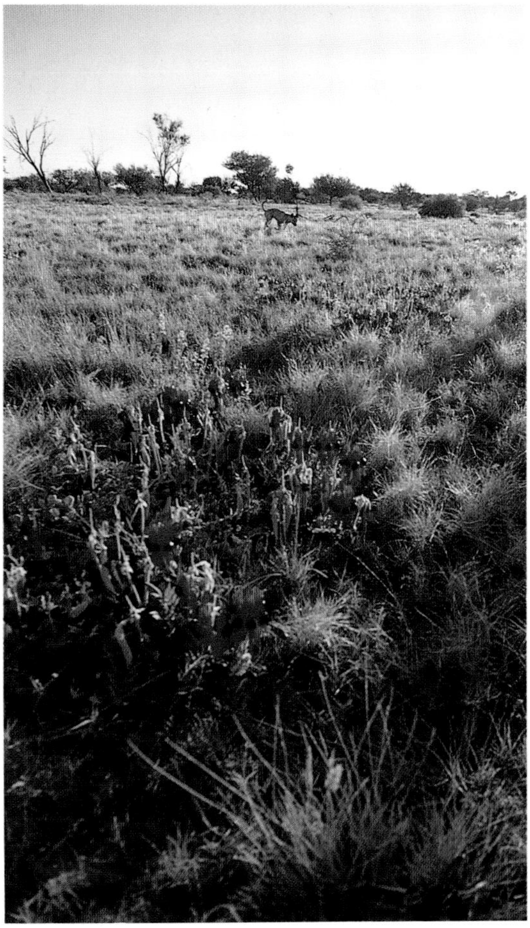

Maliki takes a break from the long drive up the Oodnadatta Track and goes for a run among the Sturt's desert pea flowering near Granite Downs. Gary Steer

by a portable chiller that stood tall among the short arid vegetation. The diesel refrigerator motor kept the rabbit carcases cool until a truck made its fortnightly visit to bring in an empty chiller and tow the full one to Adelaide. Around a bend in the track and beside a dry creekbed was the camp. It had that neat and orderly appearance given by the bushman whose only home is, or has ever been, a camp — the sort of pride in one's surroundings that can become stultifying in a middle-class suburb. Here, it gave the few sheets of corrugated iron and canvas lean-to a dignity far in excess of what could be thought possible from the crude materials used in its construction. The bough stand that carried the 44-gallon drum of drinking water was simple, yet strong enough to let you know that this camp was a home. The smiling rabbiters who greeted us were as friendly as their camp. There were two of them, father and son.

The father had been a rabbiter all his working life except for a few short breaks as a fencing contractor. The family followed the rabbits in a caravan and six children were raised along the way. In place of possessions there were photo albums with each photo meticulously mounted and the details recorded beneath. There were photos of children swimming in Coopers Creek, fishing in the Diamantina, playing with a baby wild pig caught in swamp behind a camp on the Darling River. Gary and I were given a look at their life and were awed at how rich it was — in an economic sense as well. Shooting well over 200 rabbits a night at $2 a pair, they earned more than us at our filming.

About his dingo pup? "I gave it away last week. It wasn't a real dingo. One of those half-bred things you get around here, black and brown with a patch of brindle like it was crossed with a kelpie. Fella from the chalet at Ayers Rock begged me for him so I let him have it."

We were almost next door to Curtin Springs Station — only 120 km down the road, a mere stone's throw by Territory standards, but no mention was made of the bonanza we were eventually to discover there. Another cup of tea and we were on our way to Alice Springs.

After seven long days of travel and tracking dingoes across South Australia we were loath to spend time in Alice Springs. But there was no escaping the endless round of meetings with people who perhaps knew of likely spots to observe dingoes. They were mostly officers of the Conservation Commission who travel the region in the course of their work. Some of them were also responsible for dingo control on the pastoral holdings.

It took time to sift through all the information crowded into our meetings. Then came the problem of actually making contact with the people scattered across the Northern Territory who might have been able to help us. Even today it can be difficult to contact the station folk, isolated by vast distances and rough roads. It was frustrating being outside the communication network that provides instant contact. We had to rely on the Royal Flying Doctor Service radio-telephone. This meant booking a call first thing in the morning and waiting while the Flying Doctor attempted to contact the other party who may have been out at a stock camp mustering cattle 50 km or more from the homestead. With the owner or manager away, the women were busy and not always in earshot of the phone. When they answered, they treated us with caution and were suspicious of our motives, particularly with the Azaria Chamberlain case so fresh in everyone's mind.

But after two years of tracking dingoes, we were well practised at sounding reasonable and not too demanding. Nevertheless, one forthright question had to be asked: "Can you guarantee we will see dingoes?" We knew it sounded naive but it helped cut back the distances travelled following a weak scent. And it got to the heart of the matter which the pastoralists don't seem to mind, for they would answer in that straightforward way that made our task so much easier.

"No, I ran the waters last week and didn't see a dog, haven't seen one for a few weeks now," was the sort of answer that would put that particular station off the list. We perked up when we heard, "Yes, there's been a few dogs about lately. We haven't baited out past Bluebush Dam for a few years now and I saw dingoes when we mustered last month." And "No, they hadn't been shot at or chased on motor bikes". And so we were welcomed to Allambi Station, three hours' drive east of Alice Springs.

Andrew and Livia Smith run Allambi Station with such commitment that I felt guilty at being so far away from my farm. Their homestead complex was neat and orderly and we rolled out our swags in a large hangar to sleep beneath the wings of an aeroplane. This winged Pegasus had reduced the number of horses on Allambi to a handful. Against the wall were the motorbikes that could chase cattle without tiring themselves. Over in the corner was a bar for entertaining guests who may also fly in. Along the other side was the governess' quarters and the schoolroom where the three children were taught through the School of the Air by teachers whose chalk is a radio and whose classroom is bigger than Great Britain.

I found Andrew Smith's point of view about dingoes fairly typical of most pastoralists in central Australia. He believed that a certain number were tolerable and did some good by helping to control rabbits and red kangaroos. However, once dingo numbers increased to the level where calves are being taken, he started poisoning them.

While I cannot claim a comprehensive survey by any means, I have met only one or two pastoralists who are willing to have calves killed by dingoes and not feel the need to adopt some form of control measure. But individual responses to dingoes in cattle country vary enormously and there is certainly not the universal antagonism towards them found wherever there are sheep.

There had been no baiting around the bores and dams on the outer stretches of Allambi for many years and dingoes were being seen at Bluebush Dam. The regular sighting of a white bitch at Phillipson Bore, the next water on from Bluebush, had us impatient to get out and begin filming. Before leaving, I asked Andrew for the loan of a high-powered rifle in case we needed the carcase of a feral animal to lure dingoes within camera range. He handed me a 303/25 and ten bullets.

After two hours of driving over bumpy tracks and checking every watering point for dingo tracks we arrived at Bluebush. There were plenty of tracks and even an earth wall with some small trees as cover in which to conceal ourselves. The decision to stay was straight-forward. To decide where to camp was another matter. We had discussed it endlessly over the past few days and had gradually come to believe that wherever we camped, the dingoes would know we were there so we might as well camp within sight of the dam where we could maintain a close watch every minute of daylight without having to create disturbance by walking or driving to and fro.

Using fallen mulga in a crude, woven construction, we built two hides on a long contour bank that channelled what little rain fell out there into the turbid dam. We set up camp some 200 m away where the stunted and sparsely leaved mulga provided the only shade around the long claypan dotted with clumps of low bluebush.

Barely had we unpacked and boiled the billy before, out of the corner of my eye, I saw a big yellow dingo approaching the dam from hardly 200 m away. Gary scrambled for his camera gear. Maliki was running loose and we didn't bother to tie him up, thinking that he would be of little consequence and might even help in attracting the wild dingoes. The big dog kept coming in to water and we sneaked up behind the dam wall and managed to film him drinking among some cattle.

This was the first of many occasions on that trip when we watched dingoes and cattle drinking together, quite often within a few metres of each other.

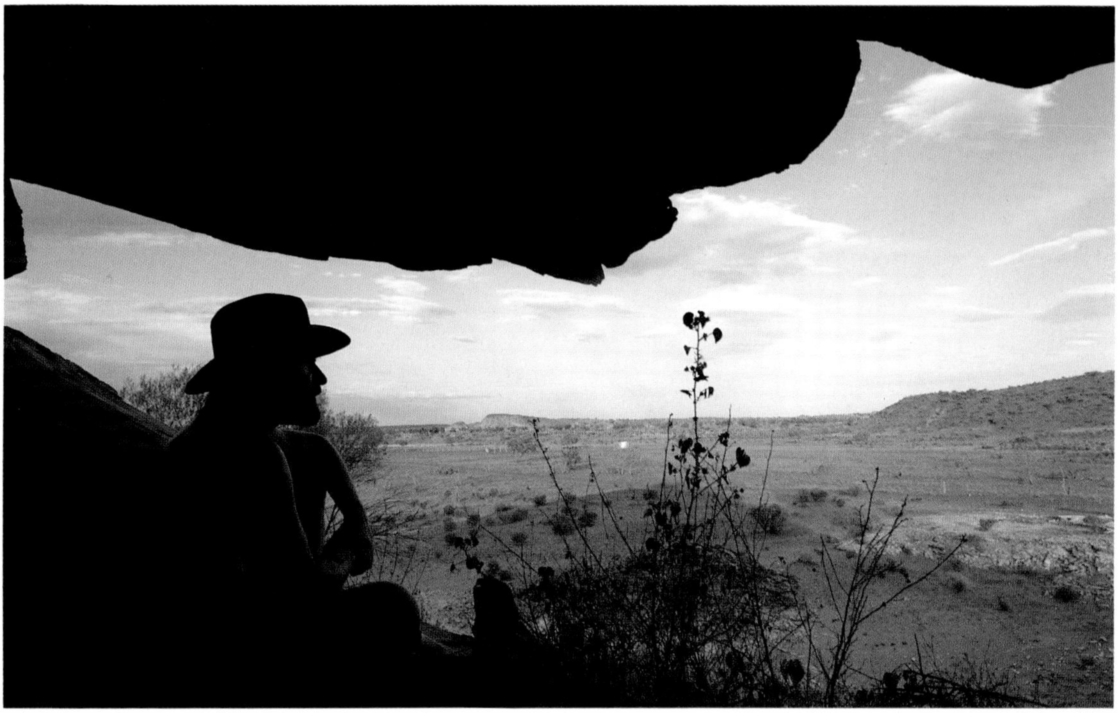

We took shelter from the intense summer heat in this cave overlooking Phillipson Bore on Allambi Station, Alice Springs. However, thousands of ticks that infest the Euros, which also use these caves, soon drove us back on to the hilltop and under the blazing sun again. This is where we filmed the white dingo catching a lizard. Gary Steer

Sometimes a curious half-grown steer would playfully chase a dingo. Once I saw a calf only a month or two old chase a dingo across a daypan near a bore. Most often dingoes and cattle ignored each other. It seems to indicate that the dingo is not seen as an enemy that frequently preys on calves; but perhaps cows have poor memories or don't hold grudges.

The big dingo looked up from his drink and saw Maliki. He stiffened and the hair stood up on his neck; he was clearly displeased at the sight and smell of a stranger at his waterhole. Maliki was also cautious and made no attempt to join the wild dingo. This surprised us enormously because until then, Maliki had been only too willing to play with any domestic dog in sight regardless of its size. There he was with a soul mate in the wild and he avoided him like the plague and came over to us instead, giving us away to the big dog which skulked off into the distance.

Gary and I were overjoyed at seeing and filming a dingo at such close quarters within an hour of setting up camp. Alas, we were not to know that this would be the first and last time that we would see a dingo here. We paid a high price for being so cavalier and letting the dingo see us. It took us two weeks of watching from dawn to dark to decide that these dingoes would not come back in daylight.

It was infuriating to hear them howl within 200 m of our camp during the night. It was even worse to make out the dull outline of at least four dingoes in the pre-dawn light, only to hear them howl once and disappear beyond the timberline into the dunes. By night they were evident by their howling and the fact that they accepted some of the offerings we left for them. An old feral donkey which we shot and laid out as bait was not so popular. The dingoes came that night, took away the donkey's penis and testicles and never touched it again.

They liked the red kangaroo carcase much better. I came by that one day when heading west to the next dam some 25 km away. Driving along, slightly apprehensive at being alone in a very isolated place and not entirely sure of the track, I looked out to my left and saw a beaten-up late model Holden weaving through the mulga. While I was trying to make sense out of this sudden apparition, the car stopped and three Aboriginal men jumped out and ran into the scrub. They grabbed hold of a wounded red kangaroo at about the same time as they spotted me.

Moving closer, I could see that they were very nervous of me, although I was a lone white man in their territory. They made a half-hearted attempt to get the kangaroo in the boot without me seeing it and then stood very quietly. I broke the ice by saying that I dearly wanted the kangaroo carcase.

They were loath to talk much at first. I learnt later that they were in fact frightened of me even though they were doing nothing illegal because Aborigines are allowed to hunt game on pastoral land in the Northern Territory. They asked if I was carrying a rifle and started to tell me how I should go about shooting a kangaroo myself. I explained that it was illegal for me to do so.

The Aborigines held conference in their own tongue before saying that I could join them and perhaps there would be a spare roo. They saw that my car was empty and Ronnie and George jumped in, telling me to follow the others. They leaned halfway out of the open front passenger window and its opposite seat in the back, gesticulating madly to the other Aborigine in the lead car while looking at the ground, apparently following a kangaroo track while yelling at me to turn this way and that and to drive at twice the speed.

We were driving at a good 30 km per hour across a stony plain littered with trees and old stumps from past fires. I was expected to see the kangaroo track we were following but couldn't see a thing except grass and shrubs. I was also beginning to think that even Aborigines could not keep track of a roo that had grazed to shade some hours beforehand, when I was ordered to a sudden halt. The marksman in the Holden pulled out a dilapidated .22 rifle and poked in a single bullet because the magazine was missing. He killed the kangaroo with one shot.

By this time we were like old friends and after another conference they said that I could have this roo after they had gutted it. The small, shy marksman took out a knife and made the tiniest hole at the roo's navel. Then with one hand applying a firm pressure on its belly, he popped the gut out. He cut a small hole in the intestine and wrung the long entrails between his fingers, forcing out the contents and cleaning it as it emerged. The whole gut was carefully picked up and dumped in the boot of the Holden.

The dingoes liked the kangaroo, but only at night and in two such nocturnal feeds it was gone. We sighted not a hair of them during the day. Nevertheless, sitting around Bluebush Dam day after day was not without its rewards. Had we been making a film about the bird life of an inland waterhole we could not have been in a better place. Just after dawn the zebra finches came flocking in by their thousands. Wave after wave of agitated, self-important little finches would fly in and land to chatter on exactly the same shrub as they sat on every morning. After a drink they would sit at the same place and have another yarn before flying off to be immediately replaced by another flock. And so it would be for an hour or more, then it would suddenly end and there would not be another finch until the afternoon.

The cattle trekked in to water in single file in the cool of the morning or late afternoon. You could see them from a great distance as they emerged from the timberline, coming in ponderously slow, but sometimes a calf would give a buck and a kick in the air, perhaps in anticipation of the cool drink. The dust rose in little swirls around their feet in the deeply rutted pads that led them in. The low angle of the sun reflected off the dust and gave them a halo around their feet. Heaven knows, they needed it to survive out here. Their thirst and eagerness were betrayed by the slobbering of their mouths as they got close to water. When they were about 100 m away they broke into a trot, then a canter as they burst over the bank and waded out to their briskets in the cool water.

Even the cattle in this part of the country have a wild edge to them and they didn't particularly like us hanging around. It showed us what we were up against with dingoes when a mob of cattle got nervous a good half kilometre away and raised their heads in the air smelling the breeze for anything different. Sometimes the mob would stop and the lead cow or bullock would walk slowly and cautiously ahead. One whiff of us and they were off in a miniature stampede. The lesson from these domesticated animals, mustered and handled at least twice a year, was not lost on us — if the cattle were twitchy, the dingoes would be even more so.

It was during a lone visit to nearby Phillipson Bore that I saw a dingo come in to drink and be chased off by a calf not much bigger than itself. Not long afterwards a second dingo came in to drink nonchalantly and unchallenged among the cattle milling around the trough. Obviously the provision of watering points by pastoralists has aided the dingo in this previously dry area and we returned at first light the next day to film this.

We stopped the car a good half kilometre from the bore and I stalked ahead to see if there were any dingoes in for an early morning drink. Poking my head carefully above the crest of a dune, I looked down to see the white bitch drinking. Running back at a half crouch I alerted Gary.

Seeing a dingo is one thing, to film it another. By the time we had the equipment ready the white dingo had long finished drinking and was heading out to the edge of the dunes. She became intent on tracking a lizard across the face of a dune and then, arriving at where it was hidden in its hole, she dug it up, gave it a quick snap and a shake then ate it. There *was* some action, but so far away! The dingo circled around wide and to our dismay saw or smelled the car and was off like a speeding bullet. Out of all that we could get only a few seconds of film. Perhaps it could be used to show that white dingoes do exist in the wild.

Nevertheless, it was a good start and we set up on the hot rock for the day. The sun began its relentless climb up the sky and took out its exertions upon us. It was November and the onset of summer saw each day hotter than the one before. The flies got into our eyes and the ants crawled up our legs and bit us in the crotch, which was no doubt suicidal for them given the heat, dust and our infrequency of bathing. We sat there for another three days and didn't see a single dingo.

And so it continued. Nothing was happening at either of the spots we were watching. Our camp at Bluebush had been moved three times, each time further away from the water to give the dingoes more space. Maliki spent his days on the chain after giving us away that first time. He ran free at night but never attempted to investigate his wild fellows. Even when they howled close to camp he did little more that prick his ears. As for running away, I think he knew he had a good lifestyle and tended to come too close at night, pushing me over on my swag to nestle as close and as warm as possible.

One afternoon I left Gary at Bluebush and headed off to Phillipson to check if the meat had been taken and if that which was left hanging in a tree near the trough had brought any dingoes around. Maliki was with me in the car.

Driving across a wide claypan, I noticed a light plane coming in low over the mulga away to my right. The pilot waggled the plane's wings so I brought the car to a halt. Without even a pass to check the claypan, the pilot landed the plane and stopped it beside me. Andrew Smith and his brother David alighted. David was flying Andrew home after he had delivered cattle to his property, Tieyon Station, just across the border in South Australia. They saw me crossing the claypan and simply dropped down for a yarn.

Sitting in the shade of the plane's wings provided some relief from the searing sun but Maliki was feeling the heat and panting with his long tongue fully extended. David got up and opened the plane door to take out an insulated foam container of cool water. He poured some into the wide lid and gave Maliki a drink. Then he splashed a large puddle of the cold water on the ground to give him a cool place to lie on. Maliki stretched out in the wet clay

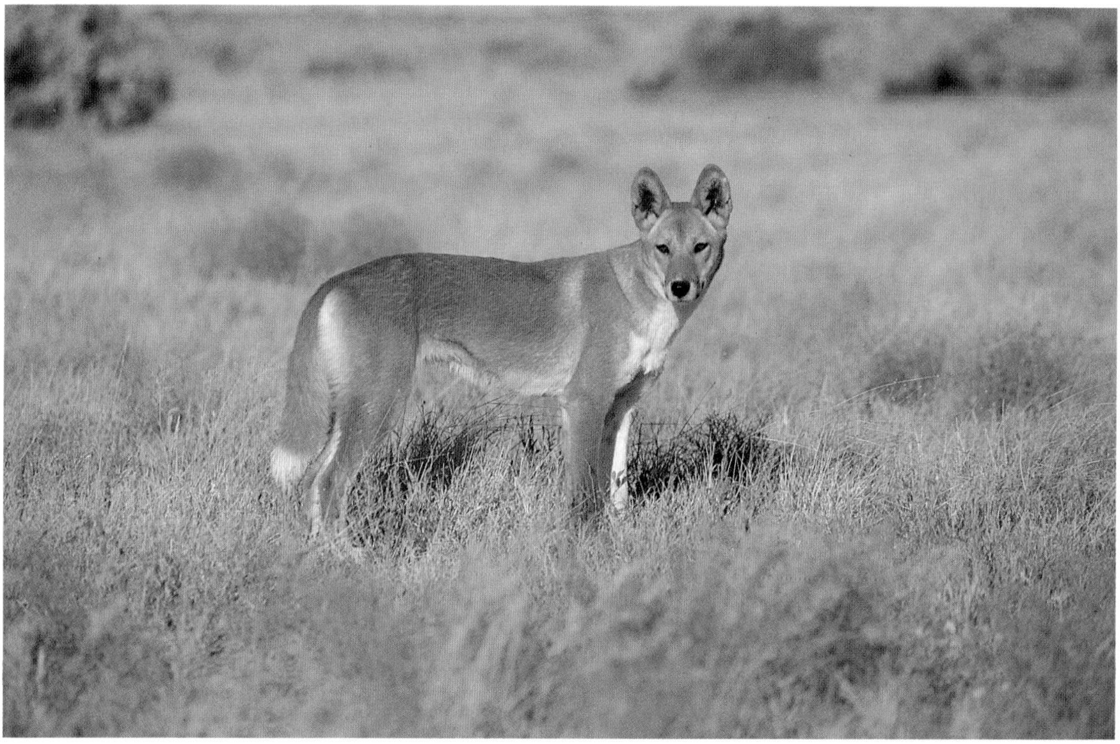

The prettiest dingo we saw on all our travels was this young female near Moomba. Roland Breckwoldt

and went to sleep while I was touched by this spontaneous show of kindness to a dingo owned by someone he had only just met. It left a lasting impression on me — this tough Territorian cattleman pilot dropping out of the sky and giving a tired and hot dog a drink regardless of the fact that it was a dingo.

We were 11 days at Allambi without much film to show for it and were questioning the wisdom of staying longer. We had almost decided to move on when some unexpected visitors arrived — a party of German zoologists employed on contract to the Northern Territory Conservation Commission to study the ecology and behaviour of wild camels in Australia. They were searching for a camel that had been caught with great difficulty and fitted with a radio-collar so that its movements could be followed with radiotelemetry. Once released it had disappeared from the face of the earth. This little party with their antennae and radio seemed a tribute to someone's folly. The gist of the local knowledge was that the camel would not have drawn breath until it had put the entire Simpson Desert between it and its trackers.

The German party provided more than an entertaining encounter. They also had useful information to pass on. In all their extensive search for camels, the greatest concentration of dingoes they saw had been around Curtin Springs Station and Angas Downs, two large cattle stations near Ayers Rock. Thus the passing comment by the tourist in Oodnadatta became more significant. The scent had strengthened and we broke camp at Bluebush, heading for Alice Springs and then on to Curtin Springs.

DINGOES DOWN THE LENS

Halfway to Curtin Springs the sky turned black with smoke and a devilish wind mixed it with red dust. The spinifex and mulga was alight in nearly every direction. The few cars and tourist buses dwindled to nothing and we wondered whether it was foolish to continue. The road was reasonably wide so we couldn't be actually consumed by the flames, so we travelled on, pulled, I am sure now, by the invisible web of wild magic that entwines you in central Australia.

The fire swept through like a tourist. It left its mark like a tourist and would come back like one, sometime in the future, when the season was right.

As we approached Curtin Springs, a lone yellow dingo crossed the blackened landscape. I turned the car to follow its tracks as it slipped through a bed of fine ash on red sand. We got a few feet of film before losing it through a fence. Still, it was possible to rationalise this paltry effort by telling ourselves that the dingo could be worked into a story about fire in the arid ecosystem.

Peter Sevron, the owner of Curtin Springs, made us feel welcome and told

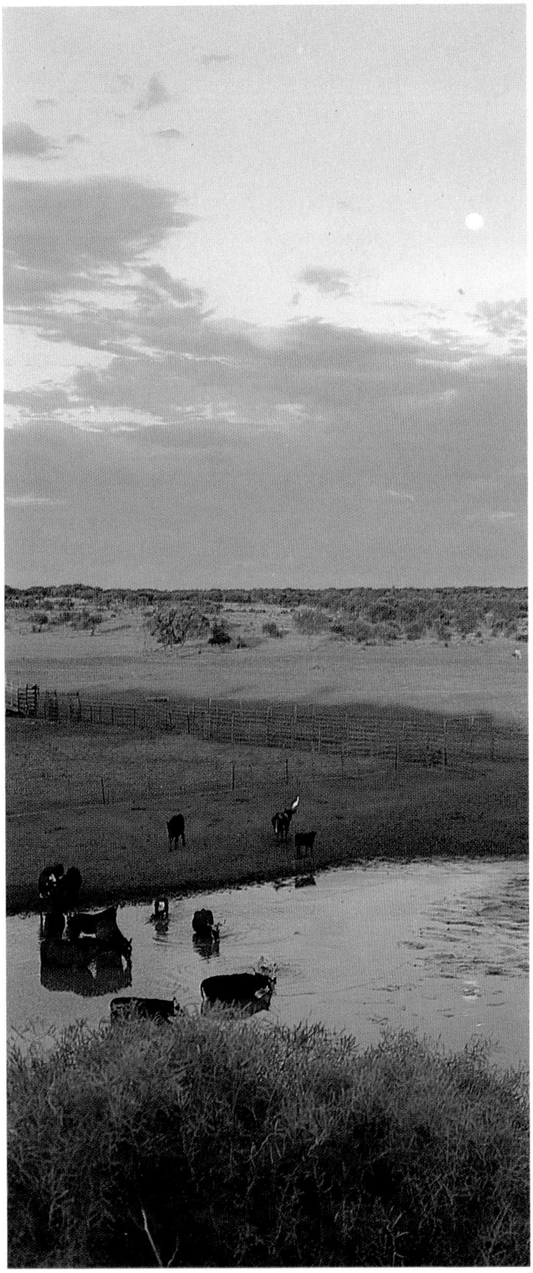

From our hide on top of a low, stony hill, dingoes could be observed using this earth tank, which was surrounded by a trap yard, at Curtin Springs Station, near Ayers Rock. The royal spoonbill that we adopted as our symbol of good fortune is sifting and sorting food in the centre of the tank. Roland Breckwoldt

us that there were "a few dogs about". Moreover we were free to travel wherever we liked on the 2,000 sq km property. I must pay tribute to all pastoralists we met; they were nothing if not generous and hospitable.

The inevitable station dump on Curtin Springs differed from its counterparts on other stations by having the remains of up to 15 bullocks dumped into it each week — an abattoir on the station supplies meat to outlying settlements. Most of these are Aboriginal communities on what were large cattle stations themselves before the land was given back to its traditional owners. The bones from this beef kept the dingoes hanging about. The dump was an ugly spot, but what else could we expect at that stage of our development as connoisseurs of outback dumps? So we drove out to an earth tank that had been sunk between two low rocky hills. The wall of the tank blocked a narrow pass between the two hills so that water ran into it.

Even as we drove in, there was a large yellow dingo with big powerful shoulders hunched over the water as he drank. A good sign on our first visit and this time we would not ruin it. We were determined that we would make a supreme effort to avoid letting the dingoes know we were interested in getting close to them. Of course, they would know that we were camped in the area but we believed that it was a great mistake to let the dingoes at Allambi see us near their water as easily as they did.

This tank looked good — water, dingoes, cover for a hide. We checked three other waterholes but they did not offer the same advantages, even though we saw both dingoes and their tracks. We set up camp among some trees nearly a kilometre away from the tank, just below a long hill that ran down to the water. From there we could climb the hill and sneak along behind the ridge on the lee side, unseen and unsmelled (which, considering our weeks without bathing, was remarkable in itself). With a hill either side of the dam we were able to set up two hides and use whichever one was downwind.

That afternoon, well before the dogs would start coming in to water, we crept to a flimsy hide of branches beneath a scraggly acacia. As the afternoon sank away the dogs started arriving from behind the dunes that fringed the wide claypan in front of us, trotting in along a maze of cattle pads that converged to form a bovine expressway in the valley behind the dam.

I kept watch and gave a low whistle to Gary when dingoes appeared. His vision was confined to the frame in the lens and I could see much more and anticipate action outside his view. The dingoes came in one by one to drink, never congregating like the birds, the cattle, the brumbies and the camels. Later we were to see some family groups but the overwhelming impression was that of the lone dingo drinking and sniffing off to hunt.

Ecstatic, buoyant and whispering "shouts" of enthusiasm, we sat until well after dark and quietly, oh so quietly, tripped our way back to camp in the pitch black night. A hot beer with a desiccated lettuce and peanut butter sandwich for us and a feed of Lucky Dog for Maliki before we rolled into dusty swags.

Dawn in a bush hide was no cross to bear as we waited in anticipation of what the light might bring. It introduced the "muscle family". A solitary dingo was attacking a pile of bullock bones we brought from the dump and the camera was trained on him but way out to my left, on the outer rim of the fringing dune, there was a distracting movement. One, two, three, four, five, six, seven dingoes all in a huddle. I reached for the binoculars and they revealed the sort of thing we had dreamed about for the past two years.

It was a family group consisting of two full-grown parents and their three young puppies which were about three months old. They were accompanied by a pair of young dingoes which were probably part of last year's litter. The entire group was in perfect condition, their coats shining in the morning sun. They put their tails in the air to show who was going to be boss of that pile of bones and raced down the hill like a platoon of Roman gladiators. Even the diminutive pups had their tails high and the single dingo already on the bones slunk away at the sight of this powerful family unit.

The "muscle family" never stayed around very long but even so, seeing them for just a little while each morning was an unforgettable experience. They obviously had a large and secure home range out beyond the dunes that was well stocked with rabbits and other game because they would spend little time, at least during daylight hours, around anything we used to attract them closer. Nevertheless, we could observe many aspects of dingo behaviour through our brief association with this family.

One such aspect was how the "muscle family" could easily bluff a subordinate outsider into leaving food, which they would take themselves. Once they were eating no other dingoes were allowed near. However, one morning the family strutted their stuff on the crest of the dune and raced down, tails up, but this time met resistance. Two adult dingoes were there first and they would not be moved. Clearly, the family had the numbers and would have won a fight for the bones, but they may have paid a high cost in injuries. After much arching of backs, curling of lips and pissing, the "muscle family" retreated and waited over an hour for the two dingoes to finish eating. This was a clear repetition in the wild of what we had observed in the compound. By the time dingoes reach adulthood there is usually a clear hierarchy and a sophisticated pattern of communication to help prevent direct conflict.

At the other end of the health spectrum to the "muscle family", and one of the most pitiful sights, were the dingoes badly affected by mange. They seemed to be almost staggering in to water and came in broad daylight when the healthy dingoes were nowhere to be seen. Their ribs poked through bare hide, which was flaking from sunburn, exposure and the interminable scratching that the mange mite causes. Dingoes

goes would be lucky to survive the coming dry period before the monsoons nudged some storms towards the centre. They were probably suffering from sarcoptic mange that is passed on from mother to pups in the first few weeks of life. Some pups are immune to it and are never affected, others with defective immune systems succumb and probably die at a young age. All the dingoes we saw with mange appeared to be young.

Mangy dingoes are more often seen than healthy ones. They are hungrier because they are not fit to hunt and a starving mangy dingo will hang around a homestead or waterhole much more readily than a healthy one. But the belief, often voiced in the outback, that most dingoes are mangy was certainly erroneous in our experience at Curtin Springs. At the time of our observations there would have been four healthy dingoes that slipped in quietly for an early morning drink for every mangy one that hung around later.

By that time we had enough film of dingoes around the water and one morning as the sun rose Gary found himself with 18 m of film left in the camera — a length of film which would only last one and a half minutes. A good wildlife film-maker would not allow himself to get caught in the middle of some unexpected action with such short rations so Gary went down to the water to film me in the hide — a "pick-up shot" as it's called in the trade, used it one is desperate or to link sequences.

Gary had only just reached the water's edge and set up his tripod when I noticed a dingo coming in to water. I

whistled just loud enough to attract his attention and watched him "freeze" behind the tripod and remain as still as any animal could. As the dingo came in closer we realised we were about to miss the shot of a lifetime. It was an old bitch and trailing behind her was a tiny pup that she was bringing to water. Gary thought the dingo would soon see

Not having any film in the camera when the 'stars' perform is a painful experience. A dingo bitch brought a tiny little pup in to drink, quite unaware that Gary was there filming the hide just to use up the last few metres of film before changing the magazine. The spoonbill doesn't seem to care. Roland Breckwoldt

him and shot off the measly one and a half minutes of film as she and the pup trotted in. He remained still and the mother and pup continued towards the water until they drank within 15 m of him.

I sat up in the hide watching and tearing my hair out in frustration. Gary remained unnoticed and the pup dived out in the water and swam around in front of its mother. Realising that it was out of its depth, the pup tried to climb on its mother's back and then came around and grabbed her tail with its tiny paws, clinging on like a baby monkey rather than a pup. And we did not get anything of this on film. It still upsets us to this day.

My photography from the hide using a still camera was severely limited because dingoes have such excellent hearing that the click of the shutter can easily scatter them even at 50 m away. But on this occasion, knowing that Gary was out of film, I took some photos. After half a dozen shots the mother pricked up her ears, looked directly at the hide, then galloped off with her tiny pup in tow. We never saw her or the pup again. It was curious that the slightest sound from such a distance away should frighten her, yet Gary, so close to her and in full view, did not worry her at all. Perhaps sound and movement are more important stimuli than the sight of still objects and perhaps the direction of the breeze that day carried any human scent away. Gary thinks that she simply did not see him at all. Maybe she had watered here on so many occasions without a human intruder that she did not notice his still figure yet was on the alert for the sound of anything that might herald danger from beyond the tank.

During the time we had been at this dam, a royal spoonbill had been wading the shallows and stooping to sift mud through its flattened bill, sorting it for tiny crustacea and other organisms. The spoonbill was our mascot, symbol of good fortune and continuity. Nothing ruffled his feathers or composure. Cattle would trample around it, brumbies snort and buck at it and dingoes ignore it but the spoonbill was always there, from dawn until dark. Wading, sifting, sorting, preening. We knew the waterhole was finished when the spoonbill flew away and when it left we also began to think about leaving. Although there was still a week or so of water for the dingoes because they could lap at the tiniest of pools, we now had enough film of them. Our filming was becoming repetitive and it was time for us to pack up. Peter Sevron came out and locked the gate around the water so the cattle had to go to the next tank some 10 km away. We made that a good point for our departure.

PART TWO

The Origin of the Dingo

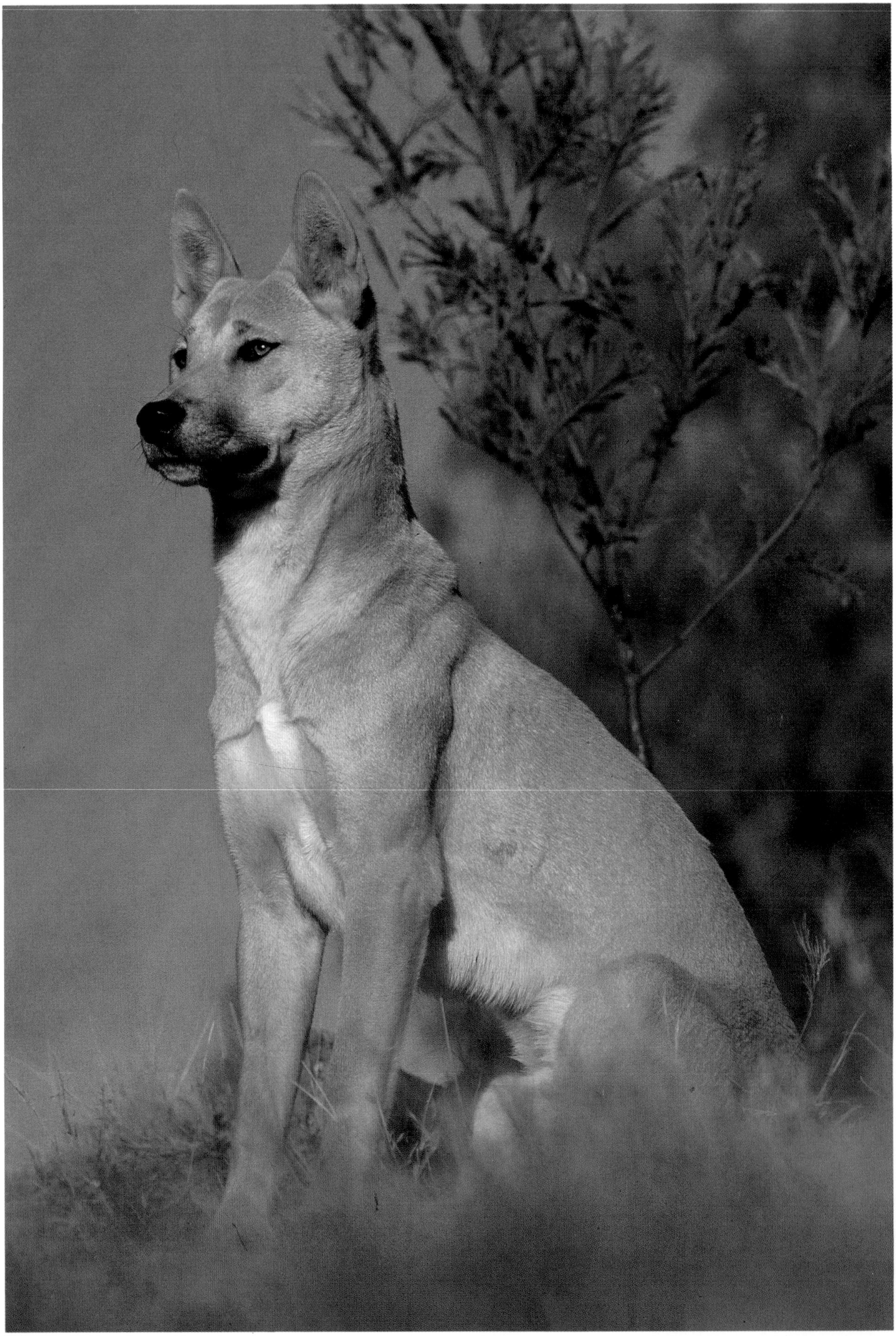

The origin of the dingo

The mystery surrounding the origin of the dingo in Australia began with the evolution of the first canids. The great wolves, the multitude of domestic dogs, the coyotes, jackals, foxes and other canids are all related to two species of small carnivores that resembled weasels and civets. One of them, called *Hesperocyon*, appeared in North America about 25 million years ago; the other, *Cynodictis*, originated in Europe 50 million years ago.

These two ancestors of the canids also gave rise to other carnivores but by the Eocene epoch, which lasted until 37 million years ago, there were at least five genera of canids which can be clearly distinguished from the other carnivores of their time. By the Miocene, which began 22 million years ago and lasted until five million years ago, there had evolved as many as 42 genera of canids. Today, only 15 genera remain, containing 35 different species that range in size from the tiny 1.5 kg fennec to the 80 kg grey timber wolf.[1] The domestic dog *Canis familiaris* is regarded as one of those 35 species.

The canids are placental mammals characterised by their adaptations for running. They have long, semi-rigid legs with a locked ulna and radius that prevents rotation of the front legs. The toes are close together and tipped with a single non-retractile claw. Canids run on these toes or on soft pads under the foot. The elongated skull with strong cheek muscles and large teeth is suited to biting, holding and killing prey. The canids have a particularly large tympanic bulla, or eardrum, which gives them superior hearing. Their complex

Places and features relevant to the origin and arrival of the dingo in Australia.

cerebral cortex indicates that they are of higher intelligence than many other carnivores.

The evolution of the canids passed Australia by. The plains of North America gave rise to the greatest diversity of canids, and they spread throughout Europe, Africa and South America, which remained joined or closely linked. Gondwanaland, which comprised Antarctica and Australia, had begun to break away from the supercontinent Pangaea around 105 million years ago, long before the canids appeared.[2] Australia drifted off on its own voyage across the southern ocean, eventually leaving Antarctica behind, to become a museum of marsupials.

UNRAVELLING A CONUNDRUM

The first Europeans to comment on the dingo were the Dutch and Portuguese seafarers who touched the western and northern shores of the Australian continent in the seventeenth century on their way to spices and riches in the East Indies. The first Englishman to record seeing a dingo in Australia was William Dampier, that vagabond explorer and soldier of fortune who first visited Western Australia in 1688.[3] His journal entry of 5 January 1688 states that "We saw no sort of Animal, nor any Track of beast but once; and that seemed to be the Tread of a Beast as big as a great Mastiff-Dog".

Dampier's curiosity was matched by a good turn of phrase and he attracted enough notice for the British government to finance him on a second voyage in 1699.[4] It was during that voyage that he wrote one of the most graphic early descriptions of the dingo:

> There are but few Land-Animals. I saw some Lizards; and my Men saw two or three Beasts like hungry Wolves, lean like so many skeletons, being nothing but skin and Bones: 'Tis probable that it was the Foot of one of those Beasts that I mentioned as seen by us in N. Holland.

This early description of the dingo as a wolf was repeated by the first British colonists who arrived in 1788. Surgeon John White of the First Fleet wrote a detailed description of the dingo: "This animal is a variety of the Dog, and, like the shepherd's dog in most countries, approaches near to the original of the species, which is the wolf..."[5]

Such was the acceptance of the dingo as a wolf-like native animal that it was formally named *Canis antarcticus* ("southern dog") by Kerr in 1792. However, this name was challenged because it had already been used for another species, so in 1793 Meyer renamed it *Canis dingo*, using what was regarded as the Aboriginal name for this dog as the species name.[6,7] The early efforts to classify the dingo show that it was widely regarded as an indigenous species — a wolf for Australia. It would take time, experience and study to prove that the dingo was a newcomer.

John Gould, the early Australian naturalist, perceived this disparity and included the dingo in *The mammals of Australia* (completed in 1863) almost as an afterthought, and certainly with an apology.[8] Gould also firmly believed that the dingo had

> all the habits of a low-bred dog, and none of the determined air and ferocity of disposition of the wolf or jackal: in confirmation of this opinion may I cite the facility with which the natives bring it under subjection...

The oddity of the dingo among the rest of the Australian fauna and the association of part of the dingo population with the Aborigines led Gould to believe that it was not indigenous to Australia, but introduced by the first Aborigines. He was scientist and gentleman enough to publish an opposing opinion and quoted correspondence from Gerard Krefft, a geologist in Victoria who, in association with Professor McCoy at the Melbourne Museum, claimed that the dingo had lived in Australia at the same time as the giant marsupials which lived until about 14–16,000 years ago.[9]

In 1843 dingo bones were found lying together with remains of the extinct "marsupial lion", *Thylacoleo carnifex*, and the largest marsupial — a "giant wombat", *Diprotodon optatum* — in an eroding sand dune at Lake Colongulac in Victoria.[10,11] Two more such finds

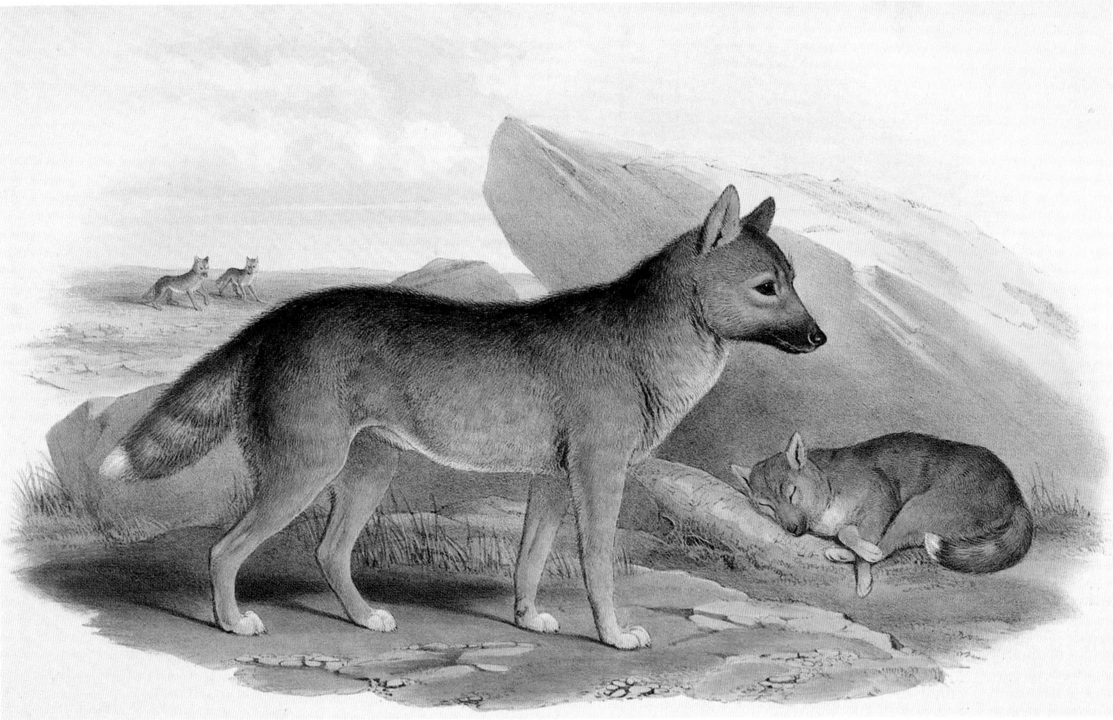

This painting by John Gould was reproduced in his book The Mammals of Australia, *published in 1863. He was one of the first naturalists to remark that the dingo was not native to Australia. Museum of Victoria*

were to follow. In 1857 the Victorian Geological Survey collected dingo bones and teeth in company with what appeared to be the fossils of species belonging to the extinct megafauna in the Gisborne Caves near Colac, Victoria. In 1867 the Wellington Caves in New South Wales were found to contain a similar association of fossils.[12]

Professor McCoy used these associations to argue that the dingo was an original element of the Australian fauna. He believed that the dingo resembled the first dogs, and that, because of its isolation, Australia had remained an ark carrying the pure wild dog, unsullied by the European predilection for selective breeding. Others were quick to accept this view, and the erroneous idea that the dingo is an example of the "purest breed of dog" remains a powerful myth to this day.

Neither Krefft nor McCoy seem to have considered that the mere association of the two groups of fossils — dingo and megafauna — did not necessarily prove that they had been deposited at the same time. From their prestigious positions in scientific institutions, they became a formidable force in the debate about the dingo. McCoy stated his position thus:

> Contrary to my preconceived notion, I have satisfied myself that the Native Dog (*Canis dingo*) is a truly indigenous animal, both from its increasing numbers (with little variety) towards the

interior of the continent remote from man, and from having identified its bones mingled with those of recent and extinct animals all in one state of preservation in the bone caverns recently opened beneath the basalt flows at Mount Macedon.[10]

McCoy was heavily influenced by a visual appraisal of the Gisborne Cave fossils that indicated that they were "all in one state of preservation". The dingo bones seemed to be mineralised to the same extent as those derived from what appeared to belong to the megafauna. The techniques for testing and measuring such phenomena were not available at that time and McCoy's conclusions certainly contributed to the debate as it drew attention from people of international repute, if not fame.

Charles Darwin entered the fray in 1868 with his publication of *The Variation of Animals and Plants under Domestication*. Darwin proclaimed the dingo to be a form of domestic dog descended from the northern wolf and brought to Australia very early in the process of Aboriginal colonisation.[13] He did not rule out the possibility of the dingo being contemporary with the giant marsupials and simply used any evidence of an overlap to point out that the dingo and the Aborigines had been in Australia for a long time. He clearly believed that the dingo had been introduced by humans. Otherwise, Darwin argued, where were all the other large placental carnivores that evolved with the canids in the Northern Hemisphere; where were the apes, the big cats, the large herbivores; and how could their absence be explained?

Was the dingo indigenous to Australia, or was it brought by the first Aborigines? These were the two main views as to its origin. Running beside them were others that had sufficient following to find their way into print. One point of origin for the dingo, it was postulated, was via the Dutch seafarers. The supporters of this view had not read the journals of these seamen to learn that the dingo was there to greet them. Yet another theory was that the dingo walked into Australia via land bridges that existed during past ice ages.

The pioneering work of A. R. Wallace brought the origin of the dingo into sharper focus. In 1893 Wallace noted that there was a clear distinction between the fauna of the Oriental Region and the Australian Zoogeographic Region and that the continental shelf of South-East Asia was the line of demarcation between the two.[14] "Wallace's Line" still holds today and is the recognised boundary between two distinct faunal regions. Wallace claimed that the dingo was not truly indigenous because none of its near relatives, or other large non-marsupials, had crossed his line and that therefore the dingo alone had been carried to Australia by people.

This theme was taken up by Wood Jones in 1921. He did not accept that an association of dingo and extinct megafauna fossils was indisputable evidence that the dingo was indigenous.[15] He examined the anatomy of the dingo and saw it as a form of wild dog, intermediate between the wild dogs of South America and the northern wolf. Wood Jones argued that, as the dingo had no evolutionary roots in Australia, it must have been introduced by people. He castigated those who believed that the dingo was indigenous to Australia with a damning zoological mouthful:

> The evolution of a modified northern wolf in an isolated portion of the Southern Hemisphere, tenanted solely by Ornithodelphians, Didelphians, and a few stray Monodelphian rodents and bats, is a thing which is Zoologically inconceivable. . . the supposition that the dingo is indigenous, that is that its phylogenetic story was unfolded in the confines of Australia, is absolutely untenable, and should, once and for all, be dismissed from any literature having pretence to scientific accuracy.

At that time, the earliest Aboriginal inhabitants of Australia were believed to have the features of the Talgai skull, so named after its discovery in 1886 near East Talgai on the Darling Downs, Queensland.[16] Wood Jones leaves no doubt about his view on Talgai man and the dingo:

> The progenitor of the Talgai man came with his wife, he came with his dog and with his dog's wife and he must have done the journey in a seaworthy boat, capable of traversing this unquiet portion of the ocean with his considerable cargo.

Professor Wood Jones was not necessarily asserting that the dingo and the extinct megafauna did not share the continent at one time. As far as he was concerned, Aborigines could have brought the dingo to Australia while the megafauna still lived. It is now known that the Aborigines and the megafauna did share Australia for at least 20,000 years.[9] However, this was not the main issue for Wood Jones. He simply believed that the dingo did not evolve in Australia and the best explanation for its presence was that it came with the Aborigines. He was supported by the earlier statements of Gould and by the work of scientists of international reputation such as Darwin and Wallace. It therefore became widely accepted that the dingo was introduced by the first Aborigines. As recently as 1953, Edmund Gill, a respected geologist, was to state:

> A fossil dingo was found with the bones of extinct marsupials in the Wellington Caves in New South Wales. It may be assumed that the Aborigines brought the dingo to Australia, and so the Aborigines can be concluded to have been here at the same time as the giant marsupials.[17]

Aborigines did hunt the giant marsupials, but the dingo did not. One by one, each piece of evidence that had been used to argue that the dingo and the megafauna coexisted, at least for a time, was shown to be false. In 1964 a reworking of the fossils found in the Gisborne Caves showed them to belong to modern species — not the megafauna.[18] The entrance to the caves is restricted and they lie in a honeycomb of basalt. It was easy for McCoy and Krefft to believe they had found fossils of dingoes and megafauna that had died long ago and been preserved within the basaltic larva flow. In their enthusiasm for a dingo that was contemporary with the megafauna, both McCoy and Krefft overlooked evidence that the dingo bones were of more recent origin. Indeed, the records of the first discovery of the caves by the geological survey state, "The roof and sides of the passages, where narrow were quite smooth and polished, evidently from animals that have inhabited the cave."[15] Animals were using the caves at the time of their discovery in 1859 and at least one dingo had recently died there.

It was not until 1973 that Gill himself proved that his earlier views of the dingo's antiquity were greatly exaggerated. He used fluorine analysis to show that the megafauna fossils from the Lake Colongulac sand dune and the Wellington Caves were deposited at widely differing times from the dingo bones found at both sites.[19] Fluorine analysis cannot indicate the actual age of bones. It can, however, show whether bones were deposited at the same time by comparing the amount of fluoride deterioration that has occurred since the death of their owner. Gill's analysis indicated that dingo and megafauna happened to die in the same place, but a long time apart.

An examination of the records of the discovery of the Wellington Caves in 1867 reveals that A. R. Thomson, Professor of Geology at Sydney University at the time, clearly noted that the fossils he found were not in their correct anatomical position and that they had become mixed.[20,21] The entrance to these caves is large, and animals had entered and died of natural causes over a long period of time. Caves can also be natural pit traps. It is possible that a diprotodon died there over 14,000 years ago and that the dingo died among its bones much more recently.

The remarkable association of dingo and megafauna bones in the sand dune at Lake Colongulac was also dismantled by modern archeological methods. Eroding sand dunes have a great capacity to mix bones. As the surface sand blows away, any bones that it holds are lowered to join those in older deposits below. This is what had happened at Lake Colongulac. The bones of a dingo were lowered to join those of a giant wombat and a marsupial lion that had died many thousands of years before.[22]

The lack of any sound explanation for the absence of the dingo from Tasmania remained a blind spot in the entire debate. Surely, if the first Aborigines brought the dingo to mainland Australia, they would have taken it south to Tasmania? The lack of any canids in Tasmania, and the presence of the thylacine, was simply ignored in the debate about the origin of the dingo.

The advent of radio-carbon dating in the late 1950s, and its widespread use to verify the ages of archeological deposits, caused a radical revision of estimates of the dingo's date of arrival in Australia and explained its absence from Tasmania. The history of the dingo was about to be rewritten. Carbon dating has ruthlessly reduced the time the

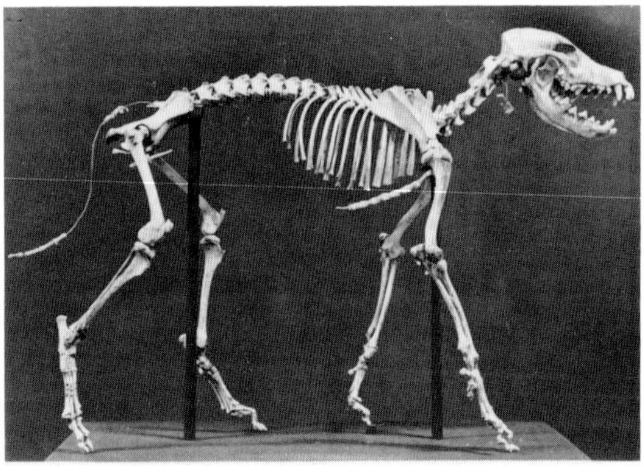

Top: *Dingo bones at Lake Cawndilla, Menindee, New South Wales, showing how the erosion of a sand dune can mix them confusingly with lower layers of fossils that are many thousands of years older. It was this process that led some earlier scientists to believe that the dingo had been in Australia at the time of the giant marsupials. Allan Fox*

Bottom: *This dingo skeleton is around 3000 years old, making it one of the oldest fossil dingoes in Australia. It was excavated in 1960 from two metres below the surface at Fromms Landing on the Murray River in South Australia. G. L. Williams*

dingo has been in Australia. This technique has revealed that the oldest dingo fossil yet found in Australia is only 3450 years old. It was found in Madura Cave on the Nullarbor Plain. Every other early fossil dingo appears about this time. An Aboriginal midden at Wombah on the north coast of New South Wales contained a dingo that died around 3230 years ago.[23] A near perfect skeleton of a young male dingo found at Fromms Landing on the Murray River is about 3170 years old.[24]

Part of a dingo found in a rock shelter at Mount Burr in South Australia was thought to be between 7500 and 8500 years old but this has now been shown to be incorrect.[25] An examination of the records of the first excavation, and a re-excavation of the same site, show that it was greatly disturbed and that the dingo bones originated from a more recent level of deposition. This earlier date still appears incorrectly in many references to the earliest carbon-dated dingo fossil. The dingo deposits at Devils Lair in Western Australia were similarly thought to have been of earlier origin but carbon dating, together with accurate archeological excavation and description, now shows that all dingo fossils are less than 3500 years old.

The decline of the thylacine (*Thylacinus cynocephalus*) on the mainland around 3000 years ago is widely accepted as further evidence that this was about the time the dingo arrived.[23] No explanation for the sudden demise of the thylacine fits as well as the theory that it could not compete with the dingo. Its survival in Tasmania until recent times also indicates that the dingo was involved in its decline on the mainland. The Tasmanian devil, another large carnivore, began its decline at the same time and was extinct on the mainland by about 400 years ago.[26] But it thrives in Tasmania where there are no dingoes.

Tasmania was cut off from the mainland when the seas rose after the last ice age that ended about 12,000 years ago.[27] The dangerous sea crossing isolated the Tasmanian Aborigines from their counterparts on the mainland who had acquired the dingo. No dingo fossils have been found on the islands of Bass Strait.

Whether the dingo did, or did not, get to New Guinea is more complicated because New Guinea does have a wild dog similar to the dingo. It is known as the New Guinea singing dog (*Canis familiaris hallstromi*) and was regarded as a separate subspecies to the Australian dingo as far back as 1881.[28] However, a debate still continues as to how and when it got to New Guinea and how closely it is related to the dingo. It has been forcefully argued that the New Guinea singing dog is quite different from the dingo and arrived in New

TABLE 1:
Timetable of events significant to the Australian dingo.

Time in years	Event
38,000	Oldest evidence of Aborigines in Australia.
14–16,000	Extinction of most of the megafauna.
12,000	Tasmania isolated by the rising sea that forms Bass Strait.
6500	New Guinea isolated by Torres Strait.
3450	Oldest known dingo fossil. Found in Madura Cave on the Nullarbor Plain.
3000	Thylacine presumed extinct on the mainland.
430	Tasmanian devil presumed extinct on the mainland.
200	British settlement of Australia.
51	Thylacine presumed extinct in Tasmania.

It is assumed that the dingo caused the extinction of the thylacine on mainland Australia because the thylacine continued to thrive in Tasmania (where there were no dingoes) until being eliminated by the European settlers who relentlessly trapped and shot it. This photograph from the collection of John Calaby was taken at Burnie, Tasmania, circa 1900, and shows the tragic result of one 'good' day's hunting.

Guinea after the dingo arrived in Australia and by quite different means.[29] New Guinea was cut off from Australia only 6500 years ago when the last of the rising seas inundated the Sunda Plain which had all but connected them.[30] The oldest dog fossils found so far in New Guinea are only 2000 years old, so it may well be that it did in fact get its dog after Australia.

We do not know how long it took the dingo to become established in Australia. Nor do we know how many colonising dingoes arrived and over how long a period. There was obviously more than one dingo, but were the first pair successful in colonising Australia? It is possible, to make an estimate of how long it would take the dingo to spread over the continent once a breeding colony had become established in the wild. We know, for example, that it took the red fox only 70 years to cross the Nullarbor Plain and a mere 60 years to reach the Kimberleys in northern Australia after it was released in Victoria.[31] The rabbit, although aided and abetted by human hand, spread throughout its present range with equal facility.

It is also quite possible that Aborigines helped the dingo to spread. On the evidence gained from the spread of the fox, a period of 500 years would be ample to allow the dingo to colonise the entire continent. With the oldest known fossil at 3450 years old, this puts the most probable time of arrival of the dingo at about 4000 years ago. Doubters may argue that because Australia is vast and the science of archeology is young, we have simply not discovered the oldest dingo fossils. The evidence accumulated so far makes it unlikely that the dingo's period of residence could be extended very much.

An arrival time of only about 4000 years ago does not solve the mystery of who introduced the dingo to Australia. Indeed, it only serves to heighten the mystique surrounding this enigmatic animal and poses more questions than it answers. Who were these visitors to Australian shores? Were they only visitors? Why did they carry dogs? Where did those dogs come from?

The New Guinea singing dog is found throughout Papua New Guinea and is regarded as a separate sub-species to the dingo, although there is still some debate about how closely related the two might be. Gary Steer

THE DOMESTICATION OF THE DOG

For a long time it was believed that the northern wolf, shown here, was the ancestor of all domestic dogs. This theory, however, has been discarded in favour of the view that some domestic dogs owe their ancestry to the smaller Asian wolves, such as the Indian plains wolf. Jean-Paul Ferrero

The next clue to the origin of the dingo is found among the bones that tell the history of the domestication of the dog. This, too, is a recent process because domestic dogs first appeared only between 8000 and 12,000 years ago. Domestication of the dog took place in different parts of the world when certain races of people adopted a way of life that was sufficiently sedentary for them to keep animals. The first attempts at domestication used wolves — either pups caught in the wild or animals that had attached themselves to human settlements by living off handouts or leftovers of the hunt. From here it was only a short step to exerting selection pressure for traits such as tractability and responsiveness to human commands.[32,33]

The diagnostic traits used to differentiate the first domestic dogs from their wild ancestors are tooth crowding, shortening of the jaw and a reduction in the size of the brain. A reduction of overall size and increasing variety in shape and form also followed domestication. Such animals make a sudden appearance in the fossil record and are always associated with human occupation sites. Some locations have yielded fossils that are clearly wolves and others that are so different that they are domestic dogs; other fossils are intermediate between the two and therefore represent the first experiments in that region of selective breeding from the wolf ancestors.

For a long time it was believed that the northern wolf (*Canis lupus*) was the common ancestor of all domestic dogs. It was further supposed that selective breeding from this wolf gave rise to a generalised dog that was called *Canis familiaris optimae*. Claims that the dingo is the purest form of domestic dog are based on the erroneous belief that it is identical to this particular form of early

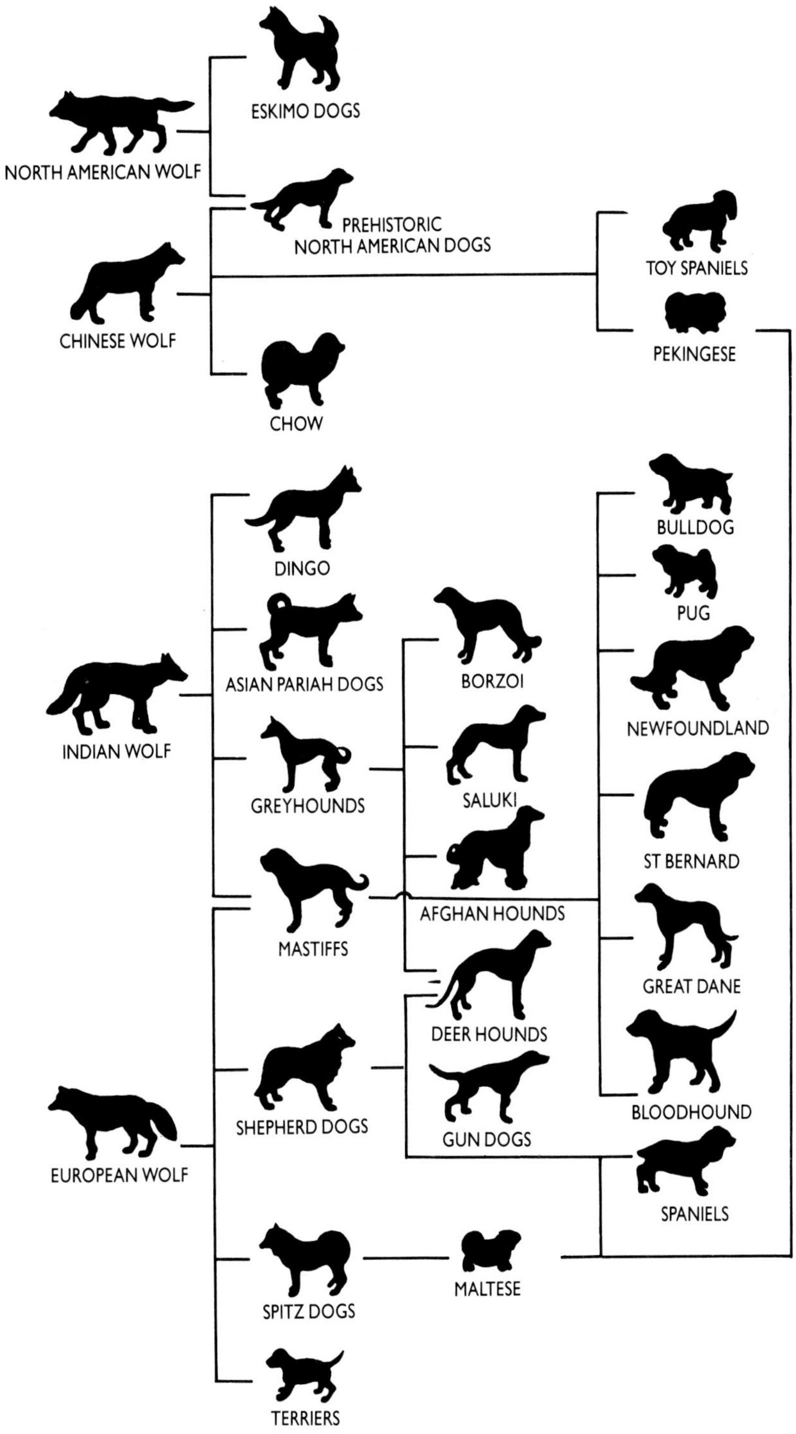

A family tree of modern dogs based on their most likely wolf ancestry. From Clutton-Brock 1984.

domestic dog. The main weakness of the theory of a generalised dog was that it was not based on the full geographical range of fossil dogs. The widespread use of the smaller species of wolf, such as the Indian plains wolf (*Canis lupus pallipes*), in the domestication of the dog is now well accepted and helps explain the differences between the Asian domestic dogs and those in northern Europe.[34] The Indian plains wolf is now regarded as the most likely wild ancestor of the dingo.

The dingo is a form of domestic dog that retains enough characteristics of its wild ancestors to put it a little to the side of the modern domestic dog. The dingo does not have the same degree of tooth crowding and foreshortening of the jaw as other domestic dogs. Second, the size of its cranium has not been reduced to the same extent as other domestic dogs when compared to the wolf.[29] Third, the female dingo is restricted to only one breeding cycle each year. These differences have provided taxonomists with the evidence to argue that the dingo is a separate subspecies of the domestic dog. Hence the dingo is known as *Canis familiaris dingo*. This rather uncertain position among the domestic dogs encourages some people to refer to any wild dingo as a feral dog. It would be more accurate to regard it as a semi-wild dog that bypassed the full domestication process exerted upon some of its near relatives.

The Indian plains wolf is the most likely wild ancestor of the Australian dingo. Alan Newsome

SEAFARERS WITH A DINGO

Laurie Corbett, a wildlife research officer employed by the CSIRO, has studied the wild dogs of Thailand where one handy source of skeletons was the local dog meat market.[35] He believes that the Thai dogs and the Australian dingo are closely related and that dogs similar to the dingo can be found in a belt that extends from Israel east towards Vietnam, bounded in the north by mountain ranges such as the Himalaya. From here they reach down through Indonesia, Borneo, the Philippines, New Guinea and Australia. Laurie recognises different forms of these Asian dogs and mentions, for example, that the Thai dogs are smaller than Australian dingoes. He does not regard this as surprising and suggests that some genetic isolation has occurred and that the difference in diet also accounts for some variation. In essence, this means that the dingo is a semi-wild dog that is widely distributed throughout Asia.

Laurie Corbett's theory on the origin of the dingo is as follows: as the people of Asia developed a sedentary life style based on agriculture they also built up a commensal relationship with some of the smaller Asian wolves; with some selection pressure they developed a dog that we now call the dingo; some groups of people were happy with the dingo as it was and did not apply any further selection pressure for domestication; they carried this dog with them as a pet and also to be used as food as they migrated throughout South-East Asia after the last ice age.

A tiny biting louse provides evidence that there may have been a two-way traffic in dingoes between Australia and mainland Asia. A biting louse (*Heterodoxus spiniger*) is believed to have evolved among the Australian marsupials yet it is also found on the wild dogs of Asia. The elusive race of seafarers who carried the first dingoes here may well have travelled back and forth and taken dingoes home that had hunted marsupials in the Australian bush.

Klim Gollan, an archeologist, presents quite a different theory.[29,36] His examination of canid fossils in museums throughout the world leads him to the conclusion that the closest relatives of the dingo were to be found among the dogs bred on the delta of the Indus River in India about 3000 years ago. Klim believes that the dingo is so like these Indian dogs, and so unlike the dogs of South-East Asia, that they must have come directly from India. He says that this is quite possible, given the long history of the Indians as traders, and points to Timor as the link in the India–Australia connection. Sheep, goats, pigs, cattle, dogs and artefacts of Indian culture arrived in Timor about 3000 years ago.[37]

Klim Gollan believes that the time of arrival of the dog in New Guinea, as indicated by the current fossil record, is reasonably accurate and will not be radically revised. This means that New Guinea did not get its dog until about 2000 years after the dingo arrived in Australia. He also believes that the Australian dingo and the New Guinea singing dog share only a very distant ancestry and that the two are separate subspecies that were carried to their respective destinations by very different races of people. According to Klim, the New Guinea dog has affinities with the smaller dogs of the Pacific region and it arrived there via the Philippines and Indonesia.

The major differences between the theories of Laurie Corbett and Klim Gollan lie in the route the dingo took to Australia and the identity of its nearest living relatives. They both agree on an Asian origin based on the Indian plains wolf. However, Laurie emphasises that the dingo is semi-wild and has only lightly felt the hand of selection pressure while Klim sees it more as a form of domesticated dog. It also follows from Klim Gollan's theory that the dingo is unique to Australia, with its nearest living relatives the village dogs in parts of India. Conversely, Laurie Corbett sees the dingo as the Australian race of a semi-wild dog that is widely distributed throughout South-East Asia.

The idea that the dingo came to Australia through South-East Asia during the active human migrations and trading voyages over the past few thousand years is easier to accept than a direct route from India which suggests an isolated event. A path down through the Indonesian Archipelago during migration or trading and fishing visits to northern Australia by South-East Asian seafarers is certainly a more straightforward theory. There is possibly another relationship between the Aborigines and people from Asia that could help us understand more about the arrival of the dingo.

THE SMALL TOOL TRADITION

The blurred picture of the origin of the dingo could be sharpened if more becomes known about "the small tool tradition". Quite suddenly, around 5000 years ago, three types of new stone tools appeared in the Aboriginal toolkit.[25] They were points fixed to spears, backed blades used as tiny knives or fixed on to spears to form numerous barbs, and adze flakes, or small stone flakes used in shaping wood. The origin of the new tools remains as obscure as that of the dingo but the fact that they both appeared in Australia at about the same time cannot be ignored.

An entry date of 5000 years ago for the points and backed blades is a little earlier than we surmise for the dingo, but it is certainly possible that their entry is connected with the arrival of the same people who carried the dingo. These migrations could have been instigated by conflicts that resulted in a loss of territory when the seas rose after the last ice age and consumed huge tracts of land, forcing the traditional owners to move elsewhere. Some archeologists disagree and say that the new tools were developed by Aborigines here in Australia. Again, there is a tenuous link, this hint that people came to Australia, brought some new tools and perhaps their dogs, and were absorbed into the culture of the Aborigines without leaving further trace.

What remains indisputable is that the dingo was a sailor, a "sea dog" that originated on mainland Asia and was carried by people to parts south and east. There would have been many reasons for carrying a dingo on such voyages. Dingoes readily eat fish, so they could have been fed on fish and then eaten as a welcome change in diet. The dingo could have been an item for trade. People who leave their homeland forever, to migrate and start life anew in a far-off land also like to take their pets with them.

The full story of the introduction of the dingo to Australia relies on the knowledge and expertise of people from different branches of science. Much of that story is integrally linked with the history of Australia, its people, and the relationship with our Asian neighbours before the coming of Europeans. It is not only the history of the dingo that is under scrutiny — it is also a history of the Australian people.

Aborigines and the dingo

The Aborigines were hunter-gatherers without dogs until the dingo was brought here only a few thousand years ago. The dingo was quickly incorporated into Aboriginal culture and some were kept in their camps. Why did Aborigines keep dingoes? What advantages did this dog confer upon its new masters? Belonging as we do to a culture that has valued the dog as a hunting animal, it is easy to assume that it enlarged the Aboriginal larder. We may have to look further. There is something else about the dog that enables it to inveigle its way into the hearts and homes of mankind.

THE DINGO AS A HUNTING AID

It has been widely assumed that the dingo was kept and used by the Aborigines as a hunting dog. Perhaps we jump so readily to this conclusion because, of the 308 breeds of domestic dog known today, over 173 are recognised as hunting dogs and many others can also fulfil this purpose. However, studies of hunter-gatherers throughout the world show that they rarely used dogs for hunting.[1] In 1965, Mervyn Meggit, an anthropologist, questioned

It has been widely assumed that the Australian Aborigines accepted the dingo so readily because it was useful as a hunting dog. However, traditional methods of hunting, such as depicted in this early illustration, did not rely on the dingo. S. T. Gill, Mitchell Library

the relationship between Aborigines and dingoes and came to the iconoclastic conclusion that:

> The available evidence, limited and uneven as it is, suggests that over wide areas of Australia the tame dingo was by no means an effective hunting dog and that it contributed relatively little to the Aborigines' larder. It seems that only in ecologically specialized regions where particular kinds of game were abundant (as in the tropical rainforest) was the tame dingo a significant economic adjunct to the family hunting unit.[2]

Meggit started a debate that ran in the anthropological journal *Mankind* for some years, and has still not been satisfactorily resolved. The argument continues because there is only a flimsy historical and anthropological record of Aboriginal life at first contact. The explorers were obsessed with charting new land and the early students of Aboriginal culture were interested in charting ritual and law. Few were interested in dogs.

The dearth of information about Aborigines and dingoes at the time of first contact has often led to a reliance on observations of contemporary Aboriginal relationships with European domestic dogs.[3] Much has changed in the Aboriginal way of life and these observations do not provide a good insight into what might have been the case with dingoes before the European invasion. European hunting dogs and the innumerable permutations of their crosses with other domestic dogs, as found in today's Aboriginal communities, are different from dingoes in both behaviour and capacity.

Some of the early explorers who observed Aborigines did believe that the dingo was primarily a hunting dog. In 1889, Ernest Giles wrote that Aborigines in central Australia used dingoes for hunting and even added that "wonderful hunting dogs they are".[4] However, Giles had other things on his mind and his cursory observations must be compared with other records about Aborigines in the same region. Herbert Basedow accompanied an early expedition into central Australia and became familiar with the Pitjantjatjara people about whom Giles had written.[5] According to Basedow:

> a native just holds the unruly mob around him for company's sake; he prefers to rely on his own skill and instinct when hunting, and rarely allows his dogs to go with him; in fact, there seems to be little inclination on the part of the dogs to accompany the chase with the master.

Basedow reversed Giles' explanation of why these Aborigines kept dingoes. He claimed that the continual pampering and indulgence lavished upon the camp dingoes made them useless for almost anything except warning about the approach of strangers. A study of the Pitjantjatjara people in 1972 supported Basedow's opinion:

> dogs are taken during the day by the women, since their presence in a hunting-blind or during a stealthy approach toward an animal would frighten away the game... Among traditional Western Desert Aborigines... dogs are seldom used in hunting, and do not receive an allotted share of the food.[6]

In 1936 Erich Kolig, a welfare officer making a patrol into remote traditional Pintupi territory, noted that dingoes were useful in following the scent of larger game such as kangaroos but rarely obtained them and that their main

Right: *This Aborigine, photographed by Charles Kerry near the turn of the century, wears a 'King Plate' gratuitously given by the white government of the day. He has chosen the dog himself, however, and it appears to be a greyhound or one of the crossbreeds based on the greyhound which the colonials named 'kangaroo dogs'. National Library of Australia*

Below: *If the dingo was a good hunting dog then it is unlikely that the Aborigines would have discarded it so rapidly in favour of European domestic breeds. Not one of the eight dogs that accompanied these two groups of Aranda men meeting at Alice Springs was a dingo, even though traditional life still prevailed when this photograph was taken in 1900. Baldwin Spencer, Museum of Victoria*

contribution lay in helping to find snakes, lizards and small mammals such as rats.[7] This is in keeping with the view that the dingo could have played only a minor role in obtaining large game because it would have frightened the animals off and put them outside the range of tradition weapons such as spears. Stalking to within close enough range to use a spear was the most reliable and widely used method of obtaining large game such as kangaroos, wallabies and emus. This technique and the dingo were totally incompatible and there are many accounts of hunters chasing dingoes back to camp as they left for the hunt.[8]

If the dingo was a good hunting dog, it would certainly be still used as such today, both by Aborigines and Europeans. Just as Aborigines gained access to new breeds of the domestic dog, so Europeans gained access to the dingo. But the dingo has not proved a successful hunting dog. It is difficult to keep a dingo focused on a task and it lacks the responsiveness to commands essential in a hunting dog. If it seems easy to presume that man was attracted to the dog because of its advantages in the hunt, it can be sobering to contemplate that the reverse also holds true: dogs are attracted to people because of *our* ability to hunt. Of course the relationship between man and dog is more complex and cannot be reduced to such simple terms but it does help to point out that we have to go beyond an aid in hunting to look for the cement that bonded Aborigines and dingoes.

THE DINGO AS A PET

To restrict an evaluation of the relationship between people and other animals to the practical and economic aspects can obscure a realisation that there are other, richer emotional bonds. One of the bonds that transcends mere utility arises when an animal is kept purely as a pet. Many Europeans noted a special relationship between Aborigines and dingoes and believed that it reflected the way their own culture embraced its pets. Why, for example, would Aboriginal women in central Australia be burdened by carrying a dingo in the way Captain White observed in 1914:

> It was very surprising to find that many of the women carried live wild dogs round their waists — the forepaws and nose being grasped in one hand, while the hind paws and tail are in the other; the extremeties of the dogs, in some cases meeting in the front. As far as the limited knowledge of the language would allow, it was ascertained that all women who were barren or had ceased bearing children were required to nurse a dog in this way.[6]

A dingo large enough to wrap around a woman's waist with both ends almost meeting was certainly large enough to walk behind a group of Aborigines. My dingo was only half-grown when it accompanied me on long walks through the central Australian landscape. Both

Above: *Aboriginal women in the arid Everard Ranges of northern South Australia carrying dingoes nose to tail around their waists. This rare photo, by an unknown photographer, taken at a date also unknown, clearly demonstrates this unusual method of carrying dingoes, which was frequently commented upon by the early explorers.*
National Library of Australia

Left: *The dingo was an ideal pet for the Aborigines. It could be fondled and cared for when young, becoming a camp dog that fended mostly for itself as an adult, or alternatively, it could try life on the wild side. This photograph of Pintupi children in the Gibson Desert in Western Australia was taken as recently as 1963, as these people had had almost no contact with Europeans up to that time.*
Jeremy Long, Australian Institute for Aboriginal Studies

Maliki and the many wild dingoes I observed, however, were frequently hampered by thorns and burrs in their feet. It is very common to see a dingo limp for some distance then lie down and try to remove the offending object. Compassion for a pet may be one reason that Aborigines carried dingoes. Even back in 1906, white Australians had acquired a reputation for indolence and were compared to the camp dingo with its propensity to lie down on the job and insist on being carried:

> The dingo suffered from the Australian "tired feeling" though — perhaps originated it — for it is on record that he "frequently refused to go further, his owner being forced to carry him on his shoulder, a luxury of which the warrigals were very fond".[9]

Aborigines often lavished dingo pups with affection. They fondled and indulged them and picked through their fur searching for scales, sores and parasites in the same way the dingoes cleaned each other. Naturalist Carl Lumholtz observed Aborigines and their dingoes in north Queensland late last century and said that "its master never strikes, but merely threatens it. He caresses it like a child, eats the fleas off it and then kisses it on the snout".[2] This is compatible with Basedow's observation in 1903 of the Aborigines in central Australia where "The dingo is also tamed and 'domesticated' when taken young. They are, however, of no use for hunting, but are generally fondled and fed up by the natives".[5]

In 1828, Major Lockyer visited Stradbroke Island off the Queensland coast and wrote the following account of its Aborigines, who at that stage had almost no contact with European culture:

> The attachment of these people to their dogs is worthy of notice. I was very anxious to get one of the wild native breed of black colour, a very handsome puppy, which one of the men had in his arms. I offered him a small axe for it; his companions urged him to take it, and he was about to do so, when he looked at the dog and the animal licked his face, which settled the business. He shook his head and determined to keep him.[10]

Further evidence that Aborigines had a special relationship with at least some

This camp dingo lived with Aborigines between 900 and 3000 years ago, at the place now known as Captain Stevenson Point near Mallacoota, Victoria. Dingo remains in archaeological deposits are found only rarely, so it is difficult to learn about the relationship between dingoes and Aborigines prior to the white invasion. This particular find is also rare because the dingo received a burial. Victoria Victorian Archaeological Survey

camp dingoes comes from the archeological excavation of an Aboriginal midden at Captain Stevenson Point near Mallacoota, Victoria.[11] Carbon dating of charcoal in the midden shows that it is about 3000 years old and was used until about 900 years ago. At some time around the middle of that period a full adult dingo was buried in the midden. That the dingo received a burial is significant in itself but an examination of its skeleton showed that it had received a massive neck injury while it was still quite young and was dependent on being hand-fed. Inside its stomach cavity was the skeleton of a large black fish, part of the Aborigines' diet in the area.

Not every Aboriginal group was equally fond of dingoes as pets. Those who inhabited the cold regions of the southeast used fur skins to keep warm and keeping these fur coats intact was incompatible with dingoes. The noted anthropologist Norman Tindale believed that the keeping of dingoes and domestic dogs actually increased in these Aboriginal communities once they gained access to European clothing that the animals did not find attractive to chew.[12]

Those Aborigines who did keep dingoes had a relationship with them that was fundamentally different from that which they had with any other animals. However, Erich Kolig cautions against jumping to the conclusion that the dingo was simply a pet on which Aborigines could exercise a nurturing instinct:

> Because a sizeable section of western society, composed of predominantly lonesome ladies, disgruntled bachelors, sentimental academics and the like, enjoys canine company so that mutual affection may enhance an otherwise emotionally barren life, does not mean that this is the standard motivation for Aboriginal society.[8]

If Aborigines wanted pets, dingoes were more suitable than other native fauna. They are easy to rear, had been partly domesticated before their arrival in Australia and could also return to the wild. This allowed the Aborigines to have young dingoes in the camp when they were most endearing and entertaining without being burdened by a large population of unruly adult dingoes. But the question still remains: if the relationship between Aborigines and dingoes was purely based on the dingo's attractions as a pet, why have Aborigines not adopted the domestic cat with similar enthusiasm? Indeed, the cat has not been given any place in Aboriginal communities. The fact that the dog remains the most favoured animal for most Aborigines encourages a search for more powerful links.

THE "THREE DOG NIGHT" THEORY

The way in which Aborigines huddled together at night with dingoes led to the suggestion that the dingo made a significant contribution to Aboriginal society as a living blanket. This notion has entered Australian folklore and a cold night may now be described as a "three dog night", or even a "five dog night" if the temperature warrants such canine extravagance.

Mammals can fight the cold by huddling together so that their combined volume has a greater heat storage capacity. Body heat can also be exchanged and the surface area through which heat can be lost from each individual is reduced. Most huddling is between individuals of the same species; different species rarely huddle together because of their different sleeping or hibernating sites. Humans are an exception and huddling with other species has been observed in various cultures. The smaller breeds of dogs, sometimes referred to as "lap dogs", are often used as a source of warmth. The poorer residents of rural England once used pigs as a source of warmth.[1]

The advantages in huddling are greater for the smaller animal because it is less able to store body heat. Consequently, the dingo would have gained the major benefit from huddling next to an Aborigine, particularly if he or she also got up during the night to stoke a warming fire! It is also possible that the dingo could be a nuisance and block the warmth from these fires or aggravate crowding. One recent observer of a group of Aborigines and domestic dogs noted that the relationship between them often came to abuse and blows in the night, as the competition for space and warmth intensified.[6] It is hard to conclude that the dingo provided any major benefits as a bed-warmer and huddling most probably reflected the more general intimacy between Aborigines and their camp dingoes.

THE DINGO AS GUARD DOG

Some dingoes do become agitated in the presence of strangers and it is highly likely that they provided early notice of intruders. Their inability to bark loudly is not a disadvantage in the closeness of an Aboriginal camp and the dingo has quite sufficient vocal repertoire and body language to warn of intruders. It is not suggested that being a guard dog was a major role of the dingo, and even less that dingoes make good guard dogs. However, it is likely that an ability to convey an early warning of intruders is a facet of the dingo that made it attractive to Aborigines.

THE DINGO AS FOOD

The dingo may not have assisted the Aborigines in hunting but there is little doubt that it was itself a source of food. There are many reliable accounts showing that the dingo was a part of the Aboriginal diet. It is likely, but by no means certain, that the dingoes that were eaten were caught in the wild, rather than taken from the camp population. The practice of eating dingoes was widespread and not confined to any particular community of Aborigines or region. It is incorrect to suggest that they were eaten only during times of meagre food supply.

Gerard Krefft, an early student of the wildlife of the lower Murray River, noted in 1866 that:

> The natives, who hate the dingo most cordially for his living off the fat of the land, kill him on every opportunity and eat his flesh, which is by no means of ill flavour, though I have partaken of it under stress of hunger, and I will not vouch that I should sit down to roast Dingo with the same gusto now as ten years ago in the Murray scrub.[13]

The Pitjantjatjara Aborigines were scattered in small clans, each with its own territory that was used exclusively for hunting and gathering. They practised dingo increase ceremonies every May at the rising of the Pleiades group of stars, which they called the Kungkarungkara. This coincided with the period when whelping began and the clans would move out to the remoter parts of their territories, collecting young pups to eat.[12]

Dingo pups are fat and succulent, and above all, portable. The following account from the diary of Michael Durack, writing in the Kimberley in 1900, shows how dingo pups could become a portable feast of fresh food:

> Open looking country. Fires away to the westward. . . Saw some blacks in the creek but they screamed at sight of us and made for their lives. . . Pumpkin and I decide to go ahead and look at the country out east. We ride over basalt downs — good black soil but no water — no sign of blacks. We dig but with poor result. . . Proceed east and down another fall where we capture a nigger at a spring. He has with him two roasted puppies which he was evidently preparing for his morning's meal. Other puppies he carries alive, perhaps to serve up later on. The sable buck is very much alarmed to find himself at our mercy and talks vociferously in his own tongue, calling in alarm to his own brethren who do not appear in his own defence. We escort him back to our own camp where we get him in conversation with our own interpreter, Tommy. He has brought all the puppies, roasted and alive, along with him — a distance of six or seven miles, keeping pace with our horses through the spinifex with less concern for it than shown

> by the horses. We start on at 3 p.m., taking the nigger as our guide to water. Here we let him go and take the horses in to water.[14]

The Jankuntjara people of the Everard Ranges in central Australia ate dingo frequently, not only in times of food shortages. Herbert Basedow noted that even adult dingoes were "keenly hunted and eaten; they are usually speared at a waterhole".[15] This is not to say that all groups of Aborigines ate dingoes. Doubtless, there were some people for whom the dingo had special significance and who therefore did not hunt it. Kolig says that the Aborigines he worked among in the southern Kimberley did not eat dingo.[8] However, the reliable reports from other parts of Australia show that the dingo frequently became a part of Aboriginal diet.

WERE THE DINGO AND THE ABORIGINES IN COMPETITION?

Although wild dingoes and Aborigines ate the same game, it is difficult to determine the degree to which they were in direct competition. Any depredation the wild dingo made upon game could have been compensated by it being eaten by Aborigines. Unfortunately, we do not know what impact the dingo had on Australian fauna. Perhaps it merely replaced the thylacine without any effect on other native animals. But it may have changed the distribution or abundance of other native animals, including some that were hunted by the Aborigines. Neither do we know whether Aboriginal predation had any effect on the abundance or distribution of wild dingoes. It is possible that the number of dingoes, as well as other game such as kangaroos and wallabies, was controlled to some degree by Aborigines.

A SOURCE OF DISEASE OR CAMP CLEANERS?

Camp dingoes ate human faeces and any foodstuffs that may have been left around. As voluntary sanitary workers, they may have been responsible for disposing of material that harboured disease. On the other hand, dingoes urinated and defecated around the camp. One way of researching the diet of the camp dingoes has been to visit very old Aboriginal camp sites and examining the dingo scats.[3]

European camp dogs were suspected of spreading the disease shigellosis during an outbreak at Papunya Aboriginal settlement near Alice Springs. However, rectal swabs taken from the dogs did not show that they were carrying the organism.[6] It is also possible that the dingoes in pre-European days carried few diseases. One exception may be hydatidosis, a subject taken up more fully in Chapter Nine. Happily, this is one disease where further research may show whether one strain, known as the sylvatic strain, was introduced by the first dingoes and whether this strain is dangerous to humans. It will be much more difficult to tell whether it had an adverse effect on Aborigines prior to European settlement.

THE DINGO IN ABORIGINAL RELIGION

The dingo appears in the religious beliefs of Aborigines from many different parts of Australia. The ubiquity of the dingo in Aboriginal religion indicates that it was quickly and thoroughly incorporated into all levels of their culture. Nevertheless, it is essential to remember that Aboriginal culture varied widely and it is misleading to portray it as homogeneous across all communities or regions. A comprehensive study of the dingo in Aboriginal religion may well illuminate its practical role among the Aborigines.

Erich Kolig examined the place of the dingo in the religious beliefs of the Wolmadjeri people of the southern Kimberley where the dingo is a villainous anti-hero.[8] He concluded that the dingo was so thoroughly entrenched in Aboriginal society because it served as a reference point for their customs and social structure. The wild and uncontrollable aspects of the dingo were woven into religious beliefs that underlay the need for order and social stability in Aboriginal society.

Kolig describes Aboriginal religious belief from many different parts of Australia to emphasise his point but begins with the Wolmadjeri where dingoes are invariably associated with mischievous acts. They are seen as

Walbiri men near the Tanami Desert, Northern Territory, singing the songs associated with the Dog Dreaming, which is also depicted in the ceremonial painting. Gary Steer

destroyers and assassins of other mythical beings, refusing to obey their masters and with a tendency to rape and thieve. One of the most feared demons of the Wolmadjeri supernatural world is a small dog called "gogur" who lives underground but can travel through the air without trace, inflicting lethal but invisible wounds to a man's throat or snatching away his life's essence or "bilur". Gogur is visible to man and can be heard howling, so it would appear that he lives among the wild dingoes. The duplicity of the dingo is also evident in the Wolmadjeri belief that their tame dingoes could see into the supernatural world and guard against dangerous spirits, particularly enemies who transformed themselves into a dingo to cause trouble. If the camp dingoes challenged another dingo entering the camp, the Wolmadjeri could be certain of its supernatural origin and evil intentions.[7]

Kolig knows of no Aboriginal beliefs that unequivocably praise the dingo for its kind deeds. There do not appear to be any that show the dingo as an aid in the hunt — an observation that supports the view that it was not primarily a hunting dog. Kolig contends that Aboriginal religious beliefs consistently portray the dingo as an unreliable thief, defiant of those who try to control it. It is precisely this lack of order that made the dingo, and now the domestic dog, attractive as a reference point for Aboriginal society. Aborigines could point to the delinquency of the dingo and be reassured of the value of their own laws in exactly the same way as Western society creates its folk devils to confirm the importance of virtue.

If we accept Kolig's theory, one important question remains unanswered. What did the Aborigines use as such a powerful symbol before the arrival of the dingo? If the underlying relationship between dingo and Aborigine is fundamentally a symbolic one, what symbol did they rely on before the dingo and how could the dingo displace it so quickly? Perhaps Kolig had not considered that the dingo is a very recent arrival. Perhaps the Aboriginal beliefs simply reflect the period following the arrival of the dingo when its rapid spread did cause a radical change.

It would be interesting to see a wider comparison than the one Kolig has made. For example, the Walbiri people of the Tanami Desert are plagued by malicious and malevolent spirits called Djanbar that can fly through the camp, stealing and looting, murdering the innocent and copulating with the women. The Djanbar are invisible to all but dogs, medicine men and totemic heroes. The arousal of the camp dingoes at night and their growling would invariably be taken as a warning that Djanbar were lurking in the dark. Today, domestic dogs have taken over from the dingo in guarding against the Djanbar.[15]

The field of Aboriginal religious beliefs about the dingo is a rich area for study. The story of the arrival of the dingo may still be told by the descendants of those who witnessed it step ashore. The dingo is the chief totem of the Mildjinggi clan who live at the mouth of the Glyde River in east Arnhem Land. One of their legends relates how the founding cultural heroes were cooking whale meat on a sandbank near the mouth of the river when the ancestral dingoes smelled the flesh. Finding the smell irresistible, they struggled to reach the sandbank, only to founder in the treacherous mud and perish. The spot is still marked by a sacred dog stone that no woman may look at. The legend is performed in an elaborate dance that depicts dogs floundering in oozing mud.[16]

Legends such as these could portray the maritime path the dingo took to northern Australia. The Kundi-Djumindju men of the Victoria River region enact a story of how the dingo came ashore from a canoe to meet the old Earth Mother with a sacred stick. The men paint themselves with dingo totems and mimic a dog leaping ashore from a canoe and then rolling in the sand and shaking itself. Meanwhile the song-man chants the story of the dingo's arrival in the Dreamtime.[17]

The dingo can feature in events that occurred long before its arrival. For example, one legend states that the dingo formed the Katherine River. It would be interesting to know whether these legends originally featured the thylacine but gradually incorporated the dingo as it displaced the thylacine. Aborigines obviously knew the difference between dingo and thylacine and knew their environment well enough not to consider them as equivalent. Aborigines apparently did not keep thylacines in their camps — had they done so, they may well have survived on the mainland. Although the thylacine is totally unrelated to the dog, it is dog-like in appearance, and it remains possible that some legends originally based on this animal came to feature the dingo instead.

The dingo was frequently depicted in Aboriginal art and artistic impressions of the thylacine and the dingo are clearly distinguishable. Either the different shape of the thylacine or its distinctive stripes were depicted until the dingo took over. The appearance of the dingo in Aboriginal art is consistent with the ages of the oldest fossil dingoes provided by carbon dating.[18] In other words, no dingoes appear in Aboriginal rock engravings that are older than the oldest dingo fossils that have yet been found.

Overleaf:

Top left: *A row of Devil Dingoes painted by the Wardaman people at Gannawalla, west of Katherine, Northern Territory. Josephine Flood*

Bottom left: *This painting at Jowalbinna, Cape York Peninsula, depicts a dingo attacking a giant wallaroo. Josephine Flood*

Top right: *The dog in this painting, found in the country of the Wardaman people at Yiwalalay, west of Katherine, Northern Territory, is possibly a European domestic breed wearing a collar. Painting was still carried out at the site well after Europeans brought their dogs into the region. Josephine Flood*

Bottom right: *A dingo and an echidna painted in red ochre in a sandstone rock shelter at Mount Manning, near Gosford, New South Wales. The appearance of the dingo in Aboriginal art found over a wide geographical area reflects its extensive natural range and, perhaps, the important place it held in Aboriginal culture. Gary Steer*

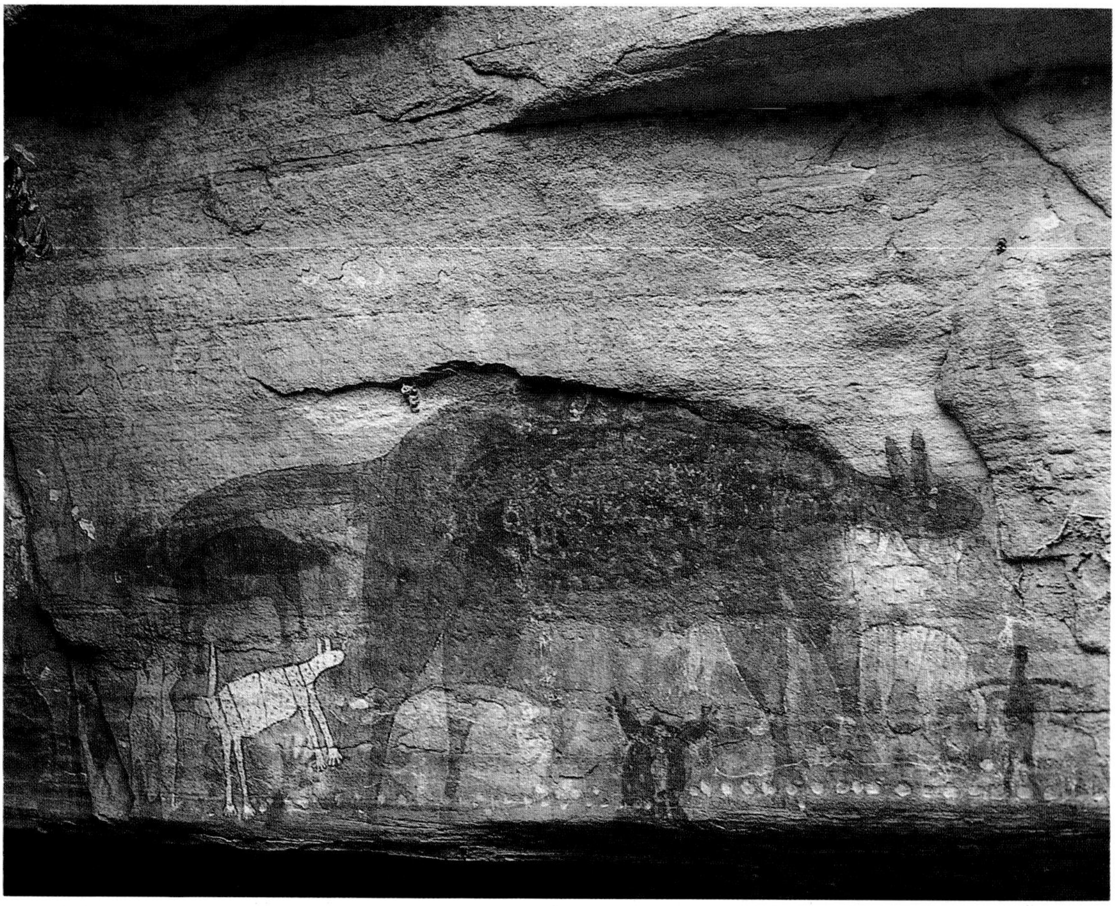

THE ABORIGINAL NAME FOR THE DINGO

Prior to European settlement the word "dingo" was only used by the Aborigines around Port Jackson to refer to their tame camp dingoes.[19] It is quite possible that the word *tingo*, which meant tame, was misunderstood by the first settlers and corrupted into "dingo". Newton Fowell, a lieutenant on the *Sirius*, kept up a steady stream of correspondence from the infant colony and described the Aborigines and their *tingoes*: "They have a number of Dogs belonging to them which they call Tingo, they do not bark like our dogs but howl".[20]

The names for the dingo in the Aboriginal languages of south-easten Australia were commonly based on "mirri", "merri", and "midi". The Aborigines around Botany Bay called their camp dingoes *mirigung* and the wild dingoes *joogoong*. However, other tribes had entirely different roots of their name for the dingo. The Aborigines of the Tweed River called their camp dingoes *noggum*. Those around Moree called them *boolomo*. *Warrigal* is also frequently mentioned as the Aboriginal word for the dingo. However, this was only used for wild dingoes in a limited area around Port Jackson and the Hunter River.[19]

It was common throughout Australia for Aborigines to have at least two names for the dingo. One name denoted the camp dingoes and another was used to refer to the wild population. The Jankuntjara people of the Everard Ranges in central Australia called all dingoes *papa* but the wild ones are called *papa inura* and were treated like any other game.[6] The Walbiri people, who live in the Tanami Desert in the Northern Territory, still refer to dingoes in the wild as *wantibirri* and any dingo associated with humans as *maliki*.

Some Aboriginal names for the dingo are very similar to the names of other animals, suggesting that when the dingo came along it was likened to other animals with which it shared some characteristics. For example, the Potaruwutji people of coastal South Australia called the marine fur seal *kadleira* and the dingo *kal*. It is not hard to see dog-like features in the seal and it is believed that the name of the dingo was derived from it.[12]

CAMP DINGOES

It is hard to avoid the conclusion that interbreeding between camp dingoes and the free-range dingoes was common in most parts of Australia. The subordinate males and females among the camp dingoes would have tried their luck at surviving elsewhere, either out of choice or because of necessity during times when food in and around the camp was scarce. Similarly, the dominant animals must have come in contact with wild dingoes. There may have been some behavioural inhibition to interbreeding, such as territoriality and intergroup competition, that did reduce its incidence. Notwithstanding such considerations, dingoes now breed with European domestic feral dogs so there is no reason to believe that wild dingoes would not breed with those that lived in Aboriginal camps. Perhaps a common cause of interbreeding between the two populations was when a pup collected from the wild for food was favoured and raised in camp instead.

It is also possible that in some parts of Australia there was no clear distinction

Left: *Many of the early sketches of Aboriginal funeral rites showed dingoes near the corpse before it was interred. 'Native sepulchre on the Daly River', S. T. Gill, Mitchell*
S. T. Gill, Mitchell Library

Below: *This photograph of a Pintupi family group in a remote part of the Gibson Desert, Western Australia, was taken in 1963, and provides a glimpse of the typical relationship between Aborigines and camp dingoes. The partly obscured dingo to the left exhibits the emaciated condition of many camp dingoes, noted by early explorers. They frequently commented that the wild dingoes were more healthy in appearance than those who remained with the Aborigines.*
Jeremy Long, Australian Institute of Aboriginal Studies

between the camp dingoes and the wild population. The association between Aborigines and dingoes would have been a very loose one, with dingoes coming and going as it suited both parties. Today dingoes will readily feed at camping areas and dumps. I have also seen a dingo that was raised as a pup by a European family in a remote area of the Northern Territory return for food most evenings but live the remainder of the time in the wild.

Very few skeletal remains of dingoes have been uncovered in a close association with Aboriginal archeological deposits. The small sample makes it difficult to determine whether the camp dingoes differed in shape and size from the wild population. Nevertheless, a comparison of the few dingo skulls found in archeological deposits with those from free-range dingoes that died about the same time has produced some interesting results.[11] Most of the skulls were similar; however, three skulls found in coastal Aboriginal sites showed some of the characteristics of domestication.

These fossils had such a degree of cranial and dental reduction — both indicators of domestication — that they were unlike every other dingo fossil that has ever been examined. Since the three specimens were all found on the coast of south-east Australia, Klim Gollan has suggested that there was a population of camp dingoes in this region that could be distinguished from their wild counterparts. This means that regular interbreeding between the camp dingoes and the free-range dingoes did not occur. Sedentary groups of Aborigines on the coast may have also had a stable camp dingo population. It does not necessarily follow that these camp dingoes were domesticated dogs. Skeletal changes can occur in the space of two or three generations in captivity and are often as much a response to diet as any deliberate selective breeding.

There is a myth that the dingo was a fully domesticated animal under the complete care and control of Aborigines until white settlement destroyed Aboriginal society. According to this view, wild dingoes are a recent phenomenon and another burden on the conscience of the European, who disrupted the happy alliance between dingo and Aborigine, giving the dingo no alternative but to go bush and become an outlaw. According to this theory, the newcomers created a feral animal out of the servant of the Aborigine.[21]

This is erroneous as it is evident that there were both camp dingoes and wild dingoes throughout Australia. First, Aborigines had separate names for camp dingoes and wild dingoes. Secondly, wild dingoes were hunted and eaten by Aborigines. Thirdly, the early explorers often sighted wild dingoes and to suggest that these were all camp dogs out for a run is fanciful. Fourthly, it was common for Aborigines in central Australia to raise dingo pups which returned to the wild when they reached adulthood. Finally, while Aborigines possess remarkable hunting skills, it is unlikely that they could eradicate wild dingoes even if they had wanted to.

THE DOMESTIC DOG AND THE TASMANIAN ABORIGINES

The Tasmanian Aborigines were without dogs and unaware of their existence until as recently as 1798 when Bass visited the island.[22] It was not long after this that the sealers established packs of dogs on the islands of Bass Strait and at least some Aborigines would have seen dogs. However, it was not until 1803 that three small British settlements were established in Tasmania. Tiny and isolated, these settlements soon ran out of rations and, in desperation, the enormously high price of three shillings and sixpence a pound was offered to anyone who could supply meat from kangaroos and wallabies.

One effect of the sudden trade in macropods was to increase the resentment of the Aborigines towards the white invasion of their traditional hunting grounds. They retaliated by attacking the European hunting parties, taking any game that had already been captured and killing their dogs. While this enmity towards the white settlers probably continued, the dogs were soon spared and kept by the Aborigines. Those Aborigines who chose to remain close to the white settlements also obtained dogs as more of them became available. Dogs were used by the whites as items of trade with the Aborigines and sometimes a white man swapped a dog for a black woman.

Within ten years after its arrival in Tasmania, several groups of Aborigines had packs of dogs. By 1816 a large group of Aborigines on the north-east coast had a pack of about fifty dogs. It soon became common for the dogs to outnumber their Aboriginal masters. These dogs were used for hunting, and the extinction of the Tasmanian form of the emu and the reduction of numbers of the grey kangaroo by around 1850 may have been a result of the dog as much as any other aspect of white settlement.

A parallel to the speed with which the Aborigines on the mainland had taken the dingo into their religion is apparent in the way the Tasmanian Aborigines took the white man's dogs into their sacred life. By 1832, entire dance routines depicted dogs and their importance. It was widely believed that the spirit of a dead man could still influence his dog. The Aborigines at West Point believed that a fierce dog living at Macquarie Harbour would devour humans who wore clothes. There may have been some hope attached to this belief, since Europeans were the principal wearers of clothing at the time. If the Tasmanian Aborigines granted the domestic dog such status in less than fifty years, it comes as no surprise that the dingo had such a secure place in Aboriginal religion on the mainland.

The relationship between the Tasmanian Aborigines and the domestic dog did not run its course. The majority of the Aborigines were killed and the remainder shipped off to the islands of Bass Strait, leaving Tasmania to the white man, his sheep and dogs. But the rapid acceptance of the domestic dog by the Aborigines of Tasmania provides an

insight to the rapidity of the dingo's acceptance by mainland Aborigines.

The Tasmanian Aborigines were without dingoes and they gained access to sheep and dogs at exactly the same time. They never accepted the sheep because to raise them would have meant a radical change to their lifestyle and social structure. The dog, however, could be easily accommodated without changing the social structure, economy or system of land use and occupation.

There are, of course, significant differences in the way the Europeans introduced the domestic dog to Tasmania and the way the dingo arrived on the mainland some 4000 years earlier. In Tasmania, Aboriginal culture was being destroyed by the white invasion. The dogs were not dingoes, but domesticated European breeds, many of which were large, fast and efficient hunting dogs such as the greyhound and its crosses. However, these differences are not sufficient in themselves to negate an excellent case study in the acceptance of the dog into a hunter–gatherer society.[22]

Some Aboriginal groups modified their hunting methods to accommodate the various breeds of European domestic dogs that became available. This old, but unfortunately undated, photograph shows a group of Aborigines using large greyhound crossbreeds to hunt kangaroos at Maloga Reserve on the Murray River. Other Aborigines are driving the game towards the group, which is hidden behind a fallen tree. The dogs will be released when the game comes near, and the spear will be used when the prey is cornered or 'baled up'.
N. J. Caire, National Library of Australia

THE DINGO AND ABORIGINES TODAY

Today, even in the remotest parts of Australia, the Aboriginal camp dog is invariably a variety of domestic dog rather than a dingo. Even dingo–domestic hybrids are uncommon. Old photographs and illustrations show that domestic dogs displaced the dingo as soon as Aborigines gained access to them.

One reason for the absence of dingoes could be that they are quickly converted into cash via the white man's bounty on their scalps. It is unlikely that this alone explains why dingoes are rarely kept. It is sometimes suggested that the destruction of the traditional way of life is implicated in the demise of the dingo as a camp dog. But Aborigines in remote settlements in northern Australia who now occupy their own land and have a degree of self-determination do not keep dingoes. If a Walbiri man wants a dingo there is absolutely no reason why he cannot have one. Dingo pups can be readily obtained in the Tanami Desert and there is no white or Aboriginal law that says he cannot keep one; after all, the Walbiri is from a long line of Dog Dreamers. While Dog Dreams are still passed down in tribal religious beliefs, the dog that nuzzles a Walbiri man's face is a domestic dog and not a dingo.

The most straightforward explanation for the preference for domestic dogs is that they are much more tractable and manageable. Specialised hunting dogs are also a feature of some settlements and an entirely new method of hunting is now based on the use of such dogs.[23] In most cases it is still hard to accept that the multitude of dogs associated with Aboriginal settlements are of any practical use and it does appear that their abundance and the tolerance shown towards them indicates a relationship Aborigines have long had with the dingo. Regardless of whether it has a practical use or not, the speed with which Aborigines replaced the dingo with the domestic dog can best be interpreted as a willingness to innovate and accept the latest development in the long relationship between people and dogs.

The Europeans

First contact with a European proved disastrous for the dingo. In 1601 the Portuguese seaman Diego del Prado saw a dingo foraging on a reef at Thursday Island and promptly shot and ate it.[1] While eating dingoes did not become fashionable, killing them was to develop into a national obsession.

The Portuguese and Dutch seafarers of the seventeenth century were the first Europeans to consistently record encounters with dingoes in Australia. Jan Carstenzoon saw "great numbers of dogs" near Cape Keer-weer, Queensland, in 1623.[2] The Dutch seaman Willem De Vlamingh led an exploration of the west coast of Australia in 1697 during which the party met a number of dingoes.[3] One of the ships on that journey was the *Nijptangh* and an officer on board faithfully recorded each day's happenings. Apparently, his men saw dingoes near Jurien Bay, Western Australia:

> We went inland nearly one and a half mile, but found neither people nor fresh water, only several footsteps of Men and prints like that of a dog and Cassowary; further no Trees, only Thistle and thorns. One of our men said that he had seen a red snake; some others said that as soon as we reached the shore, [they had seen] a yellow Dog leaping from the wild overgrowth and throwing itself into the sea as if to amuse itself with swimming.

In a delicate disclaimer the officer added: "What truth there was is unknown to me, I did not see these things myself."

The dingo was mentioned in the journals kept by Captain Cook when he sailed up the east coast in 1770. A near-fatal collision with a reef made it necessary for Cook to seek sanctuary in quiet shallow waters to repair the badly damaged *Endeavour*. There, by a river which Cook named after his ship, at a place now known as Cooktown, one of the diarists noted that "A wolf was said by one of the midshipmen to have been seen".[4]

FIRST SETTLEMENT

A dingo was party to the very first conversation between Captain Arthur Phillip and the Aborigines. Little did the dingo or the Aborigines realise what colonisation had in store for them. These were early days, accompanied by hopes for a peaceful coexistence between the two cultures. The journal of John White, surgeon-general to the First Fleet, describes how men in the first landing party scooped up sea water and mimicked drinking, whereupon a group of Aborigines watching from the shore led them to fresh water.[5] This friendly gesture from the Aborigines set the scene for:

> our first interchange with these Children of Nature — About 12 of the Natives appeared next Morning on the Shore opposite to the Supply, they had a dog with them, (something of the Fox Species); and some Gentlemen that were of his Party Yesterday went on Shore, and very soon came to a Parley with them.

Arthur Phillip was probably the first European to keep a pet dingo but the relationship did not reach the high plane of emotional bonding possible between man and dog. He described the dingo thus: "On the whole it is a very elegant animal, but fierce and cruel."[6]

One early account demonstrates that

Right: *At first the dingo was a benign observer of colonisation — but it soon became the enemy. 'Shooting the dingo, S. T. Gill, Mitchell Library*

Below: *The earliest European drawing of the Australian dingo appeared in Captain Arthur Phillip's account of the First Fleet voyage published in 1798. Mitchell Library*

DOG OF NEW SOUTH WALES.

the dingo may have had some ability as a guard dog. A dingo intimidated the governor's man when he entered an Aboriginal camp.[5] Perhaps the Aborigines encouraged the dingo to let the white man know that he should not be shooting their game:

> The Natives have frequently Dogs with them, and the Governor has procured one of them. In Colour and Shape it resembles the Fox Dog, but the tail is not so bushy, it has become very tame and domestic. The Natives set one of these Dogs at a Man, whom the Governor employs to shoot Birds and other Animals, and as he found himself in danger of being Bit, he shot him Dead on the spot, the Natives were extremely terrified at this, and took to their heels with the greatest Precipitation.

John White was the first European to provide a rounded description of the dingo, published in his journal in 1790.[7]

> The ears are short, and erect, the tail rather bushy; the hair which is of a reddish dun colour, is long and thick but straight. It is capable of barking, not so readily as the European dogs; is very ill-natured and vicious, and snarls, howls, and moans, like dogs in common. Whether this is the only Dog in New South Wales, and whether they have it in a wild state is not mentioned; but I should be inclined to believe that they had no other; in which case it will constitute the wolf of that country; and that which is domesticated is only the wild dog tamed, without having yet produced a variety, as in some parts of America.

'Border of the Mud-Desert near Desolation Camp, March 9, 1861' by Ludwig Becker, who painted it only one month before he died during the ill-fated Burke and Wills expedition. It depicts a black dingo which, although less common than the yellow-ginger, is one of the colours of the pure-bred animal. State Library of Victoria

The dingo adapted easily to the European presence and took advantage of any new source of food that it came across. One such bounty resulted from the death of many convicts from malnutrition, flogging, overwork and disease over a six-month period in 1790 at Toongabbie, west of Sydney. There was a large hole for the dead and every day fresh corpses were thrown into it. At night, the howling of dingoes could be heard around the pit as they fought over the bodies, gnawing at them until they were covered over.[8]

It did not take long for dingoes to travel to Great Britain. There was at least one in the Zoological Gardens at Chiswick by 1830 and while recording it in the official inventory, the curator took the opportunity to vent his thoughts on the Aborigines:

> We have him [the dingo] in that condition in which he may be supposed to approach most nearly to a state of nature, as the companion of a race of savages, the lowest in the scale of intellect that we have met with in the world. . . it should always be borne in mind that even amongst the most savage nations the Dogs are distinct in character as the tribes they serve, and in their degree of intellectual development frequently outstrip that of the masters who hold them in subjection.[9]

NIPPING A SHEEP INDUSTRY IN THE BUD

Captain Phillip had purchased 44 sheep and four goats on behalf of the government at Cape Town. Some officers had also purchased livestock on their own account so that at least a hundred sheep survived the passage and arrived at Port Jackson in January 1788, whereupon five of them were killed in the first week by a lightning bolt.[10] The first statistical return of livestock in Australia was published on 1 May 1788 and it showed that four months after the arrival of the First Fleet only 29 sheep were still alive.[11] Dingoes were suspected as a cause of death but Captain Phillip put their demise down to his own men supplementing their meagre rations.

Great Britain did not have the climate for the merino sheep that were spreading throughout France and Spain and threatening Britain's supremacy as a wool producer and manufacturer of woollen goods, and now looked to the colony for its wool. Political and economic imperatives saw further sheep imported to Australia. They became so valuable that officers on a fleet of three ships sent to Cape Town by Governor Hunter in 1796 to obtain more livestock crammed their cabins with sheep to sell on their own account at Port Jackson.[10] Captain Waterhouse was in charge of the fleet and set an entrepreneurial example by carrying at least twenty sheep for himself. Many died en route but the privately owned sheep must have received conscientious attention because when the fleet arrived back at Port Jackson in July 1797 it carried 37 sheep on account of the government and 84 on account of the captain and officers. Among them were some of the first merinos. Captain Waterhouse sold his portion for 15 guineas a head. There was an official inquiry into this convenient association between public service and private enterprise but Captain Waterhouse was not censured, his action being defended as a public benefit to the colony.

By 1800 there were 6000 head of sheep around Sydney. They were extremely valuable and were protected from dingoes, Aborigines and fellow colonists by trusted shepherds who stayed with the flocks by day and yarded them at night.

There were numerous dingoes around Sydney Town, running wild and in the company of Aborigines. The outskirts of Sydney were said to be swarming with dingoes and the "Dog Trap" gates, on the Rydalmere railway branch line from Granville that came with much later development, acquired their name from these early times.[12] There were 32,000 sheep running on the Cumberland Plain by 1812 but further expansion was hemmed in by the Blue Mountains until three landholders, Blaxland, Wentworth and Lawson, found a path west in 1813. Soon after, sheep flooded west into new dingo country. Michael Hindmarsh of Alne Bank near Bathurst wrote in 1824 that:

> The only enemy that attends it is the Native Dog, which commits great havock. Betimes I have known 100

> sheep to have been killed or bitten so as to occasion their death in one night. The bites of these animals are almost sure death to sheep.

By the time the first settlers of Port Phillip Bay (now Melbourne) held their first meeting in 1836, the dingo had acquired such a formidable reputation that they decided to offer five shillings a head for every dead dingo. George Russell was the manager of the Clyde Company's property Golf Hill at nearby Geelong. His journal shows that in 1837 a ewe was taken from a flock during the middle of the day; seven sheep were taken on three separate nights; 16 were killed when dingoes got into the yards one night when the nightwatchman fell asleep on the job; six were driven away at night and were never recovered. Twenty lambs were killed the following year when shepherds forgot to yard them and 34 sheep were killed in the month of June alone.[13]

Losses of this magnitude encouraged the talent for improvisation that the Australian bush induced in the settlers. One way of killing dingoes was to tie a bait to the trigger of a loaded weapon in such a way that it could not be tugged at by a hungry dingo from anywhere but in the direct line of fire. Shepherding sheep was very costly but it was the only way the flocks could be fully protected. In 1832 the Australian Agricultural Company owned 25,000 sheep dispersed in individual flocks of between 300 and 500 head, each watched by a full-time shepherd. At night they were yarded and guarded by a nightwatchman. The cost of wages and provisions contributed significantly to the loss the company was making at the time.[10]

The shepherd's life was lonely and fearful. Violent death at the hands of Aborigines was a very real possibility at the frontiers of the expanding kingdom of the sheep. The Aborigines fought against the white man's guns and poison as best they could, and one way was to eat his sheep and kill his shepherds.[14] The Clyde Company was to lose at least one of its shepherds this way:

> The shepherd returned to the hut [and encountered] the lifeless body of his mate. The shock nearly overpowered his reason; he threw off his hat, coat and boots, and ran to the home station five miles distant, climbed to the roof of the hut and sitting astride to the ridge cried "Murder! Murder!" continuously for half an hour before he became sufficiently reassured to impart his intelligence.[13]

The shepherd's task was to mind a small flock of sheep during the day and then drove them back to a central camp at night where they joined with other shepherds. The sheep were put in rudimentary yards of portable timber hurdles for the night. Everything had to be portable so that the shepherds could follow the grass. The bigger stations had hutkeepers to supply the shepherds with food and help watch the sheep at night, although special nightwatchmen were often employed. It was common for nightwatchmen to have another job during the day and double their wages by moonlighting. The nightwatchmen and shepherds often slept in tiny "dog boxes", with handles extending from each end so that they could be carried with the sheep.

The hazards associated with being a shepherd, the interminable loneliness, the boredom and poor wages and conditions, meant that the occupation did not attract the most zealous and dedicated workers. Some men regarded it as a path to higher duties as a stockman or overseer but it was more often a lowly occupation, filled by many a "ne'er do well". Sheep were often poorly supervised and the consumption of alcohol followed by sleep was more common than vigilance against the dingo. Thomas Alexander Browne, a grazier at Port Fairy in the Victorian Western District, later wrote under the name of Rolfe Boldrewood and described the troubles of the squatters: "In those days, too, when fencing was not; when the shepherds comprised perhaps, the very worst of the labour in the colonies, it may be guessed how hard and anxious a life was that of the western Victorian sheepowner."[15]

This was the background that kept the squatters on a continual lookout for ways to beat the dingo. It did provide a diversion for those with sufficient social standing to wear a velvet coat and ride a fine horse to follow the dingo to the sound of stockwhip, bugle and a pack of rangy kangaroo dogs. The colonial squatters tried to recreate the life of the rural gentry in Britain. This was epitomised by the Bathurst Hunt which rode in a green coat with a native dog embroidered in gold upon the collar.[16]

The hunt was merely a frivolous recreation and loaded pistols beside waterholes could kill but a small proportion of dingoes. Strychnine poison dealt the dingo its first major blow. By 1845 this poison was being widely used as the main method of killing dingoes and within another five years it was adopted throughout the sheeplands. Some graziers grouped together and employed a man to lay baits. George Russell at Geelong began using strychnine on a massive scale in 1847 and convinced his neighbours to contribute to the cost of employing a man for the sole purpose of poisoning dingoes. Local sources of the poison soon became scarce and its popularity can be gauged from the following letter that George Russell sent to his principals in Glasgow:

> I also wish you to send me about 20 pounds worth of the poison called Strychnia: we have for some time past found it of great use in destroying the native dog; but from the great demand it is difficult to obtain it, & only at an exorbitant rate.[13]

By 1850 Alexander Cameron, the manager of the Clyde Company's property Terrinallum (some 80 km from Golf Hill), was able to report that no wild dogs had been seen or heard at the station for some time. However, a few months later he said that he was unable to leave home for a while because three sheep in a flock had been "hit" the night before and, although they had carried out a lot of poisoning around the "rises" lately, there must be a remnant left that still had to be poisoned. There is a clear indication in this account that the sheep were no longer under constant supervision and were being left unattended.

Strychnine was being used against the dingo in south-east Queensland in 1860:

> The native dogs on Cardarga were very numerous, as owing to its scrubby and broken character, it was a natural harbour for them, but in addition, large packs of dingoes followed the trail of the travelling stock and often remained on the run. Poisoning was therefore an imperative duty. Everyone carried strychnine, and poisoned baits had to be made and laid every day. Everything available from the bones of cattle slaughtered for food to animals shot or found dead on the run had to be poisoned. I must have killed many thousands this way. On one bright moonlight night I was followed by nine large dingoes. They played and gambolled around my horse, but having a good supply of poisoned baits in my saddle pouch I succeeded in administering a dose to all of them in turn.[10]

Such was the fate of any dingo that gambolled in the moonlight with a white man and it is little wonder they soon learnt to avoid his company. Before dingoes became aware that they would be poisoned, shot, trapped or run down, they did not have the same tendency to avoid people as they do now. Australian history holds many stories, such as the one above, where dingoes came close to people either out of curiosity or to seek food.

The costly practice of guarding small flocks against dingoes became less important as they succumbed to the poison baits. Around the time that strychnine began to control the dingo, the squatters gained changes to the legislation governing their leases so that capital improvements could be fully compensated if their lease was ever revoked. This provided incentive to put up fences, ringbark trees and build grand homesteads as reward and monument to their triumph over the bush. "Camping out" was the term used to describe the sheep that spent time alone. The small flocks could now be combined in great mobs and instead of employing shepherds, the graziers put their efforts towards fencing in their runs. Fencing methods and materials developed so rapidly that within forty years pastoralists in some of the remotest sheep country in Australia began fencing dingoes out.

EARLY CONSEQUENCES OF DINGO ERADICATION

Predictably, the dingo's life became increasingly difficult with strychnine, followed by clearing and fencing. The combination of poison and lack of cover meant that dingoes could be eradicated from the more settled agricultural regions. A book about South Australia published in 1866 described how uncommon it was to encounter a dingo in the settled districts.[17]

The decline of the dingo often coincided with a sudden abundance of kangaroos. Gerard Krefft, a curator at the Australian Museum, published a book on the mammals of Australia in 1871.[18] In it he recognised the damage dingoes caused to sheep but also felt that the settlers had created their own kangaroo problem:

> In some districts the settlers are obliged to have regular battues to keep the kangaroos within bounds, because they feed voraciously and multiply so quickly that sheep or cattle would soon be outnumbered by them. The main cause of this prolific increase is no doubt the destruction of the Native Dog and the absence of the Aboriginal hunting parties.

In 1885, George Finch-Hatton described how he searched for game on a cattle station near Mackay in Queensland during his adventures as an English gentleman in the antipodes.[19] He considered that shooting Aborigines, which some of the locals indulged in to pass the boredom of a day off in the bush, was not worthy of a gentleman, but kangaroos were abundant and made tolerable, if less than ideal, game. Moreover, hunting kangaroos could be justified because:

> Since the destruction of the native dogs and eagle-hawks by the squatters who stocked the country with sheep, the kangaroos have not a single enemy left, and in some districts of Queensland they have increased to such an extent as to bring absolute ruin upon the runs which they infest.

Aflalo was also an English traveller whose impressions of Australia, *A Sketch of the Natural History of Australia: with Some Notes on Sport*, was published in 1896. In this quaint almanac about colonial life, Aflalo stated that:

> Every man's hand is against the cowardly larrikin of the brute world, relentless despoiler of the sheepfold, through which it will run amok, killing a number of animals by eating out the paunch, its favourite mouthful... There is certainly nothing very prepossessing about the half-wild companion of the Aboriginal. Like its Aboriginal master, it has been somewhat freely "dispersed" by the settler, until it is now getting scarce in many districts, where baits impregnated with strychnine have done their work well. The result of its disappearance from the cleared country has been a plague of kangaroos, which in turn have to

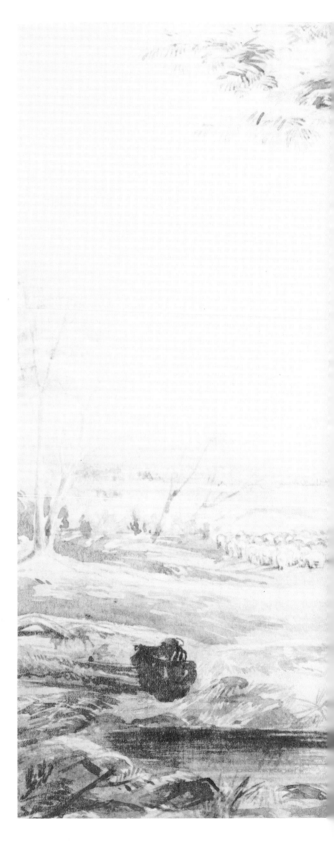

be thinned by organised "drives". If the farmers at home could but get a glimpse of the thankless fight which their Australian competitors have to maintain against dingoes, kangaroos, rabbits, cockatoos, injurious caterpillars, drought and inundation, they might bear with their own troubles a little more patiently.[20]

The scarcity of the dingo in the more settled regions is reflected in a book about the dogs of Australia published in 1897 that contained a brief section on the dingo.[21] It shows little regard for the one dog that was here before all the others were imported:

> Here we have the supposed indigenous canine curse — an untameable brute, whose depredations in the past must have amounted to millions. Fortunately, his days are nearly numbered in most parts of the colonies. For some years past the genuine dingo has been very scarce excepting in the back blocks...It will be a blessing for the squatters when the brutes are extinct.

But Rolfe Boldrewood was a squatter, and although he was a cattleman, his observation that kangaroos increased after the dingo was eradicated by strychnine caused him to reflect more deeply on the relationship between predator and prey.[15] He also commented on the relationship between the

The shepherd's life was lonely and fearful. Finding salace in strong drink, with the dangers inherent in that, was apparently very common. S. T. Gill, Mitchell Library

dingo and the cattlemen in a way that is relevant today:

> In good soothe, the pioneer squatter of that day had many and divers foes to contend with. Having done battle with one army of Philistines, another straightway appeared from an unexpected quarter. We had trouble with the aboriginals: a canine "early Australian", the dingo, had likewise disturbed our rest. He used to eat calves, with perhaps an occasional foal, so we waged war against him. We were not up to strychnine in those days. The first letter I saw on the subject was from the ill-fated Horace Wills, whose sheep had been suffering badly at the time. He had come across the panacea somewhere, and lost no time in recommending it to his brother squatters. With the help of our kangaroo dogs, and an occasional murder of puppies, we pretty well cleared them out. As cattle men, and taking a selfish view of the case, we need not have been so enthusiastic. Though he killed an occasional calf, the wild hound did good service in keeping down the kangaroo, which after its extinction, proved a much more formidable antagonist. . . but in the kangaroo battues which ensued, it more than once occurred to me that I was interfering with a natural law, of which I did not foresee the consequences.

There were many "natural" laws that were broken in the first 100 years of the European settlement of Australia. The eradication of the dingo as a predator over much of the country changed one of them, as did the destruction of the Aborigines, because they also preyed on kangaroos. Then came more watering facilities and more grass, as trees were ringbarked and stumps were burnt or grubbed out. Forest and woodland became grassland and most of the fauna that inhabited the trees and undergrowth was lost, some of it forever. A few species of kangaroos and wallabies liked the changes so well that the white man had created another pest. Still, the sheepmen did not lament the dingo.

FRATERNISING WITH THE DINGO

Various residents of Sydney fancied the dingo as a pet, but it did not prove a satisfactory town dog. It was considered quite fashionable to have a pet dingo in the 1830s, although they did not prove compatible with their new environs.[8] One dingo owner wrote:

> He was especially fond of cats: I have known him to eat six in one morning. People thought some new disease must have broken out, cats got so scarce in the suburb where I had him. I had one vocalist in this line who kept half a terrace vacant for six months, till the

> landlord bought him in self-defence. It was the pianos made him so bad. Ours was a musical suburb, and no dingo can endure that.[12]

It is not hard to guess the fate of this dingo once the landlord had purchased it. Most dingoes that were kept as pets lived short lives, as their habits in adulthood made life too difficult for the owners who had thought they may retain the appealing features of puppyhood. The difficulties associated with keeping dingoes as pets meant that the fad had passed by late last century, except for those who kept them to cross with domestic dogs. Folklore has it that the dingo was used to develop a cattle dog suited to Australian conditions.

The case for some dingo blood in the blue heeler or Australian cattle dog centres on a colonial cattleman named Hall from Muswellbrook in the Hunter Valley of New South Wales.[22] He had imported a pair of smooth-haired blue merle collies from Scotland in 1840 and they were good cattle dogs except that they barked too much. Uncontrolled barking is a most undesirable trait in a cattle dog, as it is capable of turning a peaceful herd of cattle into a bellowing mass. The ideal cattle dog will silently "heel" a straggling cow or calf with a nip on the lower leg, giving it some incentive to stay with the mob. A judiciously timed short bark can do wonders when yarding up or blocking but the timing has to be right and an excitable

Red cattle dog at work. Roland Breckwoldt

dog that barks perpetually is a severe handicap.

Hall is said to have reduced the propensity for yapping among the collies with a spot of dingo blood. The progeny of the collie–dingo cross were either mottled red or blue, did not bark very much, were excellent heelers and, unlike the pure dingo, were tractable and responsive to command. These dogs became known as "Hall's heelers" and found their way to Sydney via a butcher who operated out of the Homebush saleyards. Here they were seen by cattlemen from all over the state and were soon in demand.

Hall was not the only person to experiment with crossing the dingo. A drover named Timmins, who took cattle between Sydney and Bathurst in the 1830s, is also credited with creating a new breed of dog that was based on the dingo.[22] He was using a breed known as the Smithfield but found that it barked too much and could not stand the heat. What better canid could there be to take away the bark and give a bit of heat tolerance than the dingo? The progeny of this cross were red bobtailed pups, silent but severe heelers that earnt the name "Timmins' biters". As a drover, Timmins had plenty of opportunity to show off his new dogs and sell pups along the way.

It is not known whether Hall's heelers and Timmins' biters were then purposely interbred to arrive at the blue heeler of today. It is also likely that people in many different areas were crossbreeding dingoes with domestic dogs. The Australian classic *Dusty* by Frank Dalby Davison is a perceptive account of the difficulties involved in the relationship between a man and a dingo–kelpie cross.[23] Crossing domestic dogs with dingoes still occurs but the official stud books of the Australian cattle dog and the kelpie are closed, so it is difficult for dingo genes to get among pedigreed dogs. But oral history and folklore have it that the dingo has already made its mark.

OFFICIALLY PROCLAIMED AN OUTLAW

The inexorable process that led to the dingo being put on the "wanted" list of outlaws began as early as 1830 when "An Act for abating the nuisance occasioned by the great number of Dogs which are loose in the Streets of the Towns of Sydney Parramatta Liverpool and Windsor in the Colony of New South Wales" was assented to by the Legislative Council.[24] This Act was set in place for only three years because it was felt that the bounty of two shillings paid for the tail of any unregistered dog would soon rid the colony of the dogs that roamed the streets and frequently caused a danger to travellers and "the great annoyance of the inhabitants at large".

This was the first bounty on dogs in Australia and there is every likelihood that many dingo tails were handed in to the constables and peace officers authorised to pay it. Even the lucrative bounty could not encourage people to kill sufficient dogs to stem the supply of canine problem-makers and in 1832 the Act was extended for another three years. By the time that expired, the dog problem had spread with settlement and the creation of new towns such as Bathurst. Consequently, the Act was made permanent in 1835 and amended to include the towns and highways of New South Wales, and to raise the bounty to two shillings and sixpence.[25]

At that stage the dingo had not yet been singled out for more severe control measures but that ended with "An Act to facilitate and encourage the destruction of Native Dogs" passed on 28 December 1852.[26] This was an extremely powerful Act for its time, since it opened the way for a tardy landholder to be forced to contribute to the cost of dingo poisoning undertaken by a neighbour:

> Whereas with a view to the destruction of the Native Dog it is expedient that the owners of conterminous runs should be liable to assessment in order that they may be compelled to pay a fair contribution proportionate to the benefit that they may derive from the labor and expenditure of their more energetic neighbours.

Under the provisions of this Act a landholder who was about to poison dingoes could put in a tender to the Court of Petty Sessions describing the nature of the program and its cost. The court then had to ensure that any neighbour who would benefit also paid part of the costs. This was a recognition of the dingo as a serious pest and the desirability of getting some equity into its control. Hereafter, a zealot could extract some compensation from a less enthusiastic neighbour. The division of interest was invariably along the lines of cattleman versus sheepman and this was a way the sheepman could get action from a cattleman who did not control dingoes.

The Dog Act was amended again in 1875 to cover all police districts in New South Wales.[27] The separate Act covering dingoes was also amended in the same year to make it unlawful to lay poison baits within 100 yards (91.4 m) of a public road or any boundary of freehold land.[28] Too many drovers' dogs were being inadvertently poisoned and the amendments prevented baits being laid within "three quarters of one mile" (1207 m) from a travelling stock route. It also became necessary to put signs up saying that baits had been laid in an area. Having complied with these conditions, no landowner could be held responsible for killing any domestic dog that happened to eat a bait.

The dingo's outlaw status was finally sealed in New South Wales in 1898 with the creation of Pastures Protection Boards.[29] Hereafter, a landowner was not merely responsible for contributing to a neighbour's efforts at dingo control, but everyone was forced to control noxious animals on their own land. The

The result of being declared on outlaw is all too apparent in the fate of these dingoes on the Monaro Tobleland, New South Wales. Gary Steer

Act listed the noxious animals that the boards would attempt to eradicate and the native dog was, predictably, one of them. Nor was there much leeway in avoiding this task because a native dog was defined in the Act as including "any dingo or native dog, or any dog whatever which has become wild".

The Pastures Protection Boards were authorised to pay a bounty on dingo scalps and there were stiff penalties for anyone bringing scalps across the border into New South Wales from other colonies to take advantage of any differential in the bounty. Later amendments allowed various boards to form Wild Dog Control Boards especially devoted to controlling dingoes and feral dogs. Four such boards were established, their membership comprising delegates from the Pastures Protection Boards in the region, and they remained in existence until 1987 when the Minister for Agriculture acted upon the advice of a committee of review which recommended that wild dog control could now be handed back to the Pastures Protection Boards.

For a time, the other colonies were bound by the laws of New South Wales and the dingo was affected by the early Dog Acts. After they gained statehood they gradually developed their own laws on dingo control. The dingo received legislative attention from the Queensland parliament in 1885. An advertisement in the South Australian *Government Gazette* offered a reward for dingo scalps as early as 1837 and a Dog Act was passed in 1852, with legislation specifically on the dingo following in 1889.

THE DINGO IN LITERATURE

Aborigines handed their myths and beliefs about the dingo from generation to generation in a rich oral history. Europeans have also filled the bush with dingo myths, folklore and yarns. The dingo arouses strong emotions and its enigmatic nature has made it a subject for the writing of poets, novelists and playwrights.

Very different attitudes to the dingo are reflected in the poetry of two of Australia's best-known poets. "Banjo" Paterson was a colonial poet and bush balladeer, so it is not surprising that, in "In the Droving Days", he should paint the dingo as an outlaw, romanticise the hunt and shed few tears at its death:

We saw the fleet wild horses pass,
And kangaroos through the Mitchell grass;
The emu ran with her frightened brood
All unmolested and unpursued.
But there rose a shout and a wild hubbub
When the dingo raced for his native scrub,
And he paid right dear for his stolen meals
With the drover's dogs at his wretched heels.
For we ran him down at a rattling pace,
While the pack horse joined in the stirring chase.
And a wild halloo at the kill we'd raise —
We were light of heart in the droving days.

In "Trapped Dingo" Judith Wright, a contemporary poet, reflects upon death itself:

So here, twisted in steel, and spoiled with red
your sunlight hide, smelling of death and fear,
they crushed out of your throat the terrible song
you sang in the dark ranges. With what crying
you mourned him! — the drinker of blood, the swift death-bringer
who ran with you, many a night; and the night was long.
I heard you, desperate poet. Did you hear
my silent voice take up the cry? — replying:
Achilles is overcome, and Hector dead,
and clay stops many a warrior's mouth, wild singer.

Voice from the hills and the river drunken with rain,
for your lament the long night was too brief.
Hurling your woes at the moon, that old cleaned bone,
till the white shorn mobs of stars on the hill of the sky
huddled and trembled, you tolled him, the rebel one.

Insane Andromache, pacing your towers alone,

death ends the verse you chanted; here
you lie.
The lover, the maker of elegies is
slain,
and veiled with blood her body's
stealthy sun.

Rudyard Kipling, that great weaver of tales about animals, people and wilderness, wrote an enchanting children's story of how the kangaroo got its shape by having to jump across a river to escape a wily dingo.[30] Until then the kangaroo, according to Kipling's fantasy, was like a woolly little cat on four short legs. The Big God, whose name was Noong, responded to the short kangaroo's plea to be made more popular by teaching it a lesson on the perils of vanity. The Big God sooled a dingo on to the little kangaroo to show him that popularity could be dangerous. The only way the kangaroo could eventually escape the persistent dingo was to learn to jump the wide Wollgong River.

When Mark Twain visited Australia, he too reflected upon the dingo and its fate:

> I also saw the wild Australian dog — the dingo. He was a beautiful creature — shapely, graceful, a little wolfish in some of his aspects, but with a most friendly eye and sociable disposition. The dingo is not an importation; he was present in great force when the whites first came to the continent. It may be that he is the oldest dog in the universe; his origin, his descent, the place where his ancestors first appeared, are as unknown and as untraceable as the camel's. He is the most precious dog in the world, for he does not bark. But in an evil hour he got to raiding the sheep-runs to appease his hunger, and that sealed his doom. He is hunted now, just as if he were a wolf. He has been sentenced to extermination, and the sentence will be carried out. This is all right, and not objectionable. The world was made for man — the white man.[31]

The oppressed and victimised of our society can identify with the lowly, despised and maligned dingo. Max Williams turned to poetry while serving a life sentence in prison. He was acquitted in 1972 and wrote his autobiography which chronicles the events that can take a child in the wrong environment and carry it down a perilous track of 25 years in and out of prison.[32] An underdog for so many years, who has now found dignity and self-esteem through writing and community work, Max called his lifestory *Dingo*, and it opens with this poem:

A DINGO'S CALL

In the hardwoods my call is borne
sung from forest ridge and trail.
A warrigal padding silently
and where sheoaks hide my scent.
Alone and always listening
for other calls out there!

I used to search the quiet lake;
blue green waters of Cuttagee.
See the crane-minded fishermen
perched on timbered shores —
and watch the crouching jinker driver
bring his haul across the bridge.

Yes, I am the dingo,

trying in my way to live,
the hunted, scorned because of this.

The dingo has also been labelled as a coward. In the past the dingo did not always avoid people unless it was systematically shot, chased and poisoned. It responded to its outlaw status by vanishing into the bush at the first sight of a human, and so it was branded a coward. So strong became the association between dingo and coward that it is still regarded as a grave insult to be

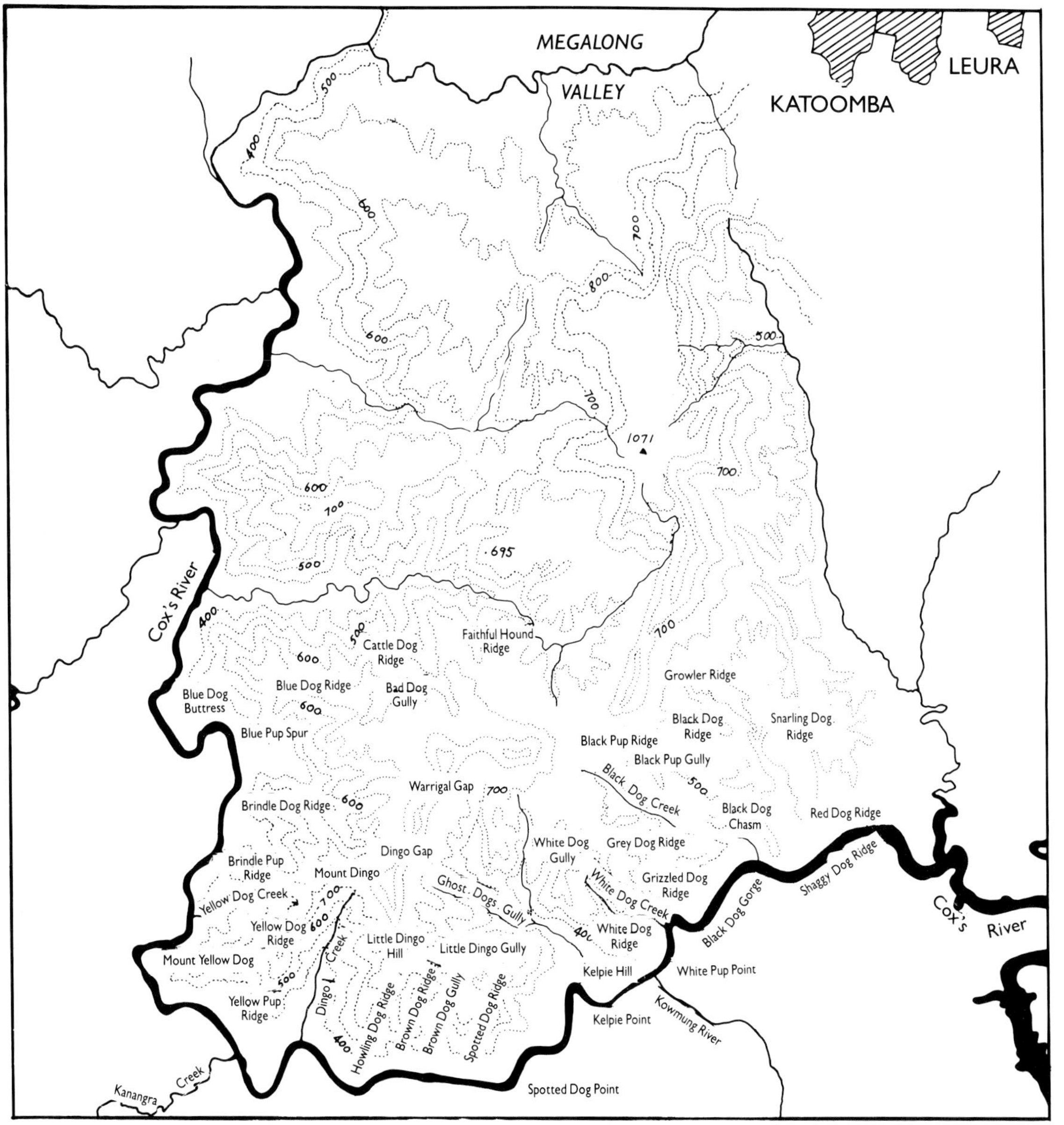

This area, not so far from Sydney, must have been well-known for its dingoes. Place names, including the lesser known Aboriginal names of Warrigal and Merrigal, reflect one way the dingo has been incorporated into European culture.

called a dingo. Used in this perjorative way, the dingo acts as a reference for socially acceptable behaviour in precisely the same way as it is depicted in many Aboriginal religious beliefs.

In the play *The Man from Mukinupin* by Dorothy Hewett, one of the leading characters is a part-Aborigine named "Touch of Tar". She provokes her white lover, Harry Tuesday, into demonstrating some emotional involvement, even if it is only the violence she has become conditioned to.[33] Harry is a broken, alcoholic Vietnam veteran, exploited himself but also representing all the exploitation Touch of Tar has suffered:

> TOUCH OF TAR: You've always been mad Harry Tuesday.
>
> HARRY TUESDAY: Stupid bitch! I'd like to king hit you with this bottle.
>
> TOUCH OF TAR: Why doncha then, you dingo?

The inference is obvious — to hit a woman is cowardly and "dingo-like". Still, the dingo label is too much for Harry Tuesday and he swings his king hit.

"Dawkins! Dawkins! Come on Dawkins! Get up Dawkins! Come on Dawkins, it's your turn! Dingo Dawkins!"

No, this was not the language of the schoolyard gang. It was the Liberal Party opposition in Parliament House, Canberra, on 11 April 1986, taunting the Minister for Trade, John Dawkins, into defending himself and the Labor government during a censure motion. When Dawkins failed to take his feet and the Special Minister of State, Mick Young, rose to defend the government, the opposition broke into loud and prolonged howling that emulated the dingo. The howling lasted a full three minutes and there was chaos in the House. Such is the power of the dingo — its howl as a weapon of parliamentary debate![34]

THE DINGO AS FOLK HERO

Australians have a tendency to venerate their outlaws by forgiving their failures and turning them into folk heroes. Ned Kelly is now seen as someone who stood up for the poor Irish and took to lawlessness only as a means of making a statement against the class that had oppressed his countrymen for so long. Breaker Morant is remembered for his horsemanship, poetry and likeable personality rather than a bit of a rogue who might hit the bottle and lose his sense of judgement.

Animals can be folk heroes too. Phar Lap was going to prove the superiority of Australian horses until he met his death in the United States under highly suspicious circumstances. Death is an important ingredient in the making of a folk hero and there is sufficient morbidity in the history of the dingo to make a dozen folk heroes.

It is this gradual elevation of the dingo to folk hero status that led to its use as a symbol to head a cause. A socialist workers' newspaper published during the Depression years was called *Dingo* as a rallying cry for its readers. It is perhaps harder to fathom the association between the dingo and a magazine devoted to "lifestyles, music, adventure, sexuality and all the other fascinations of the changing and challenging world we live in". However, a magazine called *Dingo* that focused on these issues was launched in 1984.[35] The editorial stated that the dingo was an innocent victim of the destruction of Aboriginal society and that "In many ways the dingo represents the uniqueness of the Australian character; the arrogance of independence, the cunning to survive and the spirit to remain free." This magazine did not survive beyond the first issue but if the dingo declines likewise, it is a sure guarantee that it will become even more of a folk hero.

Perhaps an image of the dingo as an independent loner persuaded the producers of an Australian television satire to call the series "The Dingo Principle". The slogan "Every bastard for himself" splashed across the screen between skits certainly reinforced that notion. The title is significant enough, but more relevant is the grim irony that followed a send-up of the Ayatollah Khomeini, the religious leader of Iran, during an episode of "The Dingo Principle" screened on 20 April 1987.

Word got back to Iran overnight that the Ayatollah had been mocked. He was not amused and the Muslim theocracy of Iran called it blasphemy. Within days, Australia's live sheep export trade with Iran was gravely threatened. In a delicious irony, "The Dingo Principle" almost killed the live sheep export trade, worth over $300 million and growing at the rate of 20 per cent each year. Of all the possible outcomes of the skit, it had to be the sheep industry that suffered. The *Sydney Morning Herald* of 29 April carried the headline "Dingo Attack Wipes the Smile off the Sheepfarmers' Faces".

THE CHAMBERLAIN CASE

My association with dingoes during the years when the Azaria Chamberlain case dominated the headlines led to my becoming involved in it. Initially, like most Australians, this was simply a personal response to the tragedy; later it evolved into a more direct involvement.

Dingoes in captivity have bitten their captors for one reason or another. A free-range dingo choosing to attack a human, either for food or in defence of its territory, is a different matter altogether. In the 200 years that Europeans have been living in the bush, there had never been an authenticated account of a dingo attacking a human. So it stood until 17 August 1980, when Lindy Chamberlain screamed into the blackness of a cold desert night at Ayers Rock, "My God, the dingo has got my baby". Even in the crowded camping ground there was no one else who could claim they actually saw a dingo carry the baby off.

Lindy Chamberlain claimed that a dingo took her nine-week-old daughter Azaria out of the family's tent. The events that followed were widely publicised but what really happened at that precise moment was shrouded in conflicting evidence, an uncertainty of what was on trial, and human propensity to spread rumour and create myths in order to make sense out of the bizarre.

If only Lindy and Michael Chamberlain had acted in a manner that most people considered "normal", they would not have been so readily accused of murder arising from strange motives such as a sacrifice in the desert. The Chamberlains are Seventh-Day Adventists and Michael was a pastor. Doubtless, their religious beliefs gave them solace in a time of grief but many found it hard to understand their behaviour and judged them guilty of murder.

The accusation the Chamberlains made against this one dingo reflected the entire European history of the dingo and people sprang to its defence. Was the dingo now going to be made a convenient scapegoat for a murder? Most Australians live in urban areas with no direct experience of dingoes and insisted that they are instinctively shy and reserved and would rather starve than enter a tent. There were those who protested the Chamberlains' innocence but their voices were drowned as the event became a media circus that spawned vicious humour in dingo and baby jokes.

Despite a predominantly suspicious public, the Chamberlains were initially pronounced innocent by the coroner, Denis Barritt, who conducted the first inquest. On 20 February 1981 he made history by announcing his verdict on nationwide television, saying "that Azaria Chamberlain met her death when attacked by a wild dingo whilst asleep in her family's tent. . .".

Reliable evidence was given at the inquest that there were indeed many semi-wild dingoes foraging and scavenging among the tourist facilities at the Ayers Rock camping ground. They had no fear of people because they survived on handouts from tourists. Some of these dingoes had already attacked children and the superintendent of the national park had even written reports to his seniors stating that a potentially dangerous situation had developed. Nevertheless, I can well remember my scepticism about the coroner's findings. He maintained that because no body had been found and because most of the baby's clothing was found relatively intact, there had been human interference after the dingo had taken Azaria from the tent. This seemed like having it both ways.

The Northern Territory government had been restless over the finding of its provincial magistrate and reopened the case in September 1981 with a second inquest based largely on the evidence of the British forensic scientist Professor James Cameron. He maintained that the baby's jumpsuit had a bloodstained handprint on it, showing that Azaria was being held while her throat was cut. The media had a field day. Every myth about wild nature — children raised by wolves and apes, Romulus and Remus, Tarzan — and every reason to put religion and motherhood on trial were exploited on behalf of a public who by now was totally confused about the issue but prepared to sit in judgement of two people who refused to conform to stereotypes.

The results of the first inquest were quashed by the second finding in February 1982 that Lindy Chamberlain should stand trial for murder with Michael Chamberlain an accessory to the fact. The trial caused a sensation, especially when on 29 October 1982 the jury pronounced the Chamberlains guilty despite evidence that a dingo could have been responsible, that no body was found, no motive was established nor was it shown that Lindy Chamberlain was anything but a caring mother. Their guilt was determined on forensic evidence alone and much of this, such as the claim that there was foetal blood in the Chamberlains' car, was heavily disputed by scientific experts.

"Acquit the dingo" invoked the car sticker on a four-wheel drive in Alice Springs and so it eventuated, because every court of appeal failed to reverse the Chamberlains' conviction. The High Court itself came to a narrow three to two judgement in favour of letting the convictions stand. Lindy Chamberlain gave birth to another daughter and then went to Darwin's Berrimah Jail to serve a life sentence. Michael Chamberlain, no longer a pastor, was given an 18-month suspended sentence as an accessory to the fact. This was thought to be the final curtain on the great Australian morality play.

Early in 1983 I was asked to work on a documentary film on the ecology of the dingo. Part of our task was to build a very large semi-natural compound on my farm so that we could obtain essential closeups of breeding and raising pups that would be impossible to obtain in the wild. We received our first dingoes on the farm at about the same time that the Chamberlains' appeals were exhausted and they began serving their sentences. By the time filming came to an end in March 1985 I had 14 dingoes under close observation. I had also travelled far and wide in search of the dingo character. Sometime during this period my attitude to the Chamberlain case changed.

The compound dingoes were well fed yet they were always on the lookout for anything that looked or smelled like food. They carried heavy objects with ease. I was also observing dingoes in the wild, and at Curtin Springs Station near Ayers Rock, I had to tie down the bullock heads used as attractants to get dingoes into camera range. Back in the compound the large males could get cheeky and pushy and even though I knew them all well and never feared them, I would certainly not leave a small child alone with them, much less a baby — a lesson learnt from personal experience and not the Chamberlain case. Our dingoes were half-tame, or semi-wild, and resembled in their behaviour the type of dingo found around camping grounds or dumps

TABLE 2:
The dingo's diary of European history.

Year	Event
1601	The Portuguese seaman, Diego del Prado, sees a dingo foraging on a reef at Thursday Island, shoots it and eats it.
1688	William Dampier sees the tracks of a dingo at Shark Bay, Western Australia. He returns in 1699 and his men see dingoes.
1770	Captain Cook sails up the east coast; near what is now Cooktown one of his men reports seeing a wolf.
1788	The British invasion begins with a small settlement at Sydney Cove. A dingo listens in on the first attempts at communication between the Aborigines and the Europeans.
1813	The Blue Mountains are crossed and sheep flow further west into more dingo country.
1824	First reports that the dingo was a serious enemy of the sheep industry.
1830	First Dog Act provides a bounty of three shillings a head for any dogs loose around the towns of the colony.
1836	A bounty of five shillings is placed on the head of the dingo by the settlers at Port Phillip Bay (now Melbourne).
1845	Strychnine poison becomes widely used against dingoes and they decline in the settled agricultural regions.
1852	First Act of Parliament specifically aimed to "encourage the destruction of Native Dogs".
1870	Various observers note that kangaroos have increased in abundance; the decline of the dingo is suspected as the reason.
1913	The era of the barrier fences begins with the construction of the New South Wales–Queensland border fence.
1921	The debate about the origin of the dingo has been running since John Gould mentioned in 1863 that it was unlikely to be indigenous. In 1921 Professor Wood Jones finally shows that this is correct. He believes the dingo came with the first Aborigines and this view is still widely held.

where they are not shot at or molested.

As a result of my work on dingoes I wrote an article for *Geo* magazine of August 1986, which included a few lines on the Chamberlain case, mentioning that it was not unusual for carnivores to become a problem if they were fed by humans and that the one thing that had not been put on trial in the Chamberlain case was our relationship with wild animals. There it would have rested, except that on the night of 2 February 1986 a tourist fell off Ayers Rock and the search party stumbled upon the matinee jacket that Lindy Chamberlain had always insisted was worn by Azaria at the time of her disappearance. There it was, six years later, only 150 m from

Year	Event
1950s	The advent of radiocarbon dating and its use on dingo fossils ruthlessly reduces the length of time the dingo could have been in Australia. The oldest fossil is only 3450 years old. It is also shown that the dingo could not have come with the first Aborigines because it did not reach Tasmania, which was isolated from the mainland only about 11,000 years ago. The Aborigines had been here over 40,000 years.
1962	Rabbits poisoned by 1080 are thrown from an aeroplane to poison dingoes in gorges near Ebor in New South Wales. This is the beginning of 1080 aerial baiting using meat baits.
1970s	Conservation movement gains strength and restrictions are gradually imposed on the use of 1080, although the regulations vary widely between the various states and territories. Aerial baiting is banned over national parks and other Crown lands in New South Wales in 1976.
1980	The Chamberlain incident at Ayers Rock where a dingo is accused of taking baby Azaria from a tent.

Year	Event
1984	Concern for the protection of the dingo begins to be voiced by organisations such as the Australian Conservation Foundation, which prepares a dingo policy for the first time. The Northern Territory takes the dingo off the vermin list and puts it on the unprotected list and it is fully protected in national parks and equivalent reserves. The dingo has been fully protected in the Australian Capital Territory.
1985	Research into the dingo sees more scientific evidence being published on its ecology. Of particular concern is the level of hybridisation with feral domestic dogs in eastern Australia.
1988	The debate continues about how the dingo may have got to Australia. It is agreed that the most likely ancestor of the dingo is the Indian plains wolf but one theorist believes that it may have come to Australia with seafarers from India travelling via Timor. The more popular theory is that the dingo came via South-East Asia carried by people in boats as they migrated or made contact with Aborigines in northern Australia on fishing or trading expeditions.

where the jumpsuit had been found the day after the event.

The missing matinee jacket was a vital piece of evidence in the Chamberlains' favour because the prosecution had maintained that either it did not exist at all or that it had been soaked in blood from Azaria's cut throat and therefore hidden as part of an elaborate cover-up. Lindy Chamberlain was released on licence the next day and a commitment was made by the Northern Territory government to hold a royal commission or judicial inquiry into the case to determine whether there had been a miscarriage of justice.

In July 1986 a Royal Commission into the Chamberlian convictions began hearing evidence under Justice Trevor Morling. Sometime after that, unbeknown to me, my article in *Geo* was tended as an exhibit to the commission. During December I was in my study overlooking the beautiful Tantawangalo Valley, writing this book, when I received a phone call from legal counsel assisting the royal commission seeking further comment on the possibility of a dingo taking a baby from a tent. My reply was that the claim that a dingo took the baby was credible.

This opinion resulted in my being asked to go to Sydney for further discussions with Chester Porter QC, Counsel assisting the commissioner. Chester Porter is an amateur naturalist whose office is embellished with paintings of birds that add a splash of colour amid the heaviness of row upon row of legal texts. He had developed a set of 12 standard questions on dingoes that he put to all "dingo experts", myself included. They probed any experience with dingo behaviour that could help determine if a dingo would go into a tent; whether a dingo could carry a 4.3 kg item of prey; and how much blood is spilled when prey is killed. The lack of blood had been a problem to both the prosecution and defence — if Lindy Chamberlain had cut Azaria's throat in the front seat of the car, as charged, how did she avoid getting blood all over the place? On the other hand, if a dingo killed the baby, why wasn't the inside of the tent a mass of blood and gore?

In the event of a dingo taking the baby, the absence of blood in the tent is not difficult to explain. There is rarely much blood shed when a carnivore makes a kill because death is usually caused by massive internal haemorrhage, damage to the throat and muscle tissue, and crushing of vital organs. The image of blood and guts is from Hollywood, not nature. I have witnessed hundreds of rabbit kills by farm dogs and many by the pet dingo I kept and there is rarely any external evidence of blood. Eighty-three red kangaroos that had been killed by dingoes in western New South Wales were examined by a veterinary surgeon and detailed autopsies were performed on 17 of them. There was rarely any evidence of blood on the dead kangaroos unless they had been partly eaten. However, once skinned there was abundant evidence of deep penetrating bite wounds that caused internal bleeding and oedema, often going so deep that they damaged the lungs and major blood vessels.[36]

The horrifying truth is that a dingo could have picked up the baby Azaria and run off with her while she was still alive. A helpless baby would not have to be killed before it was carried off and the tiny amount of blood found in the tent is entirely consistent with the ability of a dingo to grab prey quickly, hold it securely in its sharp teeth and powerful jaws and run with it.

Many more people who had direct experience with dingoes were called to give evidence before the Royal Commission; others offered their opinion and were also given the opportunity to be heard. This meant that a great deal more evidence about dingoes came to be used at this stage than was possible at the two inquests and the trial. Some still protested that a dingo would never attack a human under any circumstances but most of the new witnesses caused a shift in opinion about the possibility of a dingo being involved. One witness was Lionel Perron, who had worked as an engineer in the remote north-west of Western Australia during 1960–61. He said that he had seen a group of tribal Aborigines trying to spear a dingo that lived near their camp. When he asked the Aborigines he employed about what was taking place they replied that this dingo was "no good, him being eat piccaninni".

While waiting in the gallery in Court 19A of the Supreme Court in Sydney to give evidence and be cross-examined on my statement, I listened to two full days of testimony by a forensic pathologist from British Columbia whose particular speciality was cut throats. He was brought to Australia to give evidence on behalf of the Northern Territory government. The professor's explanation for the absence of blood was that Azaria was decapitated by a human after she was dead. The media went wild and the headlines in the more sensational newspapers turned out reports that I hardly even recognised as a chronicle of the evidence I had heard. One could hardly envy the task before Justice Morling in having to unravel thousands of pages of testimony and sift prejudice and wild speculation from the truth.

The Commissioner's findings were released to the public on Tuesday 2 June 1987, stating that the evidence brought before the inquiry was insufficient to allow a jury to properly convict the Chamberlains. A great deal of the evidence against the Chamberlains, such as the presence of foetal blood in the car, was shown to be incorrect. In a fine piece of logic, Justice Morling pointed out that if any of the Chamberlains' behaviour appeared unusual, then it was equally so whether the baby was murdered or taken by a dingo. While he could not say definitely that a dingo had taken the baby, the full weight of evidence made it the most probable explanation for the disappearance of Azaria Chamberlain. He concluded that "The evidence affords considerable support for the view that a dingo may have taken her". The immediate result was for the Northern Territory government to quash the Chamberlains' convictions. This did not entirely satisfy Michael and Lindy Chamberlain who said they would settle for nothing but a full pardon and financial compensation for wrongful imprisonment and suffering.

Many people were disappointed that a more definite finding could not be made by Justice Morling and will never be satisfied with any explanation of what took place that night if it does not fit their personal theory. But that enigma typifies the entire European history of the dingo. We have never been sure about this animal.

Jean-Paul Ferrero

PART THREE

The Life of the Dingo

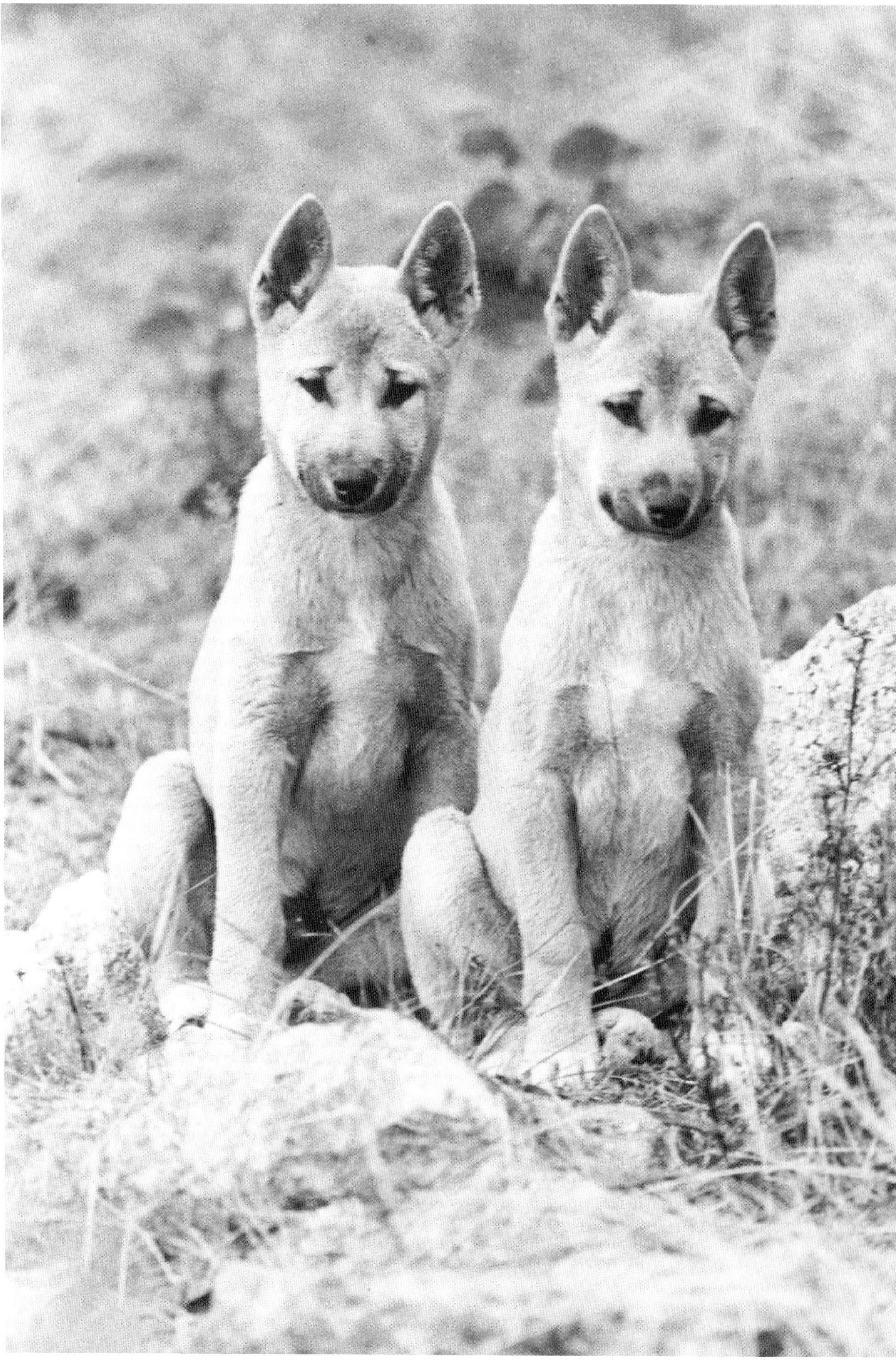

Characteristics of the dingo

So much of the life of the dingo has remained hidden from view that folklore and romantic ideas of nature have often been used to fill the gaps. As a result, many myths have grown up around the dingo and they have added to the difficulties of understanding this enigmatic animal. Although many people of the Australian bush understood the way of the dingo, there were unexplained aspects that always created controversy and conflict. However, more research into the life of the dingo is taking place and a great deal has been learnt in recent years. Modern research techniques, combined with good old-fashioned observation, are overcoming the impediments to a clear view of the dingo, from eastern forest to red centre sand dune.

SIZE

The dingo is a medium-sized canid with males weighing between 12 and 20 kg and females being lighter at around 10 to 16 kg.[1] The average total length, from nose to the tip of the tail, of 267 dingoes trapped in north-eastern Victoria was 137.2 cm. The average tail length was 26.5 cm. Only 1.5 per cent of the total number had short bob-tails instead of normal length tails.[2]

The male dingo is usually slightly

Pups at two months of age are already very independent and spend long periods of time away from the den. Gary Steer

A two-year-old female dingo. Gary Steer

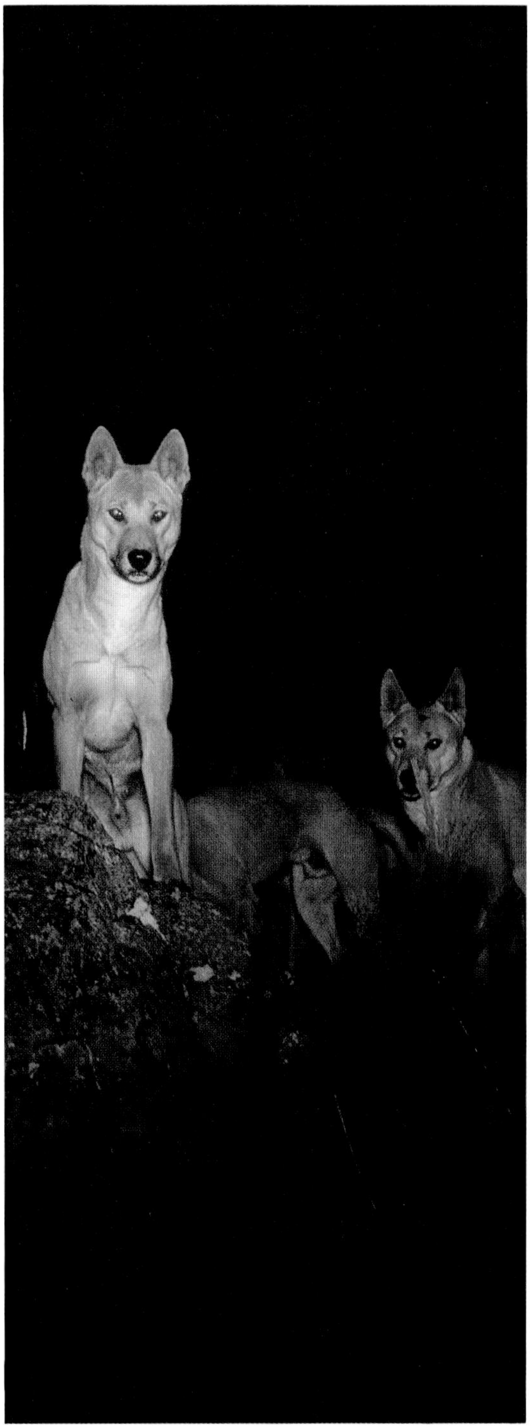

The dingo is often seen during the day, but it tends to be most active at night. Jean-Paul Ferrero

longer than the female which also has a smaller hind foot.[3] Males reach a height of about 53 cm at the shoulder. Any wild dog that is much larger than the above dimensions is almost certainly a domestic cross. Chris Cameron of Rockwood on the Western Downs country near Chinchilla, Queensland, reports that the most troublesome wild dog he encountered appeared to be a dingo – labrador cross. When it was eventually trapped it was measured at 185 cm long.

COLOUR

Even the colour of dingoes does not escape controversy. It is still commonly believed that pure dingoes are all yellow-ginger in colour. This is not correct and there are pure dingoes that are predominantly black. The first European discoverers of Australia and the explorers who followed them often noted that they had seen dingoes that were black with some tan or white markings. Together with these black dingoes there are also some that are pure white. The only characteristic common to all pure dingoes is white on the feet and a white tail-tip.[4]

One myth about the dingo that can be heard from time to time is that their coat colour is related to the environment in which they are found. Thus dingoes in the red country of central Australia would tend to be reddish. There is no evidence for such claims and all the basic dingo colours are found in all parts of Australia.

There is no way of knowing the proportion of the different coloured dingoes at the time of European settlement. A recent study into the relationship between colour and hybridisation between dingoes and domestic dogs did examine a large sample of pure dingoes in inland Australia.[5] Very few of the wild dogs in the region sampled are feral domestic dogs so this study provides the best guide to the proportion of the different colours before the arrival of feral domestic dogs. Yellow-ginger dingoes were by far the most common with 88.6 per cent falling into this category. Only 3.8 per cent were black and tan and 1.9 per cent were white. The remaining 5.7 per cent had large enough patches of white to be classified as having broken colouration. Every pure dingo in this study had white on its feet and a white tail tip. Most surprising was the incidence of a few brindle dogs that were classed as pure dingoes when their skull measurements were analysed.

Yellow-ginger is by far the most common colour of the dingo. Some within this category are distinctively yellow, similar to a golden labrador, but some run to a more russet-red like the fox. Besides white on the feet or tail tip dingoes may also carry a white chest patch or have isolated patches of white. Some individuals have a large proportion of black hairs and when these are concentrated along the back it can give them a sable appearance. Yellow-ginger is dominant to black in a three to one ratio. In other words, if a homozygous yellow-ginger dingo mates with a homozygous black and tan dingo, on average, three of the pups will be yellow-ginger and one will be black.[5]

Black and tan and black and white dingoes occur throughout Australia. They are nearly completely black and the tan or white usually appears on the chest and feet. The incidence of black wild dogs that look like dingoes is increasing with hybridisation and this is discussed further in Chapter Eight.

Pure white dingoes can still be found in central Australia but they have almost disappeared in the east. White dingoes were never common and it appears that at most they would have made up about two per cent of the population.

A few of the early explorers did note dingoes that had large patches of white or black and there were very occasional reports of brindle dingoes.[5] The recent research on colouration shows that a very small proportion of the dingoes that were classed as purebred on the basis of their skull measurements did carry broken colours. However, these were variations of the basic dingo colours of yellow-ginger, black and tan and white rather than some of the more exotic colours found among feral domestic dogs and their hybrid dingo offspring that are found in some regions today.

HABITAT AND DISTRIBUTION

At the time of European settlement dingoes occurred throughout Australia except for Tasmania. They are very adaptable and able to use every habitat from ocean beach and alpine high country, to desert dune. The war between white man and dingo has now changed the distribution map. Constant control has eliminated dingoes in nearly all the closer settled agricultural regions of eastern Australia. However, the rugged, forested spine of the Great Dividing Range still provides an almost continuous belt of suitable dingo country from Melbourne to Cape York. The distribution of dingoes in this strip is patchy, depending on past and present adjoining land use, the existence of national parks, and the use of aerial baiting.

In the absence of control by humans, the abundance of food is the most significant influence on dingo numbers. The number of pups weaned and surviving into adulthood is clearly determined by the seasons and the productivity of the environment. The availability of permanent water in the arid zone influences the amount of game and therefore the number of dingoes. The influence of water is demonstrated by research which shows that less than 12 mm of rain will allow dingoes to move away

TABLES 3:
Relationship between the number of dingoes and the availability of food in Central Australia. From Newsome et al, 1973.

Habitat	Average number of dingoes at each watering point	Average index of food abundance
Wide valleys among ranges	4.8	2.1
Open plains flanking ranges	4.0	1.6
Rugged ranges	2.7	1.2
True desert	2.4	1.2

from permanent water and extend their hunting range.[4]

The habitat that supports the highest number of dingoes in central Australia is the wide flat valley floors where rabbits are abundant.[4] The availability of prey has a clear influence on the number of dingoes, as shown in Table 3. The highest concentrations and the smallest home ranges among the dingoes at Nadgee Nature Reserve on the far south coast of New South Wales are in the forest areas where prey is more abundant. This is in contrast to the ocean beaches and estuaries where the dingoes are forced to scavenge more for their food.[6]

Right: *A black and tan dingo in the Simpson Desert. Steve Parish*

Below: *The dingo is a highly adaptable animal that quickly colonised every habitat the Australian continent had to offer — from the coast to the red centre, and from the tropical rainforest to the Snowy Mountains. Steve Parish*

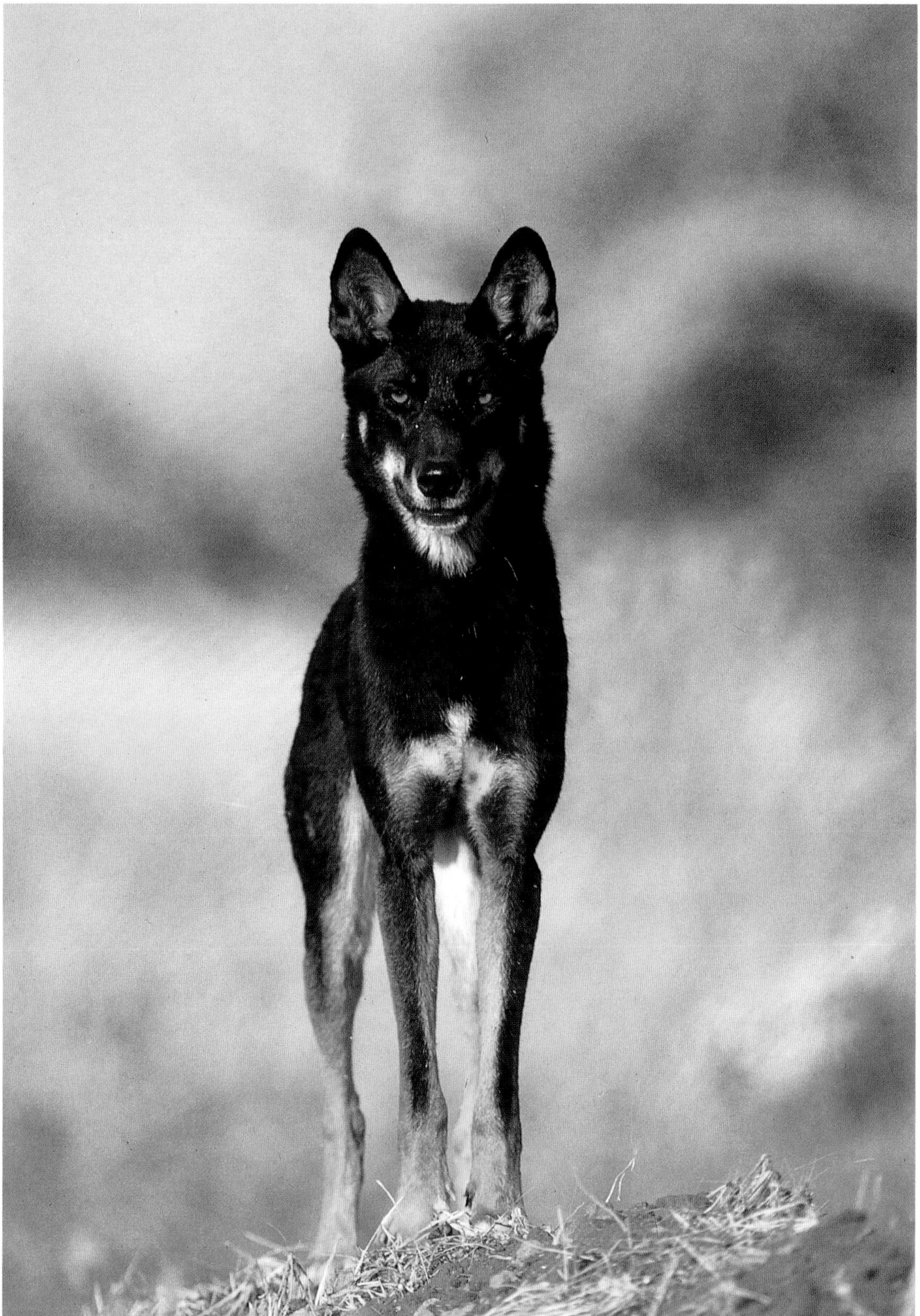

THE NUMBER OF DINGOES IN AUSTRALIA

Despite the level of control that is exercised, the dingo cannot yet be regarded as an endangered species. There are many places where control is impossible or uneconomic and there are other areas where it is considered undesirable or prohibited. Notwithstanding, some people, alarmed that the dingo is still regarded as vermin, require more substantial reassurance that it is not an endangered species. The issue of whether the dingo will be bred into extinction by domestic dogs is taken up in Chapters Eight and Fifteen of this book.

For the moment, the only available estimate of wild dog numbers comes from Queensland and results from a survey of landholders by the Stock Routes and Rural Lands Protection Board. This puts the number in Queensland at between 200,000 and 350,000.[7] An unknown proportion of these would be dingo–domestic hybrids but much of the state remains remote from settlement and contains pure dingoes.

It can be assumed that vast areas of the Northern Territory and Western Australia contain as many dingoes as Queensland. There are also many dingoes in the northern cattle country of South Australia. The situation in Victoria and New South Wales is complicated by the high level of control and the high incidence of hybridisation but there are areas within each state that still have populations of pure dingoes.

IS THERE REGIONAL VARIATION AMONG DINGOES?

Although various claims are made about distinct geographical races of dingoes, there is no scientific evidence to support them. The skeleton of any contemporary pure dingo bears a close resemblance to the skeleton of the oldest known dingo fossil.[8,9] It is also very difficult to determine the difference between a dingo and a domestic dog of the same size without detailed skull measurements and statistical analysis, so to claim that it is possible to discern regional variation among dingoes by visual appraisal is rather fanciful.

The difficulty with any system of visual appraisal is that it depends on the eye of the beholder. Without a system of objective measurement it is impossible to make valid comparisons. A study of regional variation among dingoes must be based on systematic measurement and evaluation of many individuals of known origin from all over Australia. To base any classification merely on a few animals of unknown origin is simply invalid.

Intuition may encourage a view that perhaps there evolved a dingo more suited to an alpine environment while others evolved characteristics more

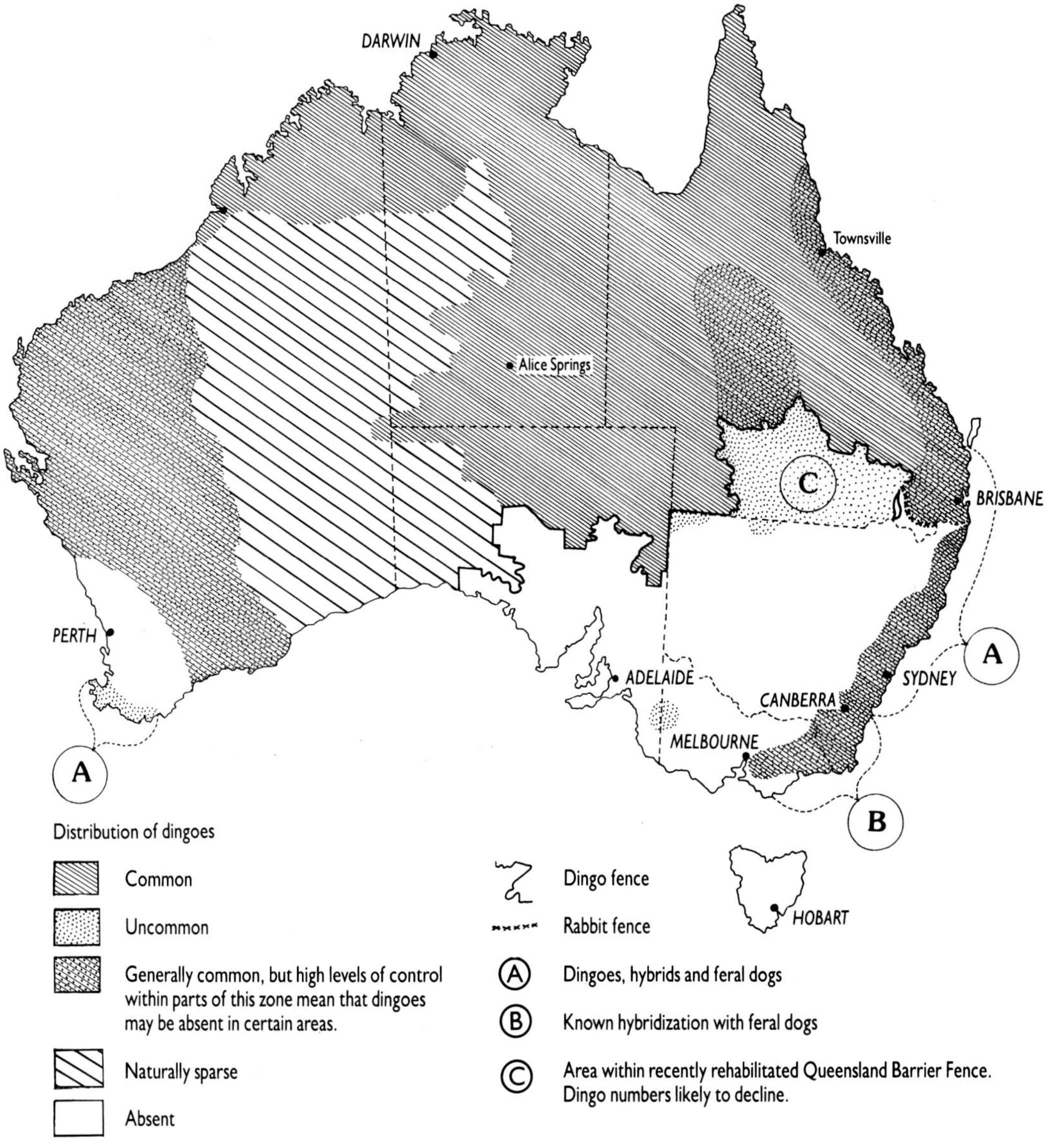

Distribution of the dingo,
Prepared by Alan Newsome and Roland Breckwoldt, 1988.

favourable to an arid or tropical climate. Research shows that mammals of the same species do make physiological adjustments to climate in a very short time but this does not necessarily separate them genetically from their peers in other climes. If there is an alpine dingo, for example, are there also alpine wombats, possums, kangaroos and emus? Was there an alpine thylacine?

It is common for species of wild canids to have a very wide range that includes radically different climatic zones. Both the grey timber wolf and the coyote are found in desert and arctic environments. The shared ability of most of the large canids to adapt to widely differing environments is believed to be a further indicator of their close ancestry.[10] There is nothing unique about the Australian dingo being found in both central Australia and the eastern highlands. Indeed, the climatic variation between these two zones is far less extreme than that found in the range of the coyote and the grey timber wolf.

Experiments have been carried out on dingoes of known origin to determine their ability to tolerate extremes of temperature.[11] Dingoes from a captive colony at San Diego Zoo were subjected to cold and hot acclimatisation. Those put in artificially cooled cages showed an amazing capacity to develop a thick cover of insulating fur. After only six months in the cold cages they had an average of three times as much fur on some body locations as those treated in hot cages. Those placed in the hot cages made equally rapid adjust-

TABLE 4:
Indicators of dingo or wild dog density. From Mitchell, J., et al, *1982.*

	Density levels		
Criteria	**High**	**Medium**	**Low**
Signs of presence	Abundant tracks, dropping etc. Howling at night.	Tracks and signs present. Some howling.	Few tracks and signs.
Animal sightings	Some sightings both day and night.	Occasional sightings.	Very few sightings.
Group size	Individuals and small groups to five; occasional groups to ten.	Individuals with occasional groups to five.	Individuals and pairs.
Approx. density	1/10 per 15 km^2	1/15 per 30 km^2	>1/30 km^2

Left: *A black and tan male and a yellow-ginger female make up this breeding pair at Moomba, South Australia. The yellow-ginger colouration is dominant to black so, providing the parents are not carrying recessive genes for either colour, there will be an average of three yellow-ginger pups to each black pup. Roland Breckwoldt*

Right: *The most commonly found colour — over 88 per cent of pure dingoes are yellow-ginger. Gary Steer*

ments to their respiration and metabolic rate. This showed that dingoes from the same colony could adapt to both heat and cold in a short space of time. This phenomenon is not confined to dingoes or other related canids — most species of mammals that reach more than 1 kg in body weight are able to vary the amount of fur covering according to climatic conditions.

There is some evidence that dingoes in the arid zone tend to be a little smaller and lighter framed than dingoes in the east, but this observation rests on measurements from only six skeletons.[12] If confirmed by further research, the slightly smaller dingoes in the arid zone would conform to other studies showing that mammals of the same species tend to grow a little larger in cold climates.[13] It is already known that the skull structure of dingoes kept in captivity will change in just one generation but this does not make them a separate species, race or type.

Speculation about distinct regional genotypes of dingoes could be nothing more than a harmless fad. Some people may believe that it is excusable if it helps the dingo as a whole by drawing attention to a rare "alpine dingo" on the edge of extinction. However, an erroneous basis for wildlife conservation may do more harm than good. The dingo already carries a heavy enough load of myth and folklore to make it extremely difficult to develop a management policy that will safeguard its future.

BREEDING

Dingoes breed only once a year, unlike most female domestic dogs which are capable of rearing two litters of pups in the same year.[14] The exceptions among domestic dogs include the basenji and some of the very large breeds. No dingo bitch has been observed rearing two litters in the same year, either in captivity or the wild. It would be extremely difficult to do so in the wild, given the limitations imposed by the seasons and food supply, and the raising of two litters would be unlikely even if the female were not biologically confined to a single breeding season.

It is not known whether dingo–domestic hybrids are capable of breeding more than once a year in the wild. Trappers in north-eastern Victoria do catch some pups in winter and others, though fewer in number, in late summer.[1] This may be evidence that some of the crossbreeds are having two litters each year but it could also indicate that they are still only rearing one litter per year but are capable of doing so at a different time from pure dingoes.

Most female dingoes are capable of breeding in their first year but a significant proportion do not do so or fail to raise their pups. Some of the younger bitches in stable family groups in the Fortescue River area of Western Australia did not breed and this was assumed to be the result of the dominant bitches preventing them mating. Other young bitches gave birth but failed to raise their pups, probably because they were denied the assistance of the dominant animals to obtain the large game in the area.

However, large prey, and the family group structure that tends to accompany it, is not the only reason why some young bitches fail to breed. Many of the solitary dingoes that feed on rabbits on the Nullarbor also fail to breed in their first year even when food is plentiful. It is therefore not only a stable group structure that prevents a proportion of the young females breeding and there is no evidence that control measures cause an increase in breeding by destroying the social hierarchy.[13]

Dingoes mate in autumn and early winter, between the months of April and June. The female stays in oestrus for between three and seven days. Climatic variation in different parts of Australia could exert some influence on

The pups are very dark at birth, although any white markings are clearly apparent. Gary Steer

whether mating occurs earlier or later in the year. Dingoes on the Barkly Tableland were observed to whelp two months earlier than those 500 km south at Alice Springs but it was not clear if this was a consistent pattern or merely due to a temporary difference in seasonal conditions between the two areas.[4] It is not known if females in the wild will mate with more than one male or whether pair-bonding or a more rigid social structure prevents multiple matings as occurs frequently among domestic dogs.

Trials with captive male dingoes in Canberra showed that they were capable of fertile matings with domestic and dingo-domestic cross females at any time of the year.[14] The central Australian dogs used in this trial produced sufficient sperm for fertile mating during summer when housed in Canberra but while they were held at Alice Springs they produced almost no sperm during summer and could not fertilise domestic bitches in oestrus. The level of the male hormone, testosterone, rises in males during the breeding season of the female dingo in response to oestrus females and copulation. The coincidence of higher levels of male hormone and the female oestrus period shows that the seasonal breeding of dingoes is set by the female.

The breeding season is accompanied by an increase in the intensity of social interaction of which frequent howling

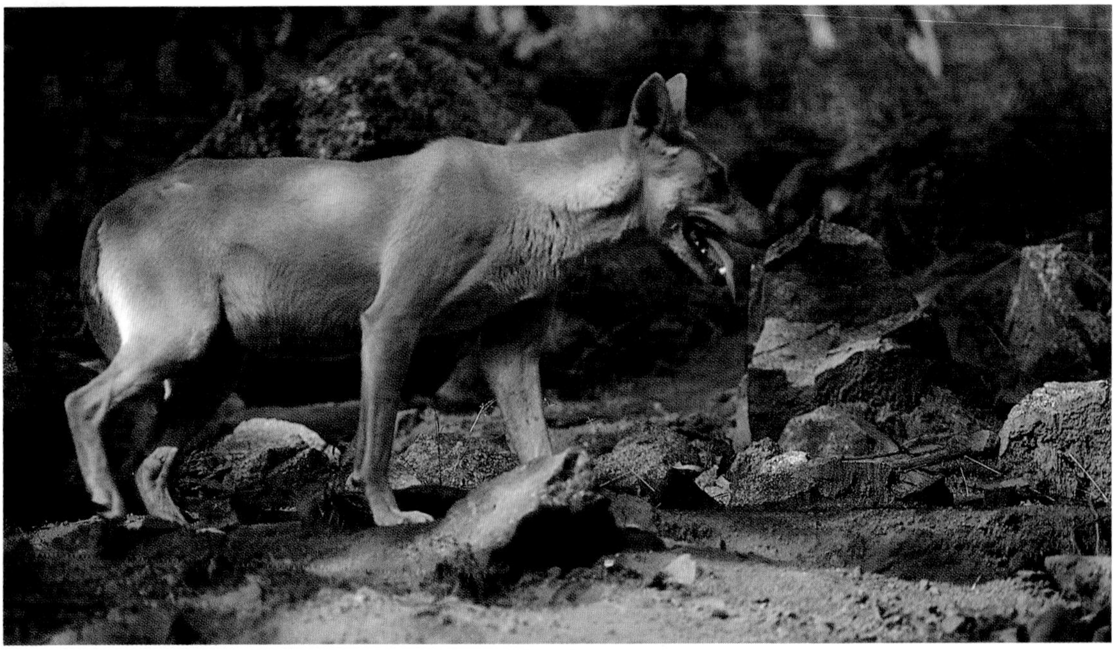

***Left:** A breeding pair at mating time in late autumn-early winter. Unlike most domestic varieties of similar size, dingoes breed only once a year. Gary Steer*

***Bottom left:** The female becomes obviously pregnant only a couple of weeks before giving birth. It is at this stage that she chooses a den site and, if it is an old rabbit or wombat burrow, will spend considerable time enlarging it or cleaning it out. Gary Steer*

is the most obvious indicator. Dingoes, either alone or in small groups, howl mainly at night and may be answered by others at some distance away, resulting in a melodious bush chorus. The increase in howling during the mating season is thought to help in locating a mate and in maintaining social cohesion and territorial boundaries. At other times, howling enables individuals to maintain contact with others during hunting. Howling may also help strangers avoid each other to reduce friction. There is also an increase in ritualised defecation and marking and scratching at conspicuous scent posts during the breeding season.[15]

Conflict increased markedly within my captive colony during the breeding season. One older female was covered in fresh wounds and scars during this period. By the time the next breeding season came around a younger female had grown bigger and stronger and, either by herself or assisted by the male, killed the formerly dominant female. This occurred at the beginning of April. The remaining bitch mated around the middle of the same month, indicating that rivalry for dominance coincided with the onset of oestrus. In the wild, the displaced female may have been able to escape without being killed.

BIRTH

Gestation lasts about 63 days which is the same as domestic dogs. The bitch becomes obviously pregnant in the final three weeks and it is about this time that the teats become prominent. She selects a suitable den for whelping and raising the pups. If the den is an old rabbit warren or wombat hole, cleaning it out or enlarging it occurs with increasing activity as the birth approaches. The most common den sites are hollow logs, enlarged rabbit warrens and rock shelters.

The pups are born in winter between June and August. The average litter size in the wild is usually between four and six pups. Litter sizes vary considerably between individual bitches depending on their age and health. Seasonal conditions and the effect they have on the nutritional levels of bitches are also important factors. I have observed healthy young females rearing five pups in the wild near Alice Springs yet an aged female using the same waterhole could raise only one pup. A trapper in the New England Tableland region reported taking 17 pups out of one log but it was not possible to say whether this comprised two litters.[16] However, even if there were two litters, they would have had to be large to make up that total.

TABLE 5:
Behaviour of a litter of 11 dingo pups in a large semi-natural compound at Candelo, New South Wales.

Age in days	Behaviour
1	Pups born in hollow log. Remain in a huddle for warmth and sleep except when suckling. Mother spends most of the time with the pups. Birth weight of pups is average of 235 g for females and 280 g for males.
5	Mother leaves pups alone for longer periods.
13	Eyes beginning to open.
15	All pups have eyes open. Pups left alone during the day but mother returns to regurgitate solid food for them.
17	Mother moves pups to an enlarged rabbit burrow, possibly in an attempt to avoid interference.
21	Pups leave den on short exploratory forays.
22	Pups eating large solid food such as rabbit and chewing bones. Begin to urinate and defecate outside den.
27	Different behaviour of individuals becoming apparent. Four males are consistently the first out for food and allow themselves to be picked up.
38	Moving freely about outside den for most of the day.
46	Both the father and mother of the pups warn them whenever a human is approaching by whining or a short, agitated bark like a cough.
48	Pups show hierarchy among themselves by fighting over food. The largest male pups are dominant.
55	Pups roaming freely about compound during day, often in company with other adults. Mother still calls them to regurgitate food but they can easily eat all forms of solid food.
60	Pups have separated into different groups. Four remain in the den, two are living in a hollow log, five are in another rabbit burrow that they have enlarged.
63	Pups have dispersed and live independently. Not seen suckling again and the mother's teats have returned to normal size.

One dingo in our compound gave birth to 11 pups and successfully raised them all on the regular rations she was fed without having to hunt her own food. Another dingo in a private wildlife park raised ten pups. I have seen a litter of eight pups raked from a hollow log by an Aborigine in the Gulf of Carpentaria back in 1960 when there were no domestic dogs in the region. These observations suggest that the dingo is not genetically restricted to small litters and that seasonal conditions, age and fitness of the mother and her place in the social hierarchy all influence the number of pups born and the proportion of those that she can raise to weaning stage.

Mating, gestation and birth were closely observed in a four-year-old captive bitch in our compound. Both dog and bitch were watched during daylight hours throughout the mating period. Only one mating was observed and this occurred on 29 April 1983. Six pups were born on 12 July. On the day of the birth the bitch refused food, was restless and vomited at least once. The birth began at 7.00 p.m. and four pups were born within 20 minutes. Two more pups were born 30 minutes later with a five-minute interval between them. The pups weighed an average of only 250 g at birth but more than doubled that within a fortnight to average 650 g.

Newborn dingo pups are dark brown with a black stripe down their back, sometimes with clearly apparent white markings. Their eyes are closed and they crowd together for warmth in an appealing huddle. The bitches in our captive colony spent most of the day and all night with the pups until they were three or four days old. Then they rapidly began spending less and less time with their pups until at seven days after birth they only spent the night with them.

The eyes of some of the pups began to open when they were 12 days old and by 14 days every pup had its eyes open. By this stage the mother was regurgitating solid food for them and carrying large bones into the den for the pups to chew. At the ripe old age of three weeks they made their first ventures, alone, into the world just outside their den. Accompanied by much immature growling, squealing and tearing they are, at this early stage, capable of eating rabbit. Life as a carnivore begins early.

RAISING THE PUPS

More than one dingo may help rear the litter. Young male and female dingoes, possibly members of the previous year's litter, as well as the mother, brought freshly killed rabbits to a den of young pups being observed by CSIRO researchers near Alice Springs.[15] The sire of the pups was not seen to assist with

their feeding although he was greeted affectionately by the pups when he approached them — shades of the nuclear human family! The mother of this litter gave the pups a drink by regurgitating water which the pups lapped from her mouth. The observers noted that the pups did not fight each other when they lapped the water as they did when the mother brought food.

Far left: *A hollow log is a common den site. These pups are only one week old but already they are left alone for long periods. They huddle together for warmth and wait for the return of their mother to suckle. Jean-Paul Ferrero*

Top: *Six-week-old pups after they were moved by their mother from the hollow log to a rabbit burrow which she had enlarged since their birth. Gary Steer*

Left: *A two-month-old pup with his father. Gary Steer*

The rabbits nearby were not preyed upon by any of the adults but as the pups got older one of the yearling bitches was observed apparently coaching the pups in hunting. The CSIRO researchers concluded that the rabbits around the den were left for the exclusive use of the pups while the adults hunted further away.

Dingo pups can be aggressive towards each other when competing for food from as early as two weeks of age. Positions in the hierarchy become apparent at around four weeks of age. This is indicated by some of the pups rapidly growing stronger and more robust than their littermates.

Dingoes will readily move their pups to a new den. Our captive females moved them if disturbed too frequently. Two bitches in the wild in central Australia moved their pups frequently to follow a scarce food supply during a poor season.[3] At one stage, these females had dens within 20 m of each other and the pups from their separate litters intermingled freely. One of the bitches was feeding four of her own pups in addition to two of the neighbour's. This level of co-operation suggests that both females were related and living in the same family group. The tendency for bitches in the New England area of New South Wales to rotate their litters around different den sites in the same order each year may also help ensure that pups have game to hunt.[17]

Cannibalism does occur, illustrating that the flexibility of dingo society may not always be altruistic. A young female in the compound ate the entire litter of an older bitch during a brief period when the pups were unguarded. Elsewhere in the wild I have observed dingoes eating another dead dingo so it is fair to assume that a dingo bitch would prey on others' pups if the social hierarchy is disturbed or a subordinate bitch breeds in a territory that she cannot defend.

GROWING UP

The pups are usually weaned at three to six months of age, although they may remain semi-dependent for a longer period. Almost fully grown pups are still likely to be seen in the company of one or more adult dogs but this may simply indicate that dingoes tend to remain in stable social groups rather than showing dependence on the pups' part. In central Australia young pups have been seen to attach themselves to one or more adult males. This is thought to occur because the young animals must stay close to water and the males tolerate their presence.[15]

A pup observes his world from the entrance of the den in an enlarged rabbit burrow — or is he just plain hungry and anxiously awaiting the return of his mother who may bring a whole rabbit or regurgiate food she has already swallowed?
Gary Steer

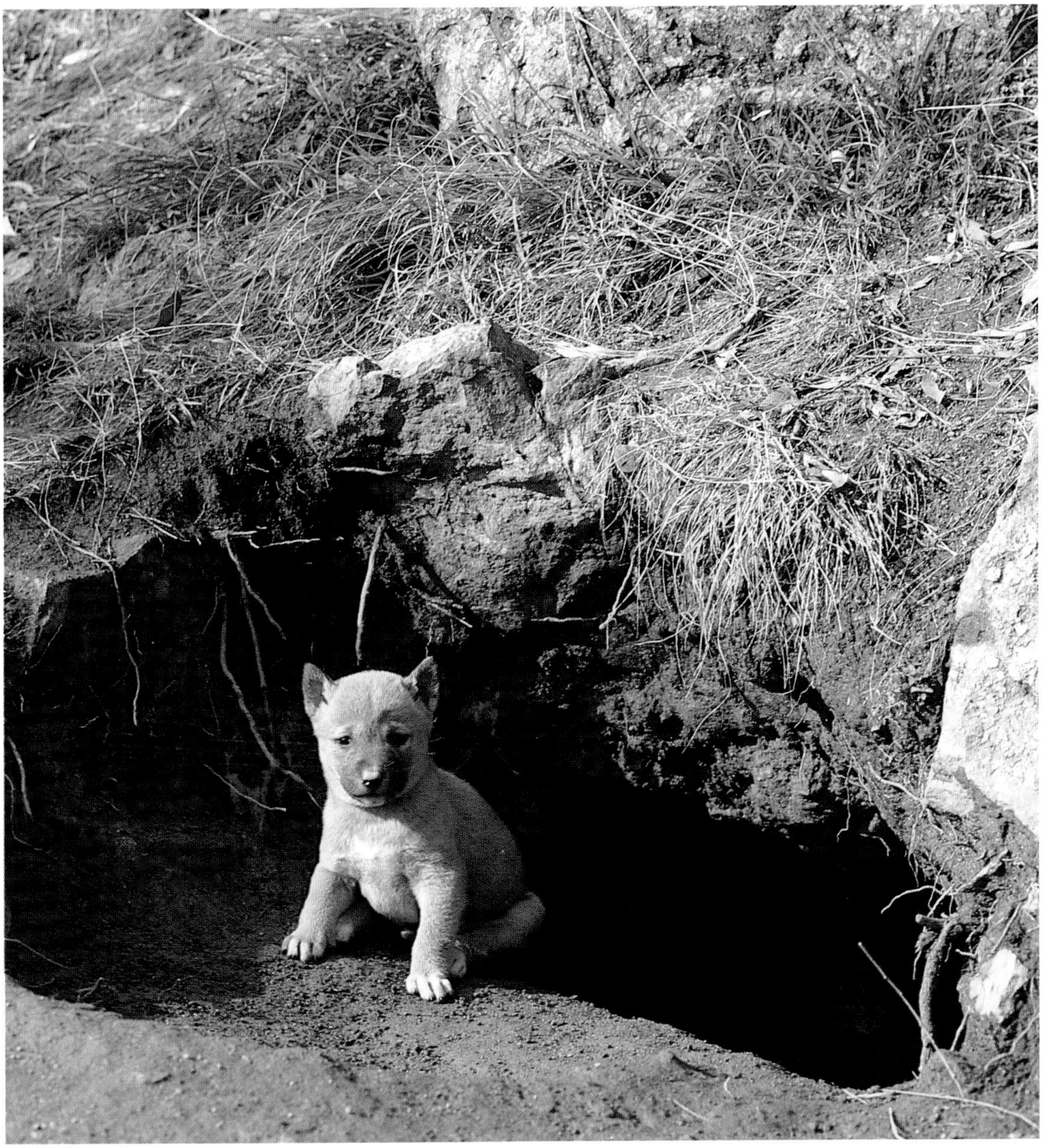

HOW LONG DO DINGOES LIVE?

The oldest dingoes trapped in the wild have been eight to ten years old and it is believed that only a very few would live longer than this.[4] Most would have a lifespan of between five and seven years in the absence of poisoning and trapping by humans. The most critical period of any dingo's life is the stage between when it is weaned and when it must find a position in the family group or travel through other home ranges until it can find a vacant niche.

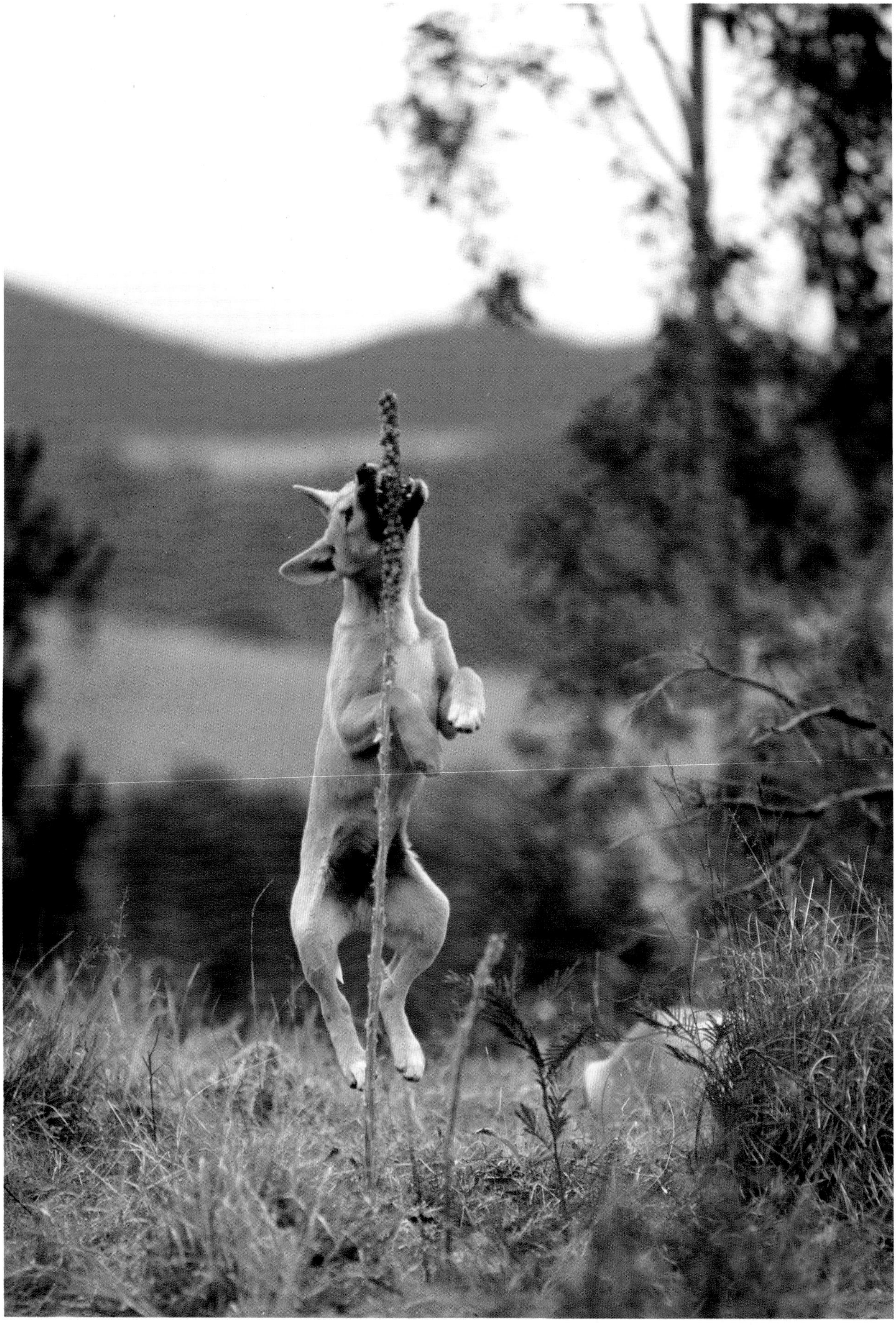

The predator and its prey

The diet of an animal tells something of where it is placed in the natural world. It can also help determine whether it conflicts with human enterprise. Both aspects are of vital interest when it comes to the dingo. What native animals does the dingo eat? How much mutton and beef actually goes down the throat of dingoes? Could it compensate for any direct economic loss by helping control prey that would otherwise increase in number to become pests? Can a knowledge of dingo diet help locate populations that do not cause any damage at all and can simply be left alone? Obtaining the answers to these questions is another step in the process of developing management strategies for the dingo.

DIET OF THE DINGO

The dingo is mainly a predator upon small to medium-sized mammals but its tastes can run to almost any animal that is available. Insects, reptiles and birds all contribute to the diet of the dingo. The dingo is highly flexible in its social arrangements and can take large prey when it hunts in a group, so kangaroos and wallaroo (or euros) are also part of its diet. Many studies of the diet

Young dingoes eat a lot of insects while they are at the vulnerable weaning stage and still unable to kill larger game by themselves. This four-month-old pup is catching insects that are attracted to the flower of the plant. Jean-Paul Ferrero

of the dingo have now been made. As a result, its role as a predator is becoming much clearer, its importance more appreciated.

There is still a great deal of controversy about how many sheep and cattle are killed and eaten by dingoes. Most studies have concentrated on natural areas and there is such a high level of dingo control over agricultural land, particularly sheep country, that it is impossible to know how many sheep and cattle would become victims if all control were lifted. Another problem is the propensity for dingoes to kill sheep well in excess of their food requirements. These issues are discussed more fully in Chapter Thirteen. The information that follows shows the food preferences of the dingo in the area where the studies took place.

The food items in the stomachs of 101 wild dingoes trapped in north-eastern Victoria showed that mammals accounted for over 99 per cent of their diet in this region and that wallaby, wombat and possum were the most common food items.[1] The identification of material in scats collected in the wild confirmed these results. Wallaby comprised 34.1 per cent of the prey, with 24.6 per cent being swamp wallaby (*Wallabia bicolor*) and the rest probably red-necked wallaby (*Macropus rufogriseus*).

Wombat (*Vombatus ursinus*) made up 29.7 per cent of the diet. Adult wombats are difficult for a single dingo to kill and it is likely that they would be hunted in pairs or larger groups. However, 25 per cent of the wombats found in the dingo stomachs were young animals which could have been killed by single dingoes.

The remaining prey consisted of almost equal proportions of possum, echidna and rabbit. The possums made up 11.8 per cent of the diet, of which 7.7 per cent was brush-tailed possum (*Trichosurus vulpecula*). Ringtail possums (*Pseudocheirus peregrinus*) were also included, as well as a surprising 2 per cent of greater glider (*Petauroides volans*), which are not known to spend much time on the ground.

Small ground-dwelling rodents and bandicoots made up only 5 per cent of the diet. Birds and insects comprised only 0.6 per cent. Dingoes were observed hunting Eastern grey kangaroo (*Macropus giganteus*), which has been found in dingo stomachs during other studies. However, no remains were found in this sample.

The young dingoes in north-eastern Victoria ate many more insects and birds than those over one year old. Insects occurred only in 2.2 per cent of the adult stomachs whereas they were found in 18.2 per cent of the young dingoes. Birds also occurred in 2.2 per cent of adult stomachs but in 36.4 per cent of the young dingoes. These results suggest that the young dingoes still shared large prey killed by adults but had to rely mainly on smaller prey.

The study included a comparison between dingoes trapped in remote areas and those trapped close to grazing land. There was only a minor difference in the diet of both groups. Seventy-three per cent of those trapped in the remote area and 45 per cent of those adjacent to grazing land had only wallaby and wombat in their stomachs. One difference in their diet was that the stomachs of dingoes caught in grazing areas contained more small prey. Rabbits, for example, occurred in 4.2 per cent of the dingoes from remote areas but were found in 13.2 per cent of those caught adjacent to grazing country. The other difference was that no sheep remains were found in dingoes from remote areas. This suggests that dingoes well away from grazing areas do not constitute a serious threat to livestock. Of the 53 dingoes caught near grazing areas only 7.5 per cent contained sheep.

Another study into the diet of the dingo in south-eastern Australia analysed the stomach contents of 530 dingoes.[2] A proportion of the stomachs were empty or contained foreign material as a result of the dingo biting at the trap to free itself so that only 372 stomachs were suitable for further analysis. Of these, only 17 stomachs, or 4.6 per cent, contained sheep and only nine stomachs, or 2.4 per cent, contained cattle. In at least 11 of the 26 cases where livestock remains were found in the stomachs, the remains originated from carrion left as a lure by the trappers. This study confirmed that the dingo prefers to eat native game. The common wombat occurred in 48.9 per cent of stomachs and kangaroos and wallabies in a further 43.2 per cent. Ringtail possum and rabbit made up most of the remainder of the diet.

Some 421 stomachs examined in the CSIRO study came from dingoes whose

TABLE 6:
Items from the diet of 101 dingoes in remote and grazing areas expressed as percentage of occurrence. From Corbett, 1974.

Dietary item	**Remote areas (48)**	**Grazing areas (53)**
Wallabies	37.5	41.5
Wombats	41.7	22.6
Possums	14.6	17.0
Echidnas	8.3	15.1
Rabbits	4.2	13.2
Rodents	2.1	9.4
Bandicoots	2.1	5.7
Sheep	0	7.5
Koalas	0	3.8
Horses	2.1	0
Birds	4.2	7.5
Insects	2.1	5.7

distance of capture from sheep country was known. Sixteen dingoes out of the 17 that contained sheep and five out of the nine that held cattle remains were all caught within 3 km of the nearest sheep. Only 16 of the 224 dingoes trapped within 3 km of sheep contained any sheep remains and, as mentioned earlier, as many as 11 of them could have eaten it when left as a carcase lure.

A study of the diet of the dingo in four different regions of the Northern Territory shows that it is a very flexible predator.[3] In the MacDonnell Ranges near Alice Springs the main dietary component is rabbit. On the Barkly Tableland it is the native long-haired rat (*Rattus villosissimus*). Where there were few small mammals, as in the drier Victoria River district, macropods and cattle were taken more frequently, along with very small prey such as lizards. In the tropical coastal wetlands the magpie goose (*Anseranas semipalmata*) and dusky

TABLE 7:
Stomach contents of 372 dingoes from south-east Australia. From Newsome et al, *1983.*

Identity	Percentage occurrence	
Large mammals		
Common wombat (*Vombatus ursinus*)	12.9	81.1
Swamp wallaby (*Wallabia bicolor*)	15.9	
Red-necked wallaby (*Macropus rufogriseus*)	12.1	
Indeterminate wallaby	22.8	
Eastern grey kangaroo (*Macropus giganteus*)	5.9	
Pig (*Sus scrofa*)	4.0	
Horse (*Equus caballus*)	0.3	
European cattle (*Bos taurus*)	2.4	
Sheep (*Ovis aries*)	4.8	
Medium-sized mammals		
Short-beaked echidna (*Tachyglossus aculeatus*)	7.0	29.4
Indeterminate bandicoot (*Perameles/Isoodon*)	0.6	
Common ringtail possum (*Pseudocheirus peregrinus*)	6.2	
Common brushtail possum (*Trichosurus vulpecula*)	2.7	
Indeterminate possum	2.7	
Potoroo (*Potorous* spp.)	0.5	
European rabbit (*Oryctolagus cuniculus*)	7.8	
Fox (*Vulpes vulpes*)	1.6	
Cat (*Felis catus*)	0.3	

Identity	Percentage occurrence	
Small mammals		
Marsupial mouse (*Antechinus* spp.)	0.3	1.7
Broad-toothed rat (*Mastacomys fuscus*)	0.3	
Swamp rat (*Rattus lutreolus*)	0.3	
Rat (indeterminate) (*Rattus/Mastacomys*)	0.8	
Bird		
Emu (*Dromaius novaehollandiae*)	0.3	
Bird (indeterminate)	2.1	
Frog, lizard, snake		
Unidentified	1.9	
Fish		
Unidentified	0.3	
Insects		
Unidentified	4.4	
Bone, meat, fat, hide		
Indeterminate	2.7	

Empty stomachs: 85; stomachs with detritus (sticks, stones, dirt), Tabanids, blowflies and dingo hair: 73; Total collected: 530.

Kangaroos and wallabies are by far the most common prey of the dingo. The large kangaroos, such as this eastern grey, are usually caught by co-operative hunting: the prey is exhausted in a chase and then ambushed or cornered by a number of dingoes from the social unit. *Jean-Paul Ferrero*

field rat (*Rattus colleti*) are the most common food items, except during the dry season when buffalo carcases became available. Common to all the areas studied was that cattle only became a significant food item during drought, and even then much of it was carrion.

Research on the diet of the dingo in the gorge country of the New England Tablelands near Armidale, New South Wales, showed that macropods made up 53.85 per cent of the diet.[4,5,6] A further 14.42 per cent comprised arboreal mammals. As much as 13 per cent of the remainder was made up by bandicoots, rabbits and echidnas. This research involved the examination of 8121 dingo scats. None contained cattle even though there were cattle in the area. Sheep were much less accessible, being isolated because of the Styx River and some dingo-proof fencing.

The New England study also showed that small prey made up a larger part of the diet of the dingo in that region between the months of May and October. These months coincide with the breeding season, so the consumption of smaller prey may reflect the need for lactating females either to catch more prey or to hunt alone. Pups that are just weaned during these months would also be limited in their ability to catch larger prey.

The dingoes studied in the New England region concentrated on swamp wallabies even though other prey species were common. They clearly preferred swamp wallaby to other macropods in the area.[7] A nine-year study into the diet of the dingo at Nadgee Nature Reserve on the south coast and Kosciusko National Park in the Alps of south-eastern New South Wales also showed that dingoes concentrated on only a few species of prey.[8] Prey could be classified to reflect the dingo's heavy reliance on particular species. The "staples", included 11 medium-sized mammals such as wallaby, wombat and possum, and waterbirds at the coastal site. "Supplementary" prey were large mammals such as the Eastern grey kangaroo, which featured heavily in the diet at times but was completely absent at others. "Opportune" prey included small prey such as rodents which dingoes would eat but did not hunt regularly or rely upon. "Scavenged" food included carrion; it is really another form of opportune prey.

One of the most interesting aspects to be uncovered in the research at Nadgee Nature Reserve was how heavily the dingoes around the estuaries and lakes relied upon waterbirds. Nine species of birds occurred in 38.4 per cent of the scats at Nadgee whereas only one bird (0.9 per cent) occurred in Kosciusko. The high incidence of bird in the diet at Nadgee was only partly due to scavenging dead seabirds washed up on the beaches. Waterbirds caught by dingoes occurred in 36.9 per cent of the scats from Nadgee, making them second only to swamp wallaby as the most common food item. The two waterbirds that were mostly taken by these dingoes were black swans (*Cygnus attratus* and Eurasian coot (*Fullica atra*). The incidence of these two species increased markedly during the moulting season when their reduced ability to take off quickly rendered them vulnerable to dingoes that rushed them in the shallow waters of Salt Lake.

A study into the food of the dog, fox and cat in Croajingolong National Park in coastal north-eastern Victoria refers only to the feral domestic dog (*Canis familiaris*) as the source of the scats that were examined.[9] No reference is made to the dingo and the authors assume that the feral dog is a damaging influence on the native fauna. However, pure dingoes still occur in this area and it is more likely that some of the 412 scats

TABLE 8:
Food items in 1983 dingo scats from north-eastern New South Wales. From Robertshaw and Harden, 1985.

Percentage occurrence defined for each species as: (total number of scats examined) × 100. Items with an occurrence of <1% are grouped as "Others", except for macropods.

Food item	Frequency	Percentage occurrence
Macropods		
Swamp wallaby (*Wallabia bicolor*)	608	30.51
Red-necked wallaby (*Macropus rufogriseus*)	222	11.14
Wallaroo (*M. robustus*)	1	0.05
Parma wallaby (*M. parma*)	91	4.57
Eastern grey kangaroo (*M. giganteus*)	5	0.25
Red-necked pademelon (*Thylogale thetis*)	76	3.81
Long-nosed potoroo (*Potorous tridactylus*)	33	1.66
Unidentified	37	1.86
All macropods		53.85
Arboreal mammals		
Common brushtail and mountain possums (*Trichosurus vulpecula and T. caninus*)	138	6.92
Common ringtail (*Pseudocheirus peregrinus*)	88	4.42
Greater glider (*Petauroides volans*)	29	1.46
Others (3 spp.)	32	1.61
All arboreal mammals		14.40
Small mammals		
Bush rat (*Rattus fuscipes*)	244	12.24
Antechinuses (*Antechinus stuartii* and *A. swainsonii*)	116	5.82
Others (6 spp.)	50	2.51
All small mammals		20.56
Other mammals		
Bandicoots (*Perameles nasuta* and *Isodon obesulus*)	136	6.82
Rabbit (*Oryctolagus cuniculus*)	127	6.37
Echidna (*Tachyglossus aculeatus*)	70	3.51
Others (7 spp.)	22	1.10
All other mammals		17.80
Other groups		
Aves	54	2.71
Reptilia	25	1.25
Others (5 classes)	28	1.40
All other groups		5.36

Left: *Many of the species preyed upon by dingoes are regarded as pests. This young pup's mother has brought a rabbit home for dinner. Gary Steer*

Above: *Dingoes often eat the entrails before any other part of their prey. Jean-Paul Ferrero*

examined came from dingoes, some from feral domestic dogs, and others from hybrids between the two. The results of the Croajingolong study are summarised in Table 9. It is interesting that the ringtail possum (*Pseudocheris peregrinus*), a tree-dwelling mammal, makes the most frequent occurrence in the scats of the three predators that were studied, although the macropods and the wombat may still have comprised the bulk of the diet over an extended period, as was found in the long-term study just across the border in Nadgee Nature Reserve.

Dingoes trapped in the rangelands of Western Australia ate mainly red kangaroo and euro (*Macropus robustus*) with both these species being found in 65 per cent of the 146 stomachs that contained food. Sheep occurred in only 4.1 per cent of those stomachs and cattle in 0.7 per cent. The very low incidence of sheep and cattle in the dingoes' diet in this study, despite their availability to at least a proportion of the dingoes trapped, suggests that dingoes prefer to eat native game.[10]

The research into the diet of the dingo shows that it eats mainly small to medium-sized native animals of which

TABLE 9:
Percentage occurrence of main prey species in dog scats. From Triggs et al, 1984.

Prey	Dog	Fox	Cat
Ringtail possum (*Pseudocheris perigrinus*)	38	58	56
Swamp wallaby (*Wallabia bicolor*)	21	5	0
Red-necked wallaby (*Macropus rufogriseus*)	13	3	0
Common wombat (*Vombatus ursinus*)	11	1	0
"Marsupial mice" (*Antechinus* spp.)	15	24	15
Rats (*Rattus* spp.)	10	15	19
Echidna (*Tachyglossus aculeatus*)	5	1	2

TABLE 10:
Food items in the stomachs of 146 dingoes collected in the rangelands of Western Australia. From Whitehouse 1977, with the addition of common names.

Food item	Number of stomachs	Volume	Occurrence
Mammals			
Red kangaroo (*Macropus rufus*)	58	47.6	40.0
Euro (*Macropus robustus*)	39	24.6	26.9
Rabbit (*Oryctolagus cuniculus*)	8	6.5	5.5
Dingo (*Canis familiaris dingo*)	6	Trace	4.1
Sheep (*Ovis aries*)	6	4.2	4.1
Feral goat (*Capra hircus*)	3	1.4	2.1
House mouse (*Mus musculus*)	3	Trace	2.1
Rock wallaby (*Petrogale penicillata*)	2	1.5	1.4
Fat-tailed marsupial mouse (*Sminthopsis crassicaudata*)	2	1.0	1.4
Echidna (*Tachyglossus aculeatus*)	2	Trace	1.4
Feral cat (*Felis catus*)	1	Trace	0.7
Spectacled hare wallaby (*Lagorchestes conspicillatus*)	1	Trace	0.7
Rabbit-eared bandicoot (*Macrotis lagotis*)	1	Trace	0.7
Cattle (*Bos*. spp.)	1	1.8	0.7

wallaby and wombat are the preferred species of prey, wherever those two species occur. It is not unusual for carnivores to rely on one or two species of prey. The lynx of Alberta, Canada, depends on the snowshoe hare for 76 per cent of its food. The timber wolf in Wisconsin, USA, relies on whitetail deer for 77 per cent of its food.[4] The heavy reliance of the dingo on only a few species is not surprising given the results of overseas research into other carnivores.

Food item	Number of stomachs	Volume	Occurrence
Birds			
Emu (*Dromaiidae*)	12	1.5	8.3
Parrots (*Psittacidae*)	7	Trace	4.0
Pigeons and doves (*Columbidae*)	2	Trace	1.4
Crows and ravens (*Corvidae*)	1	0.5	0.7
Reptiles			
Skinks (*Scincidae*)	7	Trace	4.9
Goannas (*Varanidae*)	1	1.1	0.7
Insects	8	Trace	5.5
Carrion	9	Trace	6.2
Ground matter	79	5.5	54.5
Miscellaneous	2	Trace	1.38

HOW MUCH DOES A DINGO EAT?

Dingoes in the wild consume prey equivalent to about 7 per cent of their body weight per day. This represents about 1 kg of prey for the average-sized dingo.[11] Captive dingoes require about 300 g dry weight of commercial dog food per day with a digestibility of 75 per cent, making 1000 kilocalories of digestible energy.[4] An extra 800 kilocalories of digestible energy needed for activity in the wild brings the total energy requirement to 1800 kilocalories per day. This compares to the 1750 kilocalories regarded as normal for a domestic dog of the same size as a dingo.

An average daily food requirement that is calculated from the food consumed over a long period does not mean that an animal in the wild must capture and consume an equivalent amount of prey each day. Sometimes free-ranging dingoes go without food or consume very little for days at a time and then compensate by gorging when prey is killed or large carrion is found. Timber wolves have been noted to consume as much as 20 kg of meat in 24 hours and then continue normal activity for a fortnight without food.[12]

WATER

The amount of water required by a dingo depends on the location and time of year. In central Australia the water requirements of wild dingoes were measured by trapping them and injecting them with water containing radioisotopes before releasing them.[11] When the same animals were recaptured over the next few weeks, a blood urine sample was taken so that the water turnover rate could be calculated. As can be anticipated, the period of highest water turnover in central Australia occurred in summer when dingoes required 100 ml of water per kilogram of body weight per day. A much lower rate of 70 ml per kilogram per day was required during winter.

The water requirements of lactating bitches could be lowered by a behaviour pattern common to many mammals. The bitch licks the anus and urethral openings of the pups, thereby stimulating them to void. She then consumes the urine and faeces and recovers up to 30 per cent of the moisture given to the pups in her milk.[11]

I frequently observed our captive bitches assiduously stimulating their pups to void then consuming everything that was eliminated, even in midwinter when there was plenty of water nearby, so this practice could also be associated with keeping the den clean. Moreover, the mother discontinues it as soon as the pups leave the den for elimination at around five weeks of age. But of course, consumption of the pups' urine and faeces in the first few weeks after birth would also result in more efficient use of water and nutrients.

Dingoes also receive moisture from their prey because a vertebrate is made up of about 85 per cent water. When prey is abundant and/or the weather is cool, dingoes spend less energy hunting and may obtain a major part, if not all, of their water requirement through their prey. Dingoes have been caught and observed in waterless regions of the Simpson Desert in central Australia even during summer. They obviously obtained sufficient water from prey.

I have observed dingo pups just after weaning eat from the carcase of a seal washed onto a beach on the far south coast of New South Wales then drink copious amounts of very salty water from the mouth of an estuary. They also lapped considerable amounts of salt water from the ocean beach nearby. I cannot say that they were wholly satisfied by sea water because they could easily have been also drinking fresh water elsewhere.

Dingoes rushing waterbirds in the shallows of Salt Lake at Nadgee Nature Reserve on the south coast of New South Wales. Any bird that is slow to take off because it is taken by surprise, or because it is injured or moulting, will fall victim. Jean-Paul Ferrero

HUNTING TECHNIQUE

Dingoes seem to be incessantly on the move, and moving means being on the lookout for prey. Of course, some dingo movements are for purposes other than hunting but the strong impression is that the motto of the dingo is "never let a chance go by". The dingoes I observed in our compound were always hunting while they were active. The young pups would spend hours trying to catch butterflies on the wing and tracking mice through the long grass. They ate both, even though they were well fed. I often found a pile of feathers which indicated that an unwary currawong lingered a moment too long over the dog biscuits.

The wild dingoes I observed at Alice Springs would resume hunting behaviour as soon as they had a drink. They sometimes jogged straight into water along a cattle pad but, having drunk, they began circling and sniffing among the dunes searching for rabbits and other small game.

Many accounts of dingoes' hunting behaviour come from bushmen who have been lucky enough to watch a hunt in progress. They often show that dingoes co-operate extremely efficiently. They are also able to communicate with each other in anticipation of their prey's behaviour. For example, a stockman from Quilpie in south-western

Queensland told me how he was out mustering cattle when he saw two dingoes head a wallaby towards a steep-sided valley. They made no attempt to catch the wallaby but simply ensured that it raced towards its supposed freedom down this valley. From his vantage point the stockman saw the fleeing wallaby run straight down the valley into the waiting jaws of two other dingoes that had previously positioned themselves for an ambush.

John Robertshaw witnessed a dingo force a small mob of goats across a log that straddled a creek in the New England ranges. Hidden among the roots of the log on the other side was a dingo that promptly killed three of the goats. The dingo obviously has a highly sophisticated form of communication and can achieve a high degree of co-operation in hunting.

Dingo groups at Nadgee were consistently small, with only two to three individuals, whereas at Kosciusko each group contained an average of nine dingoes.[8] The larger groups at Kosciusko reflected the larger game they were accustomed to hunting, the largest of which were brumby foals. Conversely, the smaller groups at Nadgee reflected the amount of small and medium-sized game in their diet. After Nadgee was ravaged by a major fire in 1972 there followed a period of shortage of smaller game. This resulted in a decline in dingo numbers even though grey kangaroos were abundant and actually increased in number. The explanation given for this phenomenon is that the relative instability of the coastal forests, with their frequent fires, does not allow the development of large groups of dingoes and that such groups cannot be formed quickly. Clearly, operating in a large pack does require some social skills, which take time to acquire.

The hunting success rate of the dingo is not known. Studies of wolves show that success varies enormously according to the number of wolves involved, the weather conditions and the abundance of prey. A wolf pack in Ontario, Canada, had killed 25 per cent of the white-tailed deer they started one year but managed a 63 per cent success rate the following winter due to favourable snow conditions.

PREDATOR–PREY RELATIONS

It is commonly assumed that predators control the numbers of their prey. This point of view has a strong following despite the difficulty of proving it. We see the life and death struggle between a predator and its prey and assume that the superior strength, cunning and strategy of the carnivore must control the numbers of its prey. But why couldn't the reverse apply? Why couldn't the availability of prey limit the number of carnivores? This is precisely what was

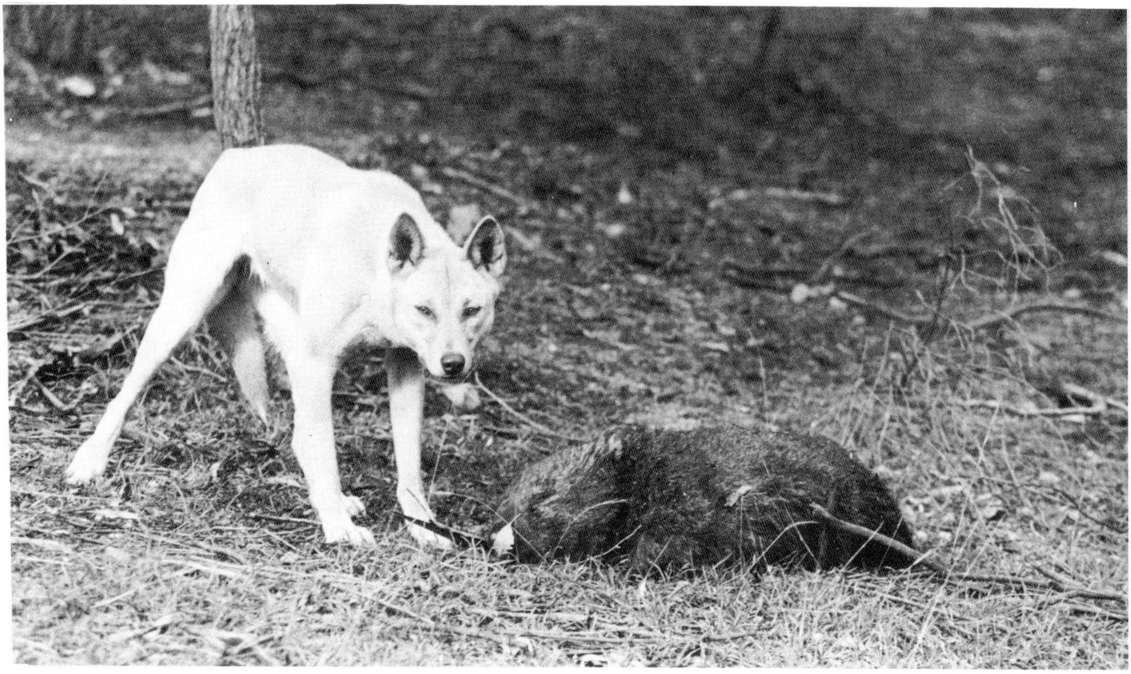

An adult dingo feeding on a common wombat, another frequent component of dingo diet in south-eastern Australia. Gary Steer

found to take place between the moose and the timber wolves on Isle Royale, an island of 336 sq km on Lake Superior, between the United States and Canada.[12]

One of the longest and most exact studies of the relationship between a predator and its prey took place on Isle Royale. Moose colonised the island at the turn of this century when they swam the 24 km from the mainland in response to overpopulation. Wolves did not reach the island until an ice bridge linked it to the mainland in 1949. These events provided a natural laboratory to study one of the most elusive aspects of ecology — the relationship between predator and prey.

The study showed that the number of moose on the island is largely determined by their food supply and the number of wolves rises and falls with the number of moose. However, when wolf numbers are high they are able to exert a moderating influence on the moose population. Before the arrival of the wolf, the moose population was characterised by a build-up in numbers to a peak that crashed when they ate themselves into starvation. Predation by the wolf has now moderated that cycle of boom and bust.

Among the forests to the north and west of the Great Lakes in Canada the moose and/or white-tailed deer reach a density of around 300 kg per square kilometre. This is all that the vegetation in the region can support in the long term. The maximum wolf density in the same area is that of one wolf to 25 sq km, giving a predator–prey relationship of one wolf to 7500 kg of prey. The density of wolves cannot increase because the prey has evolved certain mechanisms to avoid capture. The wolves are dependent on the very young, the diseased and the old and infirm.

The Nadgee dingo study indicates that what holds true for the wolf in North America also holds true with the dingo. An abundance of waterbirds in the southern part of Nadgee that lasted for four years allowed a rapid increase in the dingo population of that area compared to the northern part where waterbirds were low in number because of the absence of lakes. However, a rapid decline in the waterbird population due to factors outside Nadgee such as drought or good seasons elsewhere in Australia, resulted in a rapid decline in the number of dingoes. There was little alternative prey in the form of small to medium-sized game because of the effects of a major fire in 1972. So, long before the last native animals were killed, the dingoes themselves died or failed to rear their young. In this way, the dingo is simply part of the ecosystem and its numbers reflect the seasons, good and bad.

On the other hand, there are circumstances when dingoes can help reduce the number of macropods. Red kangaroos (*Macropus rufus*) were abundant in the Hale River valley near Alice Springs in 1960. One survey showed 96 kangaroos in a 35 km strip. But between 1969 and 1974 only 20 kangaroos were seen in the same area. There had been a severe drought from 1958 to 1965, rabbits were plentiful and together with cattle and feral horses competed with

Inside the New South Wales Border Dog Fence near Tibooburra. It has been noted that the red kangaroo population in much higher here than across the border in South Australia and Queensland where there are many more dingoes. Roland Breckwoldt

the kangaroos. All these events — drought, competition with feral animals, livestock and rabbits, plus dingo

predation — led to the decline of the red kangaroo in this particular area.[13]

In another area near Alice Springs red kangaroos were abundant but there were no rabbits because the rabbits could not burrow in the hard soil. Yet at another site near Ayers Rock where there were rabbits the kangaroos were much scarcer. The explanation given for the difference was that where there are rabbits *and* kangaroos there are also more dingoes.[13] The presence of an alternative food source enables dingoes to maintain a stable population. If one prey species became scarce they can turn to another. The number of wolves on Isle Royale is so closely related to the number of moose because there is no alternative large prey.

The 1972 fire in Nadgee reduced the number of macropods and dingo predation prevented their increase even with abundant green feed following the fire. The dingo population was not affected by the fire, or its impact on the macropod population, because black swans and coots provided an alternative food source. Dingo numbers did not decline until the waterbirds became scarce.[8]

Dingo numbers also reflect the availability of prey. The rabbit forms the greatest part of the dingoes' diet on the Nullarbor Plain in Western Australia and dingo scalp returns tend to fluctuate according to seasonal conditions that favour rabbits.[10] Dingoes were more abundant on the Barkly Tableland after a good run of seasons allowed the long-haired rat (*Rattus villosissimus*) to proliferate.[14] One of the unintended results of the South Australian dog fence is that it protects the kangaroos from dingoes. Kangaroos are abundant inside the fence, reaching plague proportions according to the pastoralists, whereas they are much fewer in the dingo country north of the fence.[15,16]

There are many more kangaroos and emus on the sheep country of western New South Wales compared to the unprotected cattle country of South Australia and Queensland just across the border dingo fence. [16] The possibility of the higher numbers of kangaroos and emus on the sheep country being a product of environmental change produced by sheep grazing was rejected because no distinct difference in vegetation on either side of the fence was evident. The most plausible explanation for the differences in the numbers of kangaroos and emus on both sides of the fence was the impact of dingo predation.[17]

At least some macropods increase their breeding in response to heavy dingo predation. Under most conditions the swamp wallaby (*Wallabia bicolor*) breeds only once a year but the New England study found that the swamp wallabies responded to dingo predation by breeding all year round.[7] Dingo predation could still reduce the recruitment of young because the analysis of bone fragments showed that a high proportion of swamp wallaby in the diet came from juveniles. Heavy dingo predation also changed the behaviour of Eastern grey kangaroos (*Macropus giganteus*) and they spent more time in groups as dingo numbers increased. The adage "safety in numbers" may be apt.

The weight of evidence is that dingoes can exert some level of control over the native animals on which they prey. This is consistent with the accounts of an increase of emus and macropods following the introduction of strychnine as described in Chapter Four. One of the interesting questions yet to be properly researched is whether the dingo can play a role in controlling introduced pests such as feral pigs. Unlike most native prey species, the introduced pests tend to be prolific breeders. Feral pigs are now widespread in Australia and represent a major agricultural pest in addition to the harm they do to native wildlife. Should foot-and-mouth disease enter Australia, it is likely to be harboured by feral pigs. These animals, particularly young suckers, should be highly vulnerable to dingoes. After all, one of the most common methods of hunting feral pigs is baling them up with a pack of dogs. Admittedly, pig dogs are chosen from among the larger exotic breeds of domestic dog but a group of dingoes hunting in their own territory should be able to compensate for their smaller stature.

The reason pig has not shown up very often in the stomachs or scats examined in dingo research to date is that most of this research has been carried out in areas where there are (or were) few feral pigs. It is somewhat ironic that Queensland, the state with the highest population of feral pigs, has carried out the least research into dingoes. A preliminary study based on a survey of dingo and feral pig bounties paid in Queensland over the 25-year period 1948–49 to 1972–73 has shown that there were fewer bounties paid for pigs in areas where the most bunties were paid on dingoes.[18] This research badly needs follow-up work on the diet of the dingo in areas where there are high populations of pigs. A positive result in favour of the dingo could well be used as evidence to prevent the indiscriminant control of dingoes in national parks and remote areas where pigs are a problem.

While the scientific evidence on whether the dingo helps control pests remains hazy, some farmers and graziers are supportive of the dingo. True, they are invariably cattlemen rather than sheepmen but farmers who grow crops sometimes have a kind word for the dingo. For example, I have met one highly successful grazier and grain sorghum grower from Kingaroy in Queensland who must be one of the few people on the land who has made representations to the Queensland government to reduce aerial baiting of dingoes. This grazier will not let anyone shoot dingoes on his property. He believes emphatically that dingoes keep down the number of emus and kangaroos that otherwise cause extensive damage to his sorghum crops. He is quite prepared to lose a few calves in exchange for the protection the dingoes give his crops.

There are other cattlemen in Queensland, such as Adam Clarke of 'Bimbadeen', Taroom, who claim that they manage the dingoes on their properties to keep the kangaroos down. If the number of dingoes increases to the stage where they feel calf losses are intolerable they undertake a control program. They cease dingo control when kangaroo numbers are high and then let the dingoes increase. These anecdotes may not have been subjected to the rigours of scientific research, but there are enough of them around to take them seriously.

KILLING IN EXCESS OF FOOD REQUIREMENTS

Dingoes sometimes kill well in excess of their food requirements. The reasons for this are poorly understood but it appears to occur most frequently when there is an abundance of prey. A group of five dingoes that got through the border dingo fence killed 83 red kangaroos (*Macropus rufus*) in only seven weeks within a 150 m radius of a watering point in western New South Wales.[19] Most of the kangaroos were juvenile females. This region has a high kangaroo population, partly because dingoes have been almost totally eradicated.

One feature associated with the predation on these red kangaroos was that not all of the carcase was eaten. The dingoes ate the abdominal contents, hindquarter muscle and the thoracic contents such as heart and lungs. The same practice is reported by sheep graziers when large numbers of sheep are killed. Indeed, the bush abounds with harsh tales of how dingoes killed dozens of sheep but ate only a small portion of one or two. Such occasions can be easily distorted into myths about dingoes killing to eat only the kidney fat or showing a preference for specific organs or tissue.

Notwithstanding the propensity for folklore to provide more colourful explanations, research has confirmed that dingoes do indeed kill sheep far in excess of food requirements. It became a major task for a research team to keep a record of the number of sheep being killed in the Fortescue River region of Western Australia when a grazier agreed to let them use his property to investigate the impact of dingoes on sheep.[20,21] A kill of over 70 sheep in one night at Moles station near Kybeyan on the Monaro Tableland in southern New South Wales during 1985 was not unusual. I have spoken to many sheepmen who have said that they would not mind if the dingoes only killed as many sheep as they needed to eat.

Some results of the New England study suggest that killing in excess of food requirements may be more common when prey is abundant. This study took place over a period of 17 years during which the dingo population increased. In the early years there was evidence that carcases of the larger macropods were only partly eaten. However, as dingo numbers increased there was a marked tendency towards more efficient use of each kill, suggesting that the dingoes changed their hunting behaviour with an increase in their numbers. They tended to concentrate on the larger macropods and eat the entire carcase. This led to the interesting conclusion that an increase in dingo numbers does not necessarily mean that more prey is killed.[6] This has implications for those who assert that a build-up of dingoes will have an adverse effect on other wildlife. It also suggests that killing in excess of food requirements is more likely to occur when dingoes are low in numbers compared to the amount of game.

THOSE WHO PREY ON THE DINGO

As a large carnivore at the head of the food chain, the dingo suffers from very little predation by other wildlife. Sometimes a pup or a young dingo may be taken by a wedge-tailed eagle or large snake such as the carpet snake or amethystine python. Large goannas would also be capable of taking small pups from an unguarded den. Salt-water crocodiles have been known to take dingoes. Such predation upon the dingo is only opportunistic and there is no species of wildlife that includes the dingo as a regular feature of its diet.

But there is one species of animal that is a highly successful predator of the dingo — humans. The species *Homo sapiens* is a very proficient dingo killer. Before white man, the Aborigines ate dingoes and can be described as true predators upon the wild population. White man's predation goes by euphemisms such as "management" or "control" and comes in many forms: shooting; trapping; poisoning; chasing on horseback with dogs or by motor vehicle; and exclusion dog fences which reduce the dingo's range.

A dingo at full pace is a formidable predator that can catch a wide variety of game. Gary Steer

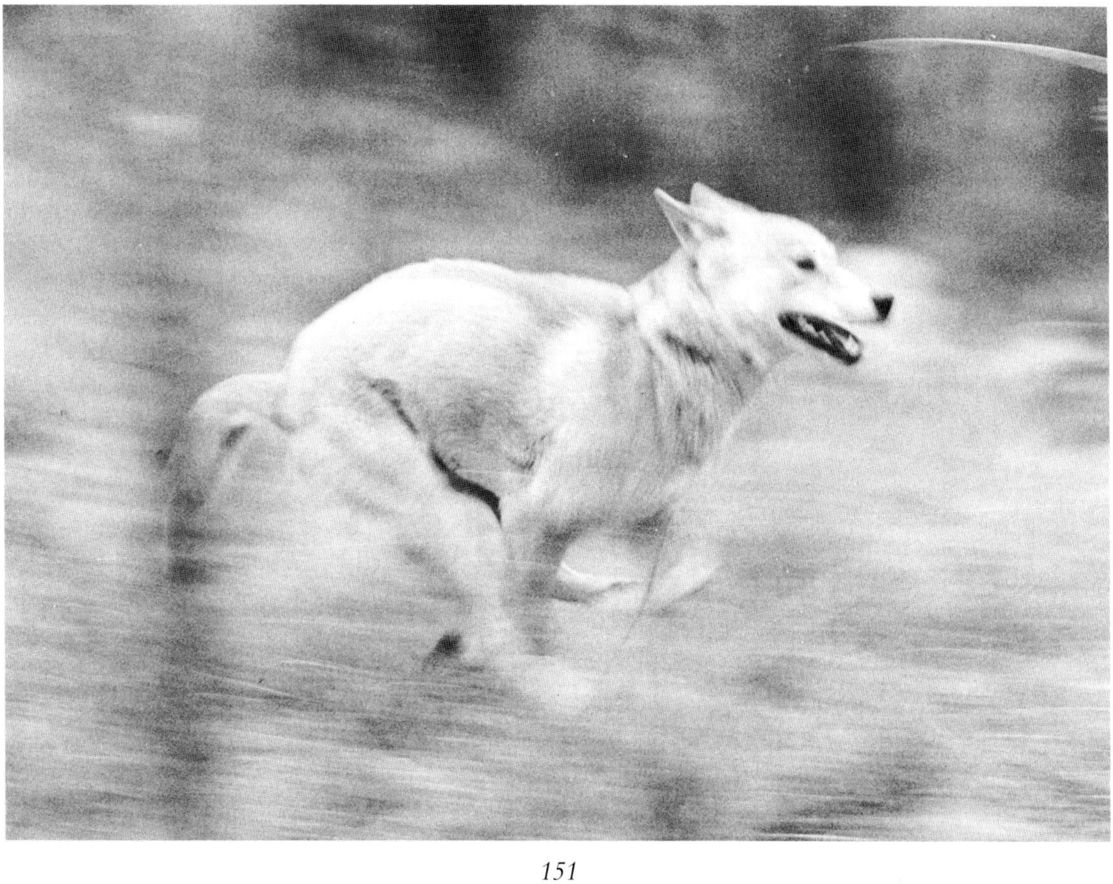

The social life of the dingo

Many an argument about the dingo has been caused by people placing different meanings on inoffensive words such as "migration" and "territory". In zoological circles they have very specific uses; in the world at large, however, they are often used so broadly that it is difficult to know just what it is about the dingo that is being debated. Reaching agreement on terminology is task enough, but then comes the long and difficult process of finding out whether the dingo behaves according to stereotype and folklore or not.

The most powerful tool for gaining an insight into the social life of the dingo is radio-telemetry. It is now possible to trap wild dingoes and fit them with a collar carrying a small radio transmitter so that their movements can be followed with a portable receiver on the ground or from an aircraft. This enables us to explore the life of the dingo in the bush, shrouded by night, forest or the vastness of the interior.

THE SOCIAL UNIT

The wild canids are classified into three broad behavioural groups.[1] The first includes the solitary hunters such as the small species of foxes which, because of their size, are relegated to hunting small game such as mice, rabbits and birds as well as feeding on carrion. At the other end of the spectrum lie the pack animals such as the northern wolf and the Cape hunting dogs of Africa that can hunt very large game by co-operative hunting. Between these extremes sits the dingo.

The dingo is not generally recognised as a pack animal because it has too flexible a social repertoire. Flexibility is the hallmark of dingo society. The dingo is a very efficient solitary hunter but its size imposes an upper limit on the size of its game. It is able to overcome this disadvantage by engaging in co-operative hunting. While its size alone would relegate it to small game, it can obtain large prey by co-operation.

For some inexplicable reason the dingoes in this family group would suddenly turn on one individual and, while falling short of a total beating, would harass it until it showed complete submission. Gary Steer

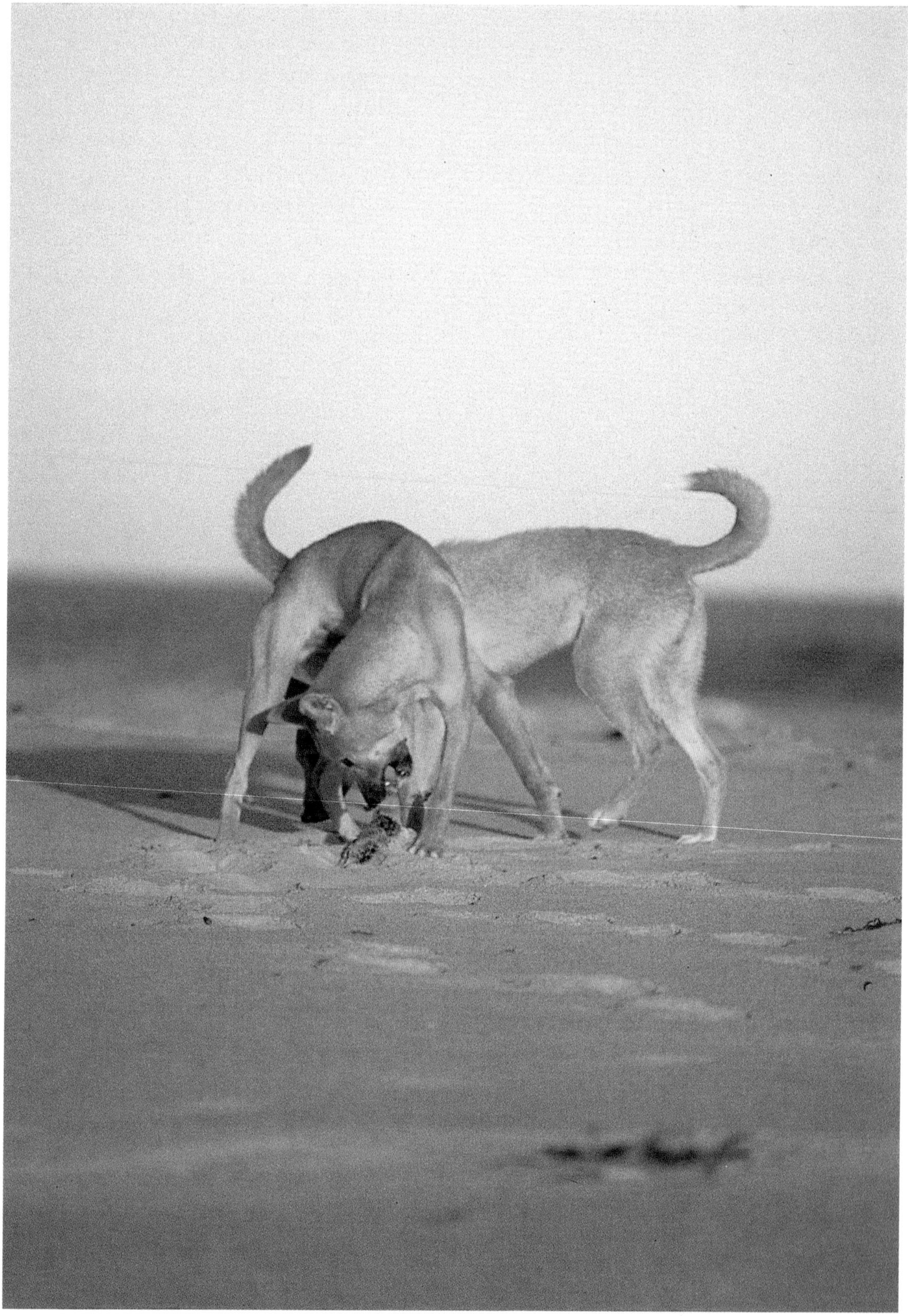

HOME RANGE

The home range of an animal is where it spends most of its time and gains food and shelter. Adult dingoes have a clearly defined home range which they seldom leave. The home range may be shared with other dingoes that make up a social group that sometimes co-operates in hunting. Alternatively, the home range of one individual may overlap with that of another.

The area of each home range depends largely on the amount of prey and, to a certain extent, the size of the principal prey species. In the New England Tableland region of New South Wales the average home range was shown to be 2700 ha each for four adult males and 900 ha each for four juveniles.[2] Most of the home ranges were elongated along valleys and the ridges between them formed natural boundaries. One juvenile had a home range that consisted of two larger areas separated by a narrow corridor. It always passed through the corridor very quickly to get to the larger areas. Five of these dingoes shared some common ground because their home ranges overlapped. The other two dingoes had overlapping home ranges some five km away.

The dingoes did not give equal preference to all parts of their home range.

Left: *Tails up. Dingoes signal their position in the social order by the position of their tail. Here, two young dingoes believe that they both own the dead bird they have found on the beach, and a fight for possession will follow if one of them does not relinquish it. Gary Steer*

Below: *Submission. The dingo standing over its littermate has its tail up: the two will already have established their position in the hierarchy during fights over a share of the food. Gary Steer*

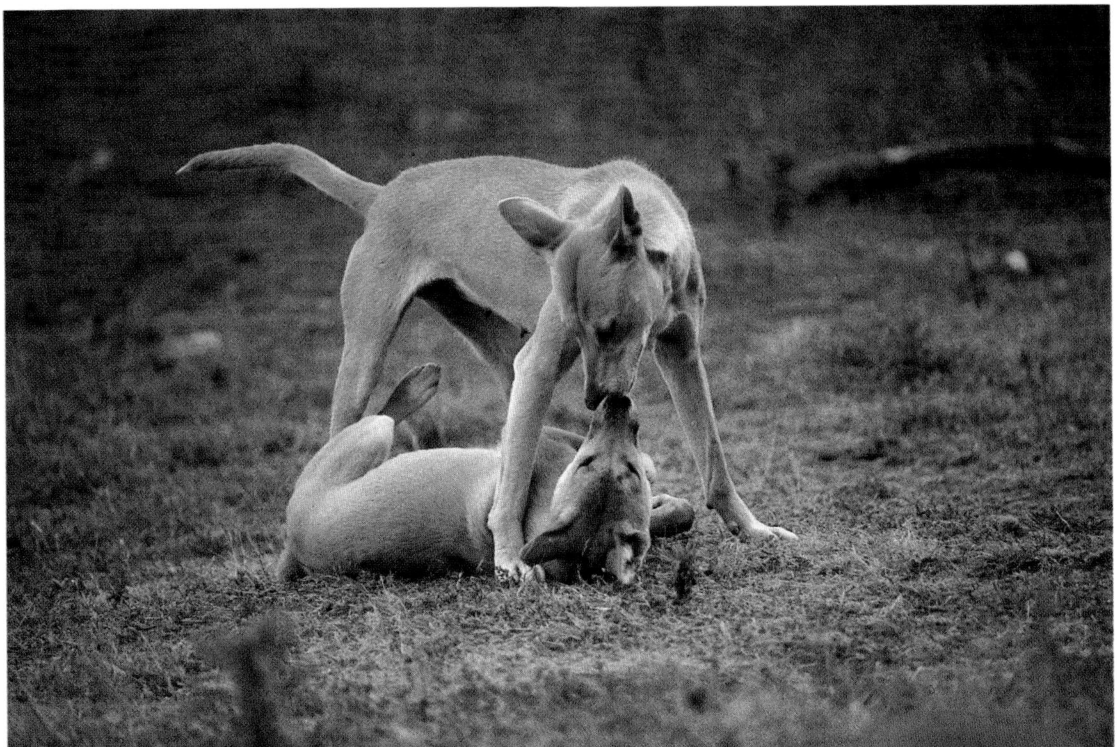

They used some parts often and others not at all. This differential use of the home range allowed a high degree of overlap while minimising conflict. It also allowed a group of dingoes to congregate for hunting, breeding or defence of group territory. Some dens were used in common — another indicator of co-operation between dingoes with overlapping home ranges.

A study in the Pilbara district of Western Australia made similar findings.[3] Each group of dingoes in the Fortescue River area of the Pilbara occupied a home range that varied in size between 70 and 125 sq km. This gave a density of about one dingo per 7 sq km in the better country to only one per 42 sq km in the poorer areas. A group of seven dingoes that occupied the river valley with abundant game had a home range of 70 sq km and one group of 15 required only 75 sq km. But a group of three dingoes on poor habitat away from the river needed 125 sq km.[4]

The home ranges of these groups did slightly overlap their neighbours' but they tended to avoid each other, although some fighting between members of neighbouring groups was observed. The groups that occupied each home range were based on the family but they frequently broke into subgroups, each of which used a particular part of the home range. These smaller groups were flexible in numbers but often reflected associations between a dog and a bitch or a bitch and her pups.[3] Most sightings were of small groups of between two and six animals with occasional sightings of the large groups of up to 15 dingoes that occupied the entire home range. These groups invariably consisted of a dominant breeding pair and younger animals from various litters.[4] An interesting sidelight to this research was the occurrence of a few solitary dingoes that moved through the home range of other dingoes. Older non-breeding dingoes whose home range extends beyond that of the main breeding group have also been observed in Queensland.[5]

The high proportion of sightings of dingoes in small groups in the Pilbara is in contrast to the dominance of solitary sightings in central Australia.[6] Dingoes on the Nullarbor have very large home ranges and tend to remain solitary because the main prey species is rabbit. The home ranges on the Nullarbor varied in size from 90 to 300 sq km. They were much more loosely defined and not defended as strongly as the home ranges in the Fortescue River region where the predominant social structure was a group that preyed on euro.[4]

The use of a defined home range has been confirmed in every study of the dingo. Among the wide valley floors of central Australia, the home range of a pair of dingoes had a radius of 8 km.[6] In the Kosciusko mountains of eastern Australia, the home ranges of three females and one male were 14, 17, 18 and 21.5 sq km respectively. At Nadgee Nature Reserve on the far south coast of New South Wales the size of the home range of three females was 9, 9.5 and 13.5 sq km and for two males it was 9 and 10 sq km.[7] A dingo obviously needs a very large area to meet its food requirements.

TERRITORY

There is a significant difference between showing that the dingo has a certain home range and then asserting that this is also a territory that it will defend against intruders belonging to other social groups. *Home range* is where an animal lives; a *territory* is a home range that it will defend to exclude other dingoes. Radio tracking shows with certainly that the dingo is not an inveterate wanderer, but it is another step to argue that it is also a territorial animal.

The strongest evidence of territoriality among dingoes comes from the Pilbara. These dingoes lived in stable family groups and were observed repelling strangers that entered their home range. At least four dingoes died after moving into other territories. They were either killed in fights or died from starvation after being forced into poor country by the residents.[8] However, the dingoes that remained solitary on the Nullarbor did not defend their home ranges with a similar determination and were much more inclined to move freely among other dingoes.[4]

MOVEMENTS AWAY FROM THE HOME RANGE

Despite the stability of dingo society and its focus on a particular home range or territory, some dingoes have to leave home. Unless there is an exceptional run of seasons, some juveniles must move out in search of a vacant niche. If they don't find one they will die; if they don't go and search for one, they will also die.

Eight radio-collared dingoes in the Pilbara region moved rapidly through occupied territories before they settled down in an area that was free of dingoes because of past control measures. A total of 29 dingoes reached vacant country; only three of them died, compared to the four dingoes that died after attempting to remain in foreign territories.[8]

Little is known about the social dynamics in a group of dingoes but it is highly likely that an increase in the population leads to the aggression that forces particular individuals out of the group. In my captive colony, an older female was killed in a fight with a younger female during the mating season. They were not fighting because of shortage of food or other essential resources because all their needs were met. Their altercation was over dominance; had it occurred in the wild the bitch that was killed may have escaped serious injury by keeping her distance and taking a subordinate position.

The research in the Pilbara also measured the distance dingoes travelled.[9] One hundred and eight young pups were caught at their dens and ear-tagged when they were between four and eight weeks

There are less subtle postures than the position of one's tail to let others know that they are not yet welcome to dine. Still, if the offender keeps its distance, there is a chance of avoiding a fight that might cause injury. Gary Steer

of age. Another 12 adults were trapped in padded traps, ear-tagged and released. A total of 12 tags were returned by full-time doggers and station employees. The average distance these dingoes had travelled from the point where they were ear-tagged was only 21.7 km for males and 11 km for females. In a similar study in the same region, 39 out of 46 radio-collared dingoes travelled less than 20 km from their original capture site. Only four dingoes were involved in long-distance movements. Three dingoes travelled between 30 and 50 km — and even this can hardly qualify as a long distance in the rangelands of Western Australia. Only one dingo travelled 150 km before settling in unoccupied territory.

Over 200 dingoes were marked with either radio collars or ear tags and colour-coded collars in central Australia so that their movements could be traced. More than 75 per cent of the recaptures, resightings and relocations of these dingoes occurred within 8 km from where they were first caught, and 95 per cent were within 20 km. Even the greater distance of 20 km is within the size of most home ranges of dingoes in central Australia. The longest recorded movement was for a pair of dingoes that travelled 33 km down a valley over a 15-month period.[6]

THE MIGRATION MYTH

Migration can be said to occur only when the entire population of a species moves annually between two locations. Migration is predictable, the destination predetermined and it is binding for the entire species. No Australian land mammals are known to be migratory. Migration is more common among birds, some of which move between Australia and other countries to the north. A significant number of bird species also migrate within Australia.

However, "migration" is one of those words that can mean different things to different people. For one person it may simply mean the movement of an individual animal between two areas; for someone else it may mean an aimless wandering. So the statement that dingoes migrate can refer to quite a range of dingo movements, and may not necessarily imply that large packs of dingoes actually migrate in the formal sense of the word.

J. S. Bacon, a dingo trapper from the New England Tablelands of New South Wales, published his experience with dingoes in a rambling but fascinating account of his life that includes details of every good horse and dog he ever owned.[10] In a chapter titled "Getting to know the enemy", Bacon discussed the "migratory habits" of the dingo:

> We proved beyond doubt that in different areas dingoes migrate and often move considerable distances. It is in their nature to wander and search out new areas with more food available. Also, they often move over certain areas at almost exactly the same time twice a year. One special example of this was the Great Dividing Range, which runs north and south through New South Wales. On the New England section of this range dingoes used to come up from the eastern fall or coastal side and reach the top almost to the same week or fortnight twice every year, viz., the last two weeks of April and the last two weeks of October. Then they would move on down the western fall of the range top, striking the sheep in that area by the end of May or early June and again by the end of November.

This myth of dingo migration was not confined to the bush. It became widely accepted, even in the halls of academia. A report published in 1947 by the organisation that was the forerunner of today's CSIRO stated that the dingo "is to be found mostly in hilly country where cover is abundant but in winter-time he migrates to the coast".[11] This idea that dingoes migrate between coastal retreat and mountain fortress still persists in south-eastern New South Wales. It is said that the large national parks, reserves and state forests on the south coast are refuges for dingoes that move between them and Kosciusko, marauding the flocks of the Monaro sheepmen during their travels.

Coincidence may underly the migration myth because it is quite likely that bushmen have observed larger groups of dingoes during the breeding season than at other times of the year. Larger packs could easily be interpreted as groups of dingoes on the move through an area where, most of the time, sightings were of single animals. Social interaction also intensifies during the breeding season and there is therefore a greater chance of seeing the local dingoes together.

Dingoes also have a tendency to look alike, particularly when one gets only a fleeting glance as they disappear into the bush. If two big yellow dogs are seen killing 50 km apart, it is easy to assume it is the same animal. And it makes for a better story. The native intelligence of the dingo can be embellished with tales of its ability to fool the trapper by killing on Sam Jones' place and then moving over to the other side of the range to Bill Wilson's just as it was about to be trapped or shot by the big drive that had been organised. Maybe it is part of the human condition to try and make sense out of coincidence. And plenty of good dingo yarns are true. I have sat quietly fascinated beside many a camp fire listening to such dingo stories. I have no doubt that some dingoes do move over a few properties within or around their home range, but there is no evidence that dingoes migrate.

A pair of dingoes rest together in the sun after gorging on a kill. Gary Steer

THE PATTERN OF DAILY ACTIVITY

Hunting, travelling to water, marking territory and maintaining the social hierarchy keeps dingoes constantly on the move within their home range. While there are similarities in the routine of dingoes throughout Australia, the pattern of activity does reflect the season of the year and regional climate. For example, the dingoes of central Australia are characterised by nocturnal activity because they avoid the heat of the day.[12] On the other hand, the dingoes studied in the temperate New England Tablelands tended to move more during the day with a distinct peak of activity around dawn and dusk.[2]

The New England dingoes spent about two-thirds of the day on the move and about one-third resting. However, movement was not continued for long periods; activity lasting up to 45 minutes was followed by shorter rest periods. Seventy per cent of the rest periods were 30 minutes or less. Only one dingo in this study remained active for a long time. It kept on the move for five hours but covered only 9.8 km. The average distance travelled during the activity periods of three dingoes was 1.2 km, 0.8 km and 1.2 km. The average speed of travel for the adults was 1.3 km per hour. The most common speed of travel for juveniles was 0.9 km per hour with the average speed of all their movements being 1.1 km per hour.

This study identified two separate

types of activity. The first type, "searching movement", was associated with intense activity over a small area with frequent changes of direction. While searching movement did occur at all times of the day, it was carried out mainly at dusk. It was impossible to observe the dingoes during this type of activity because of the vegetation and terrain — all the information was gathered by radio-telemetry. Nevertheless, it is believed that searching movement is involved in hunting prey.

The second type of activity, "exploratory movement", involved traversing greater distances with a much more purposeful direction. It often connected two centres of searching movement as if hunting was being carried out in two separate areas. At other times exploratory activity following searching movements moved out in a loop to the boundaries of the home range. This suggested that exploratory activity was associated with maintaining territorial boundaries and the social hierarchy by marking scent posts and by other social interaction.

COMMUNICATION

For some, the howl of the dingo is sinister and eerie. Others find it friendly and melodious. For patriots it is the sound of the Australian bush. To the early settlers, who still longed for their homelands, it was the howl of a wolf. There are romantics who, deprived of lion, tiger or jaguar, cling to the howl of the dingo as a symbol of something wild and primeval in a bush that is so easily passed off as a monotone of eucalypts and cryptic marsupials. The howl of the dingo is wilderness in sound.

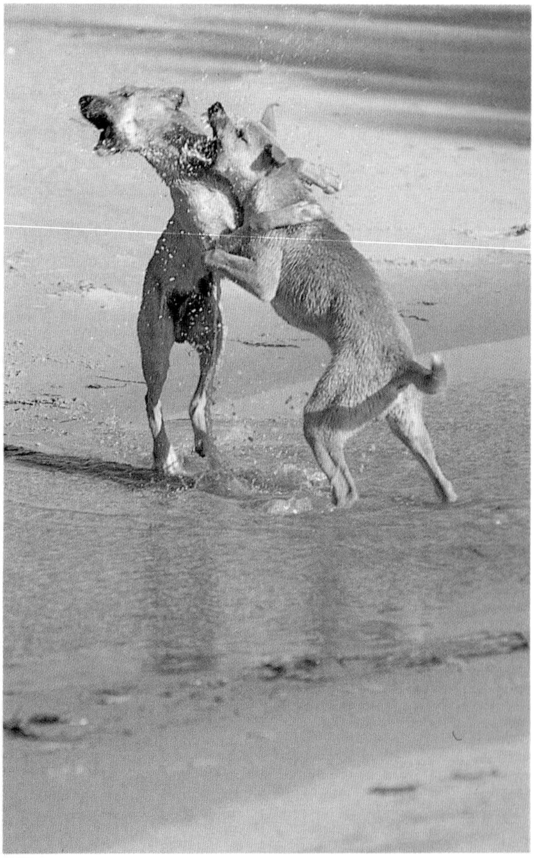

An animal that requires a large home range yet is able to form groups, disperse and regroup whenever necessary for co-operative hunting, breeding and raising of young must have a sophisticated communication system. Howling enables long-distance communication between a number of dingoes. It is not uncommon to hear one dingo begin to howl, then be joined by a chorus of other dingoes at different locations. Just as howling may serve to locate other dingoes in the same group, it can also be used to keep separate groups apart thereby avoiding direct confrontation.

The incidence of howling increases markedly during the breeding season when it probably helps select a mate, maintain group cohesion and keep out strangers.[12] The fact that howling is used to attract other dingoes is confirmed by the practice of trappers "howling up" dingoes in order to shoot them. This technique of imitating a dingo howling has been developed to an art form by some doggers. It always works best during the breeding season, and may be more effective on young and inexperienced dingoes.

Some instinctual mechanism may initiate howling in response to certain sound frequencies. One of the most delightful times to be among my dingoes in the compound was in the late afternoon when the Fokker Friendship passed overhead on its way to Cooma. All the dingoes — adults and pups alike — would break into an extended session of howling as the Fokker flew over. No other sound, animal or mechanical, could elicit howling as did the particular sound emanating from a Fokker Friendship. The Forestry Commission aeroplane that dropped incendiaries on the nearby Glenbog State Forest was totally ignored as were other light planes that passed over from time to time.

A great deal of fighting that seems to be fairly playful occurs between littermates. It probably serves as practice for the real thing, while at the same time establishing and maintaining the hierarchy. Gary Steer

The full tonal range of the howl of the dingo has not been adequately studied but howling appears to have the following functions:[12]

1. To locate mates for breeding.
2. To locate members of the same group for co-operative hunting.
3. To define territory and to avoid strangers.
4. To call pups to a kill.
5. To signal members of the same group that they are moving.

The statement that "dingoes don't bark" is more than half true. They do not bark as do most domestic dogs and howling is the main vocal communication. However, dingoes kept together with domestic dogs have learnt to bark.[13] Otherwise the closest they come to barking is a short bark when surprised or in greeting. I was often greeted by a single bark that could break into a howl when I turned up to feed the compound dingoes. This sound was typically uttered by the dominant male and female.

There are at least three other forms of vocalisation beside the full-blown howling commonly associated with dingoes. These are the bark-howl, the moan and the agitated cough. The short bark-howl was noticed among wild dingoes near Alice Springs when they were suddenly alarmed or agitated. The same observers noted another form of vocalisation that consisted of a low-pitched howl resembling a moan. This was sometimes uttered by dingoes coming in to water as if to warn other dingoes of their approach to avoid confrontation.[12]

I noticed another common vocalisation in the two bitches in my captive colony. Whenever I got too close to their pups, they warned the pups of danger with an agitated little cough that almost ran into a weak bark. The sound was rather like an amalgam of sneeze, cough and quick, soft bark. This sound was uttered so frequently and with such good effect that I am certain it is a regular feature of the dingo repertoire. Sometimes the pups, being less shy than their mothers, would begin to mill around for food but one little cough would have them scattering for cover.

The same little cough was infuriatingly effective over quite long distances. I well remember trying to catch a three-month-old escapee only to be frustrated by the mother, still in the compound, but letting her pup know of every move I made and, as it seemed to me, every move I was about to make.

I knew the pups squeezed out between the bars of the gate to pick up dog biscuits that dropped as they were poured from the garbage tin outside because I could see their tracks. But foolishly, it did not concern me because I believed that they would soon grow too large to get through the mesh and that they would not leave the bitch. One afternoon I arrived to feed the dingoes and was dismayed to see four two-month-old pups run off into the surrounding bush. I followed as fast as I could on foot and found a well-worn pad leading to an old wombat burrow. The pups were obviously down there and unbeknown to me, they must have been making nocturnal forays to the wombat hole for some time and had now decided to make it home.

I sat by the wombat hole in mild panic. Digging or smoking them out was impossible — wombat holes are a vast labyrinth. So I decided to wait in the bush and see if they would come out of their own accord. Only minutes went by before three of the pups came out and in their youthful insecurity raced back to the gate and squeezed into the compound. That relieved some of my anxiety but it left one truant still down the burrow.

It was getting dark so I was forced to place wire netting across the meshed gate. This kept the pups in but just as surely kept the escapee out. But these were early days and I thought I would return early next morning on horseback and sneak around the back of the compound to catch her.

That was the week I really learnt the power of the "agitated cough". Every day I tried a new method of catching that pup but I could not get within cooee of her before the mother inside the compound warned her of my approach. It did not matter what time of day it was or from what direction I approached. Nor did it matter that the mother had a bevy of ten pups to care for. She always kept watch for me and warned the lone pup of my approach. I seriously considered shooting the pup but by this stage she and her mother had such a good early warning system that I would have been lucky to get a shot at her.

It took me over a week of employing the "superior" human intellect to get

Misha, as she was later named, back in alive. There was a double gate system into the compound so the inner gate with its wire mesh covering could be left closed and the outer gate left open and used as a trap door. I had employed other gates into the holding pens as traps on numerous occasions. I simply tied a heavy weight to them and propped them open with a stick to which I tied a piece of meat. The dingo would grab the meat and pull the stick out, whereupon the counterweight would slam the gate shut and hold it overnight until I arrived in the morning to chain it.

But something always went wrong with the traps I laid for Misha. Either the counterweight was too light, the trap went off and she forced her way out again, or the counterweight was too heavy and she ate the meat without setting it off at all. During all this time I was treated to the sounds of the agitated cough. I eventually got Misha back into the compound by leaving the outside gate open and building a ramp so that she could climb up above the wire mesh on the inside gate and jump back down to her mates in the cover of night when hunger overtook her caution.

Apart from these vocal means, there are other avenues of dingo communication. Stance, posture and facial expression are the visible means of conveying the message at close range. The position of the tail is a certain sign of dominance or submission. Any dingo that thinks it is dominant, or would like to test its position in the social hierarchy, carries its tail high, a beacon of its status or pretensions. This will be either accepted by the other dingoes or challenged with all the preliminaries that accompany the familiar neighbourhood dog fight. Growling, snarling, curling back the lips to expose teeth and arching the back with hair standing on end all precede any violent confrontation, thereby giving each dingo ample opportunity to lower its tail, urinate, smell the other dog and begin a ritual of submissive behaviour.

The regular occurrence of fresh wounds on dingoes trapped in the wild is evidence that displays of aggression are a feature of dingo society. Surprisingly, the incidence of wounds does not increase during the breeding season when other signs of interaction, such as howling, are known to intensify. This implies that a certain amount of aggression exists all year round and is necessary to maintain a stable social structure (see Table 11).

Pups use submissive body posture to obtain food from adults. I have seen pups begin sliding along on their bellies up to 3 m away from a powerful big male that was chewing at a delectable rabbit. With their eyes carefully averted, their tails between their legs, ears back and behaving in the most obsequious

Overleaf: *A dingo, showing its subservient position by a lowered tail, approaches two members of the social group who signal very clearly, with their tails held high, that its close company is not required.*

Edging closer it raises its tail to establish that it, too, has some rights in social intercourse.

But the tails of the top dogs become even more erect and their backs arch in readiness for a further demonstration of dominance. The interloper quickly decides that a lowered tail is a much safer proposition — as is . . .

. . . retreat. Series by Gary Steer

manner possible, they have sidled up to take the rabbit from the hungry male. Any adult dingo that attempted the same manoeuvre would have been most severely dealt with. Providing that a pup does not challenge the dominant male, it can get away with murder. But among themselves, the feeding behaviour of the pups is one continuous session of exercising skills in dominance and learning when submission is the better strategy.

Dingoes spend a lot of time travelling their home range and marking scent posts. They urinate, defecate and scratch the ground at the same places to create olfactory communication sites. Chemicals in the urine and secretions from the anal gland are believed to be important pathways of communication. What exactly is communicated through these sites is not certain but it appears that they help to keep members of the same group together and keep foreign groups away.[12] The long exploratory movements noted in the New England study often covered ridgetops, creeks and fire trails where scent posts were located. These geographical features were also associated with the boundaries of home ranges so there is every likelihood that olfactory communication is part of territorial demarcation.

TABLE 11:
Annual distribution of fresh wounds among dingoes trapped in central Australia. From Corbett and Newsome, 1975.

Month	Number of dingoes examined	Percentage with fresh wounds
Dec–Jan	161	3.4
Feb–March	164	4.3
April–May	283	2.8
June–July	286	3.5
Aug–Sept	139	2.9
Oct–Nov	88	3.4

Interbreeding between dingoes and feral domestic dogs

One of the most frequently asked questions about dingoes is "How pure are they?". This question occurs persistently when livestock has been killed. Is it the work of purebred dingoes, feral domestic dogs or some genetic permutation between the two? This intrigue is not always divorced from ideology. Those who wish to protect the dingo may suggest that livestock killing is the work of feral dogs. Conversely, many graziers, not slow to see the advantage in referring to dingoes as feral animals, call them all feral dogs.

Opportunities for domestic dogs to breed with wild dingoes began from the time of first settlement. The problem of stray dogs was the reason for the first dog laws. Many of the explorers also took dogs on their expeditions that were lost or abandoned. Those explorers were at the forefront of pioneers who brought even more domestic dogs into dingo territory. In 1916, the eminent natural scientist Robert Etheridge bemoaned the fact that pure dingoes could no longer be readily found for his research.[1] His concern was somewhat misplaced because there were plenty of purebred dingoes left at that time. Even today there are many parts of Australia where most of the wild dogs are still pure dingoes. However, the proportion of purebred dingoes to hybrid and straight domestic dogs in the wild has developed into a major issue. Running alongside it is the problem of discerning the difference between dingoes and their crosses with feral domestic dogs.

The incidence of dingoes cross-breeding with domestic dogs is of concern to those who wish to conserve the dingo

Domestic dogs found their way into the bush and among dingoes very soon after the European invasion because they were carried into remote areas by the early explorers and settlers. The greyhound that accompanied the explorer depicted in this illustration by J. Doyle (circa 1854-63) will have to fend for itself among the dingoes that are already eating its master's faithful steed. Mitchell Library

as well as those who want to control it. There are good reasons to believe that the dingo will become extinct in Australia by being swamped with domestic genes. On the other hand wild dog control authorities fear that the addition of some large domestic breeds to the wild dog population will create a more difficult pest problem. Already, it is generally believed that between 50 and 90 per cent of the "dog problem" in eastern Queensland is a result of hybrids.[2]

DOMESTIC DOGS IN THE WILD

The high risk of domestic dogs finding their way into the wild is clearly demonstrated by the number that are impounded as strays each year. Some 11,000 stray dogs are impounded each year in the Adelaide metropolitan area — a staggering 10 per cent of all registered dogs. No less than 7000 of these dogs cannot be traced to an owner.[3] The town of Bega on the far south coast of New South Wales, with a population of only 4500 people, has about 160 dogs impounded each year, most of which are of unknown ownership.[4] Mumbulla State Forest and Mimosa Rocks National Park are within 10 km of Bega. These forest areas are linked to the rugged Great Dividing Range where there are dingoes, so there is no geographical barrier to the intermingling of dingoes and stray dogs. Feral dogs are seen in the forest around Bega and dog scats, be they of dingo, domestic dog or hybrid origin, are common.[5]

Domestic dogs do kill livestock. They need not be running wild to do this, and the well-fed and pampered pet by day can turn into vicious sheep killer by night. In 1981–82 1145 head of livestock, nearly all sheep, were killed by dogs in the Adelaide metropolitan area. Most attacks involved several dogs and the breeds identified ranged in size from terrier to great dane. The large breeds were involved more frequently than smaller dogs and the German shepherd and labrador were the most common offenders. However, in only 50 per cent of cases where livestock were killed were the dogs actually seen.[3]

Domestic dogs gone wild are caught in traps and shot by landholders. Some descriptions of dogs seen in the wild fit domestic dogs better than any known dingoes. John Coman, the dingo trapper at Delegate, New South Wales, trapped a German shepherd wearing a collar bearing a five-year-old registration tag from Tumut, some 200 km away. An extraordinary range of domestic dogs has been caught in the wild. Even Afghan hounds and corgis have been caught by dingo trappers in Victoria.[6] It is rumoured that workmen on the Snowy Mountains Scheme often released their pet dogs upon the completion of their contract. There are allegations of wild huskies and samoyeds and their dingo crosses in the high country which are said to stem from these releases.

During the summer of 1969 my wife and I camped in Nadgee Nature Reserve on the far south coast of New South Wales and every morning and evening we could hear the distinct baying of hounds hunting in the bush around the Nadgee River estuary. It was not long before we discovered that the baying came from two harrier hounds. These dogs had established such a regular hunting pattern that I was able to shoot them without any difficulty — with the ranger's rifle and blessing. How two well-bred hounds got to such a remote location is anyone's guess but illegal hunting might not be too far from the truth. Such personal experience leaves me in no doubt that domestic dogs find their way into the wild and are quite able to survive there.

The degree to which feral domestic dogs interbreed with dingoes is still the subject of debate in the bush. John Coman has been trapping dingoes in south-east New South Wales for the past 45 years and steadfastly maintains that the dogs he catches are still pure dingoes. He argues that, although domestic dogs are found in the wild, very few of them get to breed because of the dingo's superiority in the competition for a mate. John believes that most domestic dogs would be killed by dingoes in territorial disputes. If an occasional feral domestic dog mated with a dingo, the progeny would most likely mate with pure dingoes and gradually remove the domestic genes.

Despite doubts such as these there has not, to my knowledge, been any scientific refutation of CSIRO research that indicates that hybridisation is occurring on a large scale. CSIRO scientists measured the skulls of 1300 dingoes in central Australia and 300 in the eastern highlands. Whereas over 90 per cent of the central Australian dingoes were considered to be pure dingoes, only 25 per cent of those trapped in the east were pure.[7] Another study of wild dogs in north-eastern Victoria concluded that only 10.8 per cent of them were dingoes; 51.6 per cent were hybrids and 37.6 per cent were feral domestic dogs.[6]

Unfortunately, the weight of evidence shows that hybridisation is well under way in south-eastern Australia. It is important to emphasise that this research does not claim that there are no pure dingoes left in this region. The estimates of a pure dingo population stand at between 10 and 25 per cent. This is an overall figure and there are undoubtedly pockets of remote country where a higher proportion of the wild dogs are pure dingoes.

Hybridisation has not yet resulted in the proliferation of larger, more cunning, faster and more ferocious wild dogs. Perhaps it is the nature of the Australian environment but after almost two hundred years of European settlement, the size and abilities of Australian wild dogs appear largely unaltered. This does little to allay the fears of farmers concerned about the evolution of a "master race" of wild dogs through crossbreeding with large domestic breeds such as German shepherds and Dobermans. Pig hunters have now developed some formidable pig dogs based on bull terriers, Rhodesian ridgebacks and other exotic breeds. There is concern in western Queensland that abandoned or lost pig dogs will increase the size and capacity of wild dogs and their inclination to attack livestock.[2]

A BLOOD TEST

It would be convenient if a simple blood test could differentiate between dingoes and domestic dogs. However, no differences have yet been found between the blood of dingoes and domestic dogs. This is another indication that dingoes and domestic dogs are closely related.[8] There is little biochemical variation among all the canids and the similarity between dingo and domestic dog reflects the evolutionary path shared by all canids, from tiny fennec to great timber wolf.[9]

SKELETAL DIFFERENCES BETWEEN DINGOES AND DOMESTIC DOGS

One of the first Australians to look for differences between dingoes and domestic dogs was the late Professor Macintosh, Challis Professor of Anatomy at the University of Sydney. From his interest in anatomy, Professor Macintosh began to look beneath the skin-deep assessments of the dingo that preceded his work. He examined, measured and compared dingo skeletons and found that there was little variation among the skeletons of adult dingoes and that the contemporary wild population did not vary from the 3000-year-old fossil found at Fromms Landing.[10,11]

Macintosh then took the same measurements on domestic dogs and concluded that while there was great variation among domestic dogs because of different breed characteristics, the skeletons of dingoes and domestic dogs of the same size were similar. The next step was to take a closer look at the skulls of dingoes and domestic dogs. Here some reliable differences began to emerge. Eleven characteristics were eventually isolated which could distinguish dingoes from domestic dogs of the same age and size.

More recently, Alan Newsome and a team of research workers at the CSIRO Division of Wildlife and Rangelands Research further investigated the problem of differentiating between pure dingoes and dingo–domestic hybrids.[7,8,12] They found that eight particular discriminants were reliable enough to tell the difference between a pure dingo and a domestic dog of similar size. They are:

1. *Bulla size*: the length of the bony box that houses the inner ear. The bulla of the dingo is an average of 4.3 mm larger.

2. *Maxillary width*: the maximum distance between the big shearing teeth on the upper palate. The gap between them is an average of 2.6 mm narrower in the dingo.

3. *Mid crown width of the upper carnassial tooth*: the maximum width of the biggest shearing teeth in a dingo skull. The dingo is an average of 0.8 mm wider.

4. *Upper canine*: the canine teeth of the dingo are narrower at the top when measured along the row of teeth but they are longer. The canines of the dingo are an average of 0.8 mm narrower.

5. *Opisthion to inion height*: the minimum height of the back of the skull. The dingo is an average of 4.5 mm larger.

6. *Width of nasal bones*: the width of the two narrow bones on the upper snout. The dingo is an average of 1.2 mm wider.

7. *Cranial height*: the height of the skull measured at the narrowest point. The dingo is an average of 2 mm less giving it a flatter skull.

8. *Alveolar distance along lower premolars*:

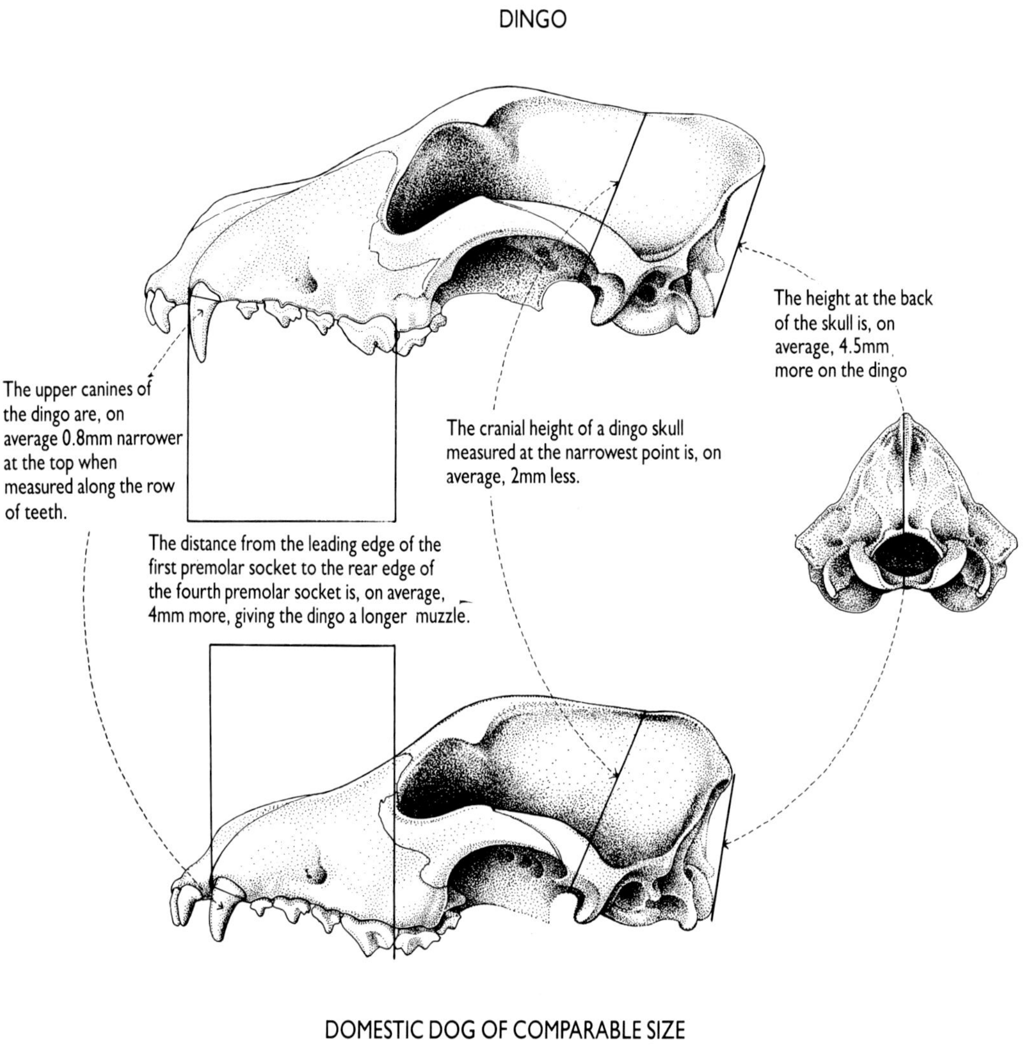
DINGO
The height at the back of the skull is, on average, 4.5mm more on the dingo
The upper canines of the dingo are, on average 0.8mm narrower at the top when measured along the row of teeth.
The cranial height of a dingo skull measured at the narrowest point is, on average, 2mm less.
The distance from the leading edge of the first premolar socket to the rear edge of the fourth premolar socket is, on average, 4mm more, giving the dingo a longer muzzle.
DOMESTIC DOG OF COMPARABLE SIZE

Differences between the skull of a dingo and a domestic dog of comparable size.

the distance from the leading edge of the first premolar socket to the rear edge of the socket of the fourth premolar (carnassial). The dingo is an average of 4 mm longer which gives it the longer muzzle.

These eight traits give the dingo a longer muzzle, larger main teeth, longer and more slender canine teeth, larger bulla (housing for the eardrum) and a larger cranium than its domestic counterpart of similar size. The dingo's superior hearing is reflected in a much larger housing for the eardrum. The overall effect is to give the dingo a more massive skull than that of the domestic dog. These differences between dingoes and domestic dogs of the same size convinced the researchers that the dingo's

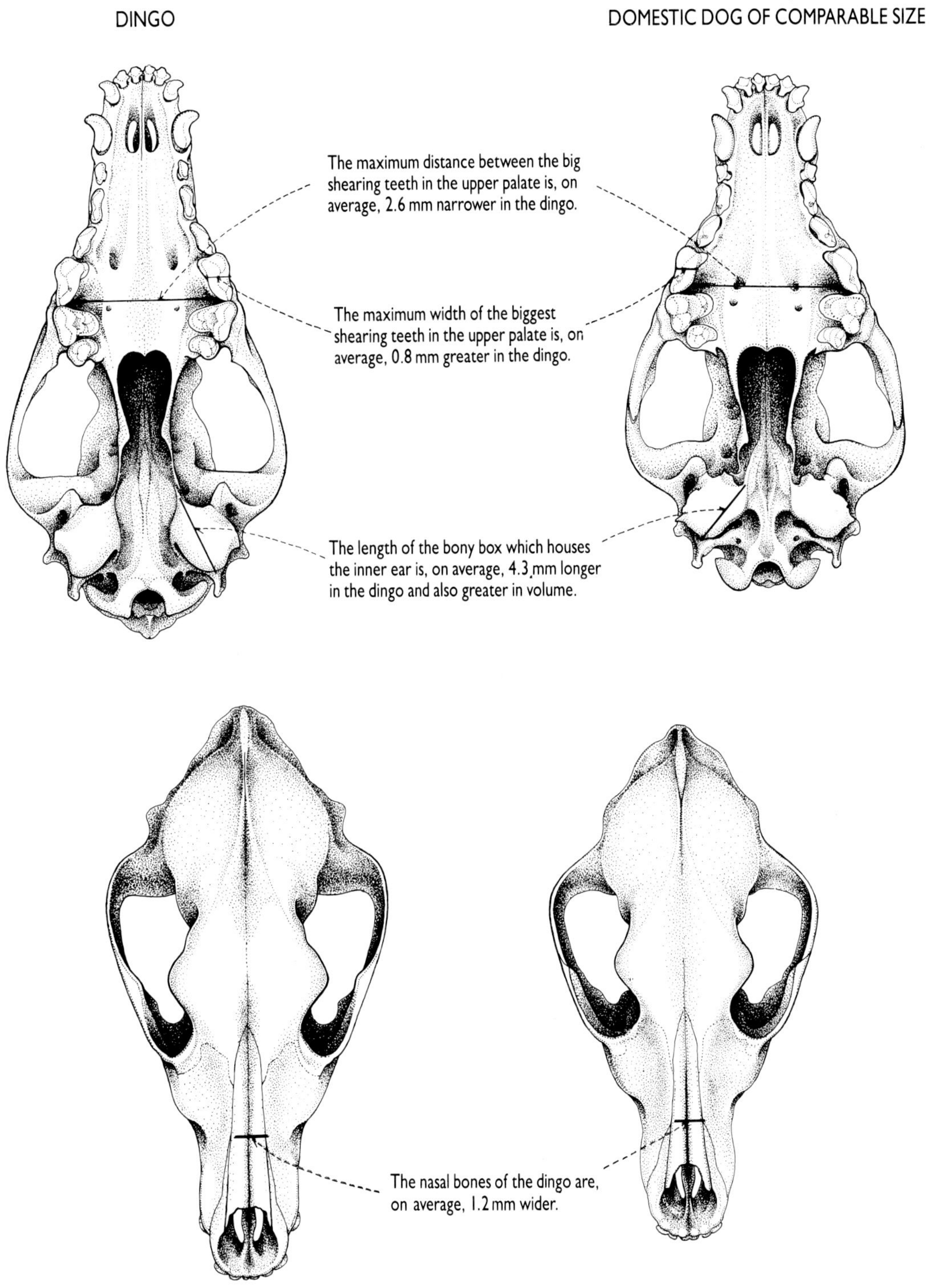

DINGO
DOMESTIC DOG OF COMPARABLE SIZE
The maximum distance between the big shearing teeth in the upper palate is, on average, 2.6 mm narrower in the dingo.
The maximum width of the biggest shearing teeth in the upper palate is, on average, 0.8 mm greater in the dingo.
The length of the bony box which houses the inner ear is, on average, 4.3 mm longer in the dingo and also greater in volume.
The nasal bones of the dingo are, on average, 1.2 mm wider.

Differences between the skull of a dingo and a domestic dog of comparable size.

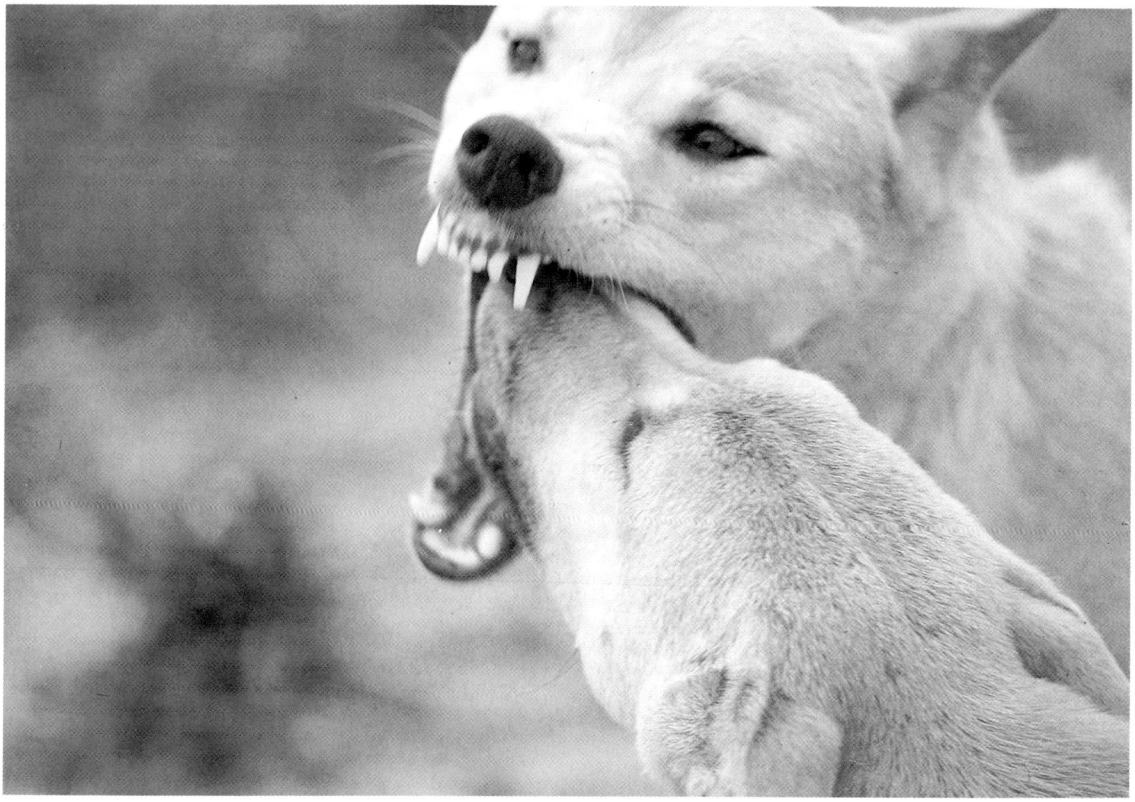

The dingo has a larger skull, involving a much bigger housing for the eardum and longer canine teeth, than domestic dogs of similar size. Gary Steer

status as a separate subspecies was legitimate and the name *Canis familiaris dingo* should stand to mark it as such.[12]

The diagnostic traits make it possible to separate pure dingoes from domestic dogs of a similar size. It is more difficult to differentiate between pure dingoes and the dingo-domestic hybrids. Hybrids share characteristics from both parent groups but the inheritance of these traits can be inconsistent so that some may show one or two strong dingo characteristics but not others. This makes it difficult to be certain about the degree of dingo parentage among some hybrids.

A group of dingo-domestic hybrids was specially bred to test some of the conclusions made from skulls collected from the wild. Dingoes were mated with blue heelers, kelpies, white labradors, dobermans and beagle hounds. All these dogs, with perhaps the exception of the doberman, occur commonly in rural areas and are likely to interbreed with wild dingoes. The first cross pups from the matings in the research program were either bred back to pure dingoes or further outcrossed to domestic breeds to give various degrees of dingo ancestry. Skull measurements were made on 41 known hybrids from this breeding program.

Most of the known hybrids fitted neatly between pure dingoes and domestics but there was some overlap. The doberman–dingo hybrids were more like pure dingoes; the labrador and kelpie were midway between dingoes and domestics; the beagle–dingo hybrids were more like domestics. This tendency for the proportion of dingo or domestic traits to depend on the size or breed of the domestic parent led to the conclusion that it is impossible to be certain about the ancestry of any wild dog of unknown parentage.

The progeny of the hybrids frequently showed stronger dingo characteristics than their parents. In bush parlance, some of them threw back to the dingo. Clearly, some dingo traits are persistent and it is impossible to show exactly what proportion of dingo ancestry exists in hybrids. All that can be said is that the skull of a certain individual resembles that of a dingo, dingo–domestic hybrid or straight domestic.

The hybrids bred in captivity were compared to 50 wild dogs caught by professional trappers in the mountains of East Gippsland, Victoria.[7] Only 36 per cent of the wild dogs from north-eastern Victoria resembled pure dingoes. A further 52 per cent of them were classified as hybrids and 12 per cent as feral domestic dogs. The uneven inheritance of dingo traits was evident in the Victorian sample, with most having maxillae and upper canine teeth similar to domestic dogs but with tympanic bullae and carnassial teeth similar to dingoes.

COLOUR DIFFERENCES BETWEEN DINGOES AND DOMESTIC DOGS

The colour of wild dogs caught in Victoria was noted by the trappers and then skull measurements were taken and analysed to determine whether there was any relationship between colour and the degree of hybridisation.[7] Unfortunately, it was found that colour alone was not a reliable guide to dingo ancestry because many of the hybrids were yellow-ginger and looked like pure dingoes. This is partly because the yellow-ginger in dingoes is dominant to other colours. The other difficulty in using colour as the guide to dingo purity is that there is so much room for argument and differing interpretation about colour that it tends to create conflicts rather than resolve them.

However, a comparison between the colour of pure dingoes in remote areas of inland Australia and dingoes and wild dogs in eastern Australia did show that incidence of the dominant dingo colouration reflected the degree of hybridisation in the two regions.[7] In the remote areas of central Australia 88.6 per cent of the dingoes are yellow-ginger, 3.8 per cent are black and tan, and 1.9 per cent are white. Only 5.7 per cent have unusual colours such as complete black, broken yellow-ginger and white, or brindling. Most of those with unusual colouring in central Australia were still classified as pure dingoes based on their skull measurements.

In south-eastern Australia the percentage of yellow-ginger wild dogs was found to have decreased to 45.9 per cent, while the incidence of black and tan wild dogs has increased to 19.1 per cent, with white dingoes having almost disappeared. The proportion of wild dogs with broken colours, brindling, all black or all brown, patches of blue, black and white and other colour patterns not normally associated with dingoes has increased to almost 34.8 per cent. This higher percentage of broken and mottled colouration among the wild dogs of the east is reflected in the skull measurements that show that this is the area with the most hybrids.

Notwithstanding the disadvantages, colour can still be used as a rough guide to the parentage of wild dogs. Most pure dingoes, both yellow-ginger and black and tan, have white on their feet and have a white tip on the tail and its absence from these locations is one indication that the wild dog in question may be a hybrid or a pure feral domestic dog. Those wild dogs that have large patches of the colours associated with domestic dogs or show extreme brindling are also unlikely to be dingoes.[13] Colour was the criteria used by a CSIRO research team to conclude that the wild dogs in the part of Kosciusko National Park where they were working were mostly hybrids.[14]

BEHAVIOURAL DIFFERENCES BETWEEN DINGOES AND DOMESTICS

One difference between dingoes and domestic dogs could be their behaviour. The problem is that one must first have a secure definition of a domestic dog. And here again the experts disagree. Even the great Konrad Lorenz appears somewhat contradictory when he says "the dingo of course is a domestic dog gone feral, and not so feral as that", but then states that those who think they can domesticate a dingo are self-deluding.[15] What Lorenz probably means is that the dingo was travelling on the path of domestication until a chance migration in the company of humans landed it in Australia. From then on it became established in the wild without further selection pressure for tractability and responsiveness to human commands and control.

A satisfactory definition of "domestication" is most elusive and the animals it describes vary with the culture and technology in which they exist. Wild animals that are kept merely as pets are not generally regarded as domestic animals, even though they might be loosely referred to as such from time to time. For example, a budgerigar in a cage could hardly be described as domesticated. On the other hand, there are other animals such as horses, cattle and sheep which we recognise immediately as domesticated. There are others such as the Indian elephant which is put to work but does not fill the stereotype of a domestic animal as easily as the others.

The dingo does not fall into the category of controllable animals that we commonly associate with domestication. My experience is that dingoes can be tamed but cannot be controlled as readily as domestic dogs. Sometimes a dingo will respond to commands; at other times it will go about what interests it at the time, ignoring all commands until it is ready. Those who have trained dingoes for obedience classes are loathe to let them off the leash when they are with other dogs. Attempts by the New South Wales Police Department and the Royal Guide Dog Associations to train them as working dogs have failed despite the high degree of expertise and experience of the dog trainers of both these organisations.

There is a marked difference in the behaviour of dingoes and domestic dogs. To show the full extent and nature of this difference would require an experiment that compares a wide range of domestic breeds with dingoes in learning, and reliably performing, a set of tasks. The experiment would need to be repeated many times by different trainers to remove bias such as favouritism and other idiosyncrasies. The cost would be enormous and therefore this research is unlikely to occur. In the meantime, we can do little but treat with caution the ascription of certain traits to the dingo which may not exist. Regardless of how much it may appear to favour the dingo, such conjecture will only add one more blind alley to the already considerable maze constructed from myth and folklore.

IMPACT OF DINGO HYBRIDS AND FERAL DOMESTICS ON NATIVE FAUNA

Feral animals such as the pig and buffalo can have a disastrous effect on native wildlife largely because the native plants and animals did not evolve with any comparable animals. However, the Australian fauna did evolve with large carnivores and it may not really matter whether a predator is a dingo, feral domestic dog or hybrid between the two. As the dingo becomes regarded as a native animal, it will be more aesthetically pleasing if the only canine predator in Australia is the pure dingo, but from an ecological perspective it is unimportant. The only exception to this would be if feral domestic dogs killed more wildlife than dingoes. This seems unlikely, given the close affinities in the ancestry of domestic dogs and dingoes. One hopes that people will press for more research rather than simply accept that all wild dogs are feral animals and are therefore undesirable. The Australian environment is capable of supporting only a certain number of higher order carnivores. But the numbers of wild dogs of today, and tomorrow, will be limited by exactly the same factors as the numbers of wild dogs of yesterday — availability of prey, disease, the social hierarchy and predation by humans.

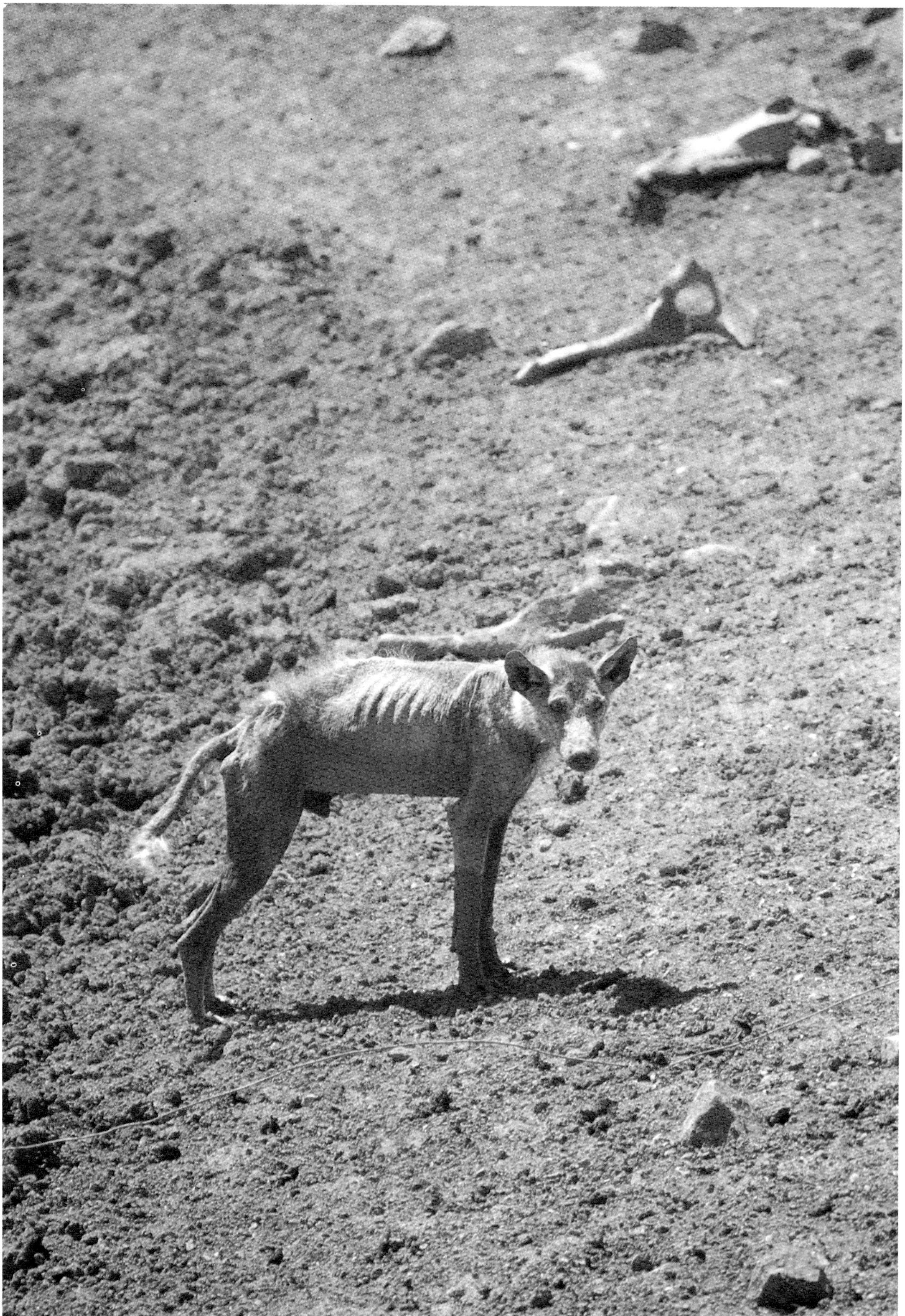

Diseases of the dingo

There is a great temptation to believe that Australia was free from canine diseases until that fateful day in 1770 when James Cook stepped ashore at Botany Bay and opened the way for British colonisation. On that voyage Sir Joseph Banks, the botanist who travelled with Cook, carried with him his faithful greyhound, which assisted him to examine the fauna. Just 18 years later the First Fleeters started an animal invasion the likes of which the continent had never before experienced. It is not known how many of the livestock diseases introduced to Australia since European settlement have affected native wildlife. It is generally accepted, however, that the impact has not been very great because the Australian fauna is very different from domestic livestock.

The one glaring exception is the dingo. It is closely related to the domestic dog and was here before the European. It is unlikely that the first dingoes to step onto Australian soil were free of disease. When the white settlers arrived with their domestic dogs, there were almost certainly some canine diseases and parasites already here. Although the domestic dogs brought from Europe may have carried diseases foreign to the dingo, it would be naive to believe that all diseases of canids have been here only since the coming of Europeans.

Sarcoptic mange is a common disease among dingoes in central Australia, although it is a mistake to say that all the dingoes are mangy merely because individuals such as this are more readily seen hanging about watering points. This dingo will probably die, not directly from the disease but from secondary infections and/or being unable to fend for itself. Roland Breckwoldt

DISEASES WITH A DIRECT EFFECT ON DINGOES

There is nothing in the basic physiology of the dingo that gives it any protection from the many diseases common to domestic dogs. The life of a wild, free-ranging animal may, however, give it some advantages over domestic dogs that are confined to small areas where disease organisms accumulate and provide a constant source of infection. Natural selection for resistance to disease may also play a greater role in dingo society. On the other hand, wild dingoes may not be regularly exposed to disease and therefore cannot develop an immunity. Nor do they receive a shot of vaccine from the friendly local vet. The dingo must hunt its own food, often in times of shortage, which may render it susceptible to diseases from which the pampered family pet is buffered.

There are parts of eastern Australia that appear to be very good dingo habitat, yet dingoes are few in number there, even when there are no control programs.[1,2] A higher incidence of disease in the cooler and wetter climate of the east has been suggested as the reason for these low populations but more research is required to confirm this theory.

Table 12 (p. 190) shows the more serious parasites and pathogens recorded among dingoes in Australia. Nearly 80 such diseases and parasites have been recorded among domestic dogs in Australia and the number that also affect dingoes is probably higher than the table indicates. The lower number of diseases recorded among dingoes is more likely to reflect the lack of research rather than the dingo's resistance to disease.

Some of the diseases listed in Table 12 are known to be common causes of death among dingoes and may therefore exert a considerable control on their numbers, as the following information indicates.

Distemper

Periodic outbreaks of distemper cause death among natural populations of dingoes. An outbreak across the Barkly Tablelands in the Northern Territory in 1969 and 1970 was estimated to have killed up to 90 per cent of the dingoes in some areas.[1]

Parvovirus

Parvovirus was introduced into Australia in 1978. Its source is unknown but some veterinary surgeons suspect that it came as a laboratory mutant among vaccine commonly used for the same disease in poultry. It causes high mortality among non-immunised pups and those that have not developed antibodies by surviving an infection.

It is not known what effect Parvovirus has had on wild dingoes but an epidemic could kill a large proportion of pups. Enough dingoes, trapped or shot in the wild, have been found to carry Parvovirus antibodies for it to be assumed that this disease is now well established among wild dingoes and that it will kill pups until resistance becomes more widespread.[3]

THE LUNGWORM (FILAROIDES OSLERI)

The parasite *Filaroides osleri* is a nematode worm that causes lesions in the trachea, or windpipe, of dogs. The disease has been associated with the mastiff breed of domestic dog, which introduced it into South Africa in the early 1940s. It is not known how or when the disease arrived in Australia. Curiously, it has been found in only a few domestic dogs but is common in dingoes and feral dogs in the Southern Tablelands of south-eastern Australia.[4]

This disease can be transmitted directly between animals but its absence from many young animals, where the chances of direct infection would be highest from parents that feed them, suggests that some other mechanism is involved in spreading the disease. It is capable of causing death as the lesions restrict breathing. This is more likely to be fatal during periods of food shortage that result in a sustained hunting effort. There is no obvious reason why *F. osleri* should remain largely confined to the wild dog

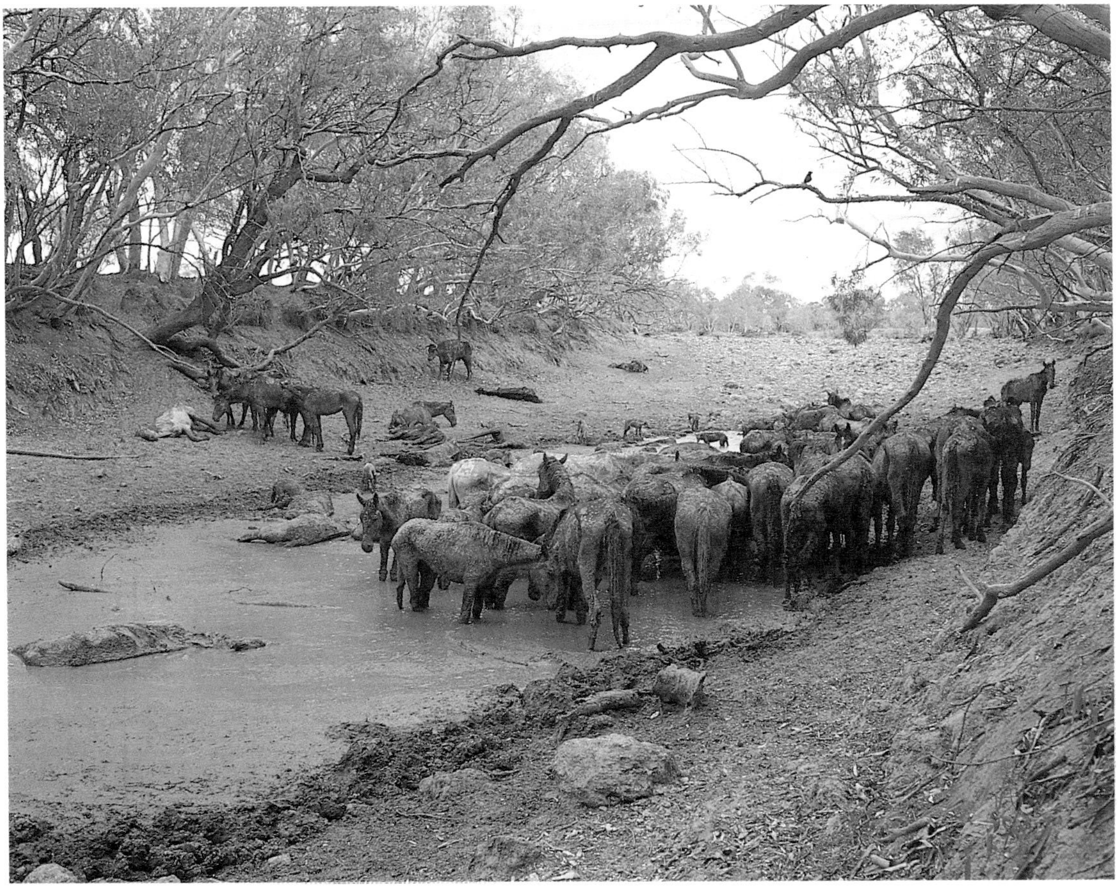

Brumbies dying, in 1980, at Parrabeena Waterhole on Bulloo Downs, south-west Queensland, during a long drought. There were dozens of dingoes scavenging from the carcases, but they, too, were dying, possibly from the disease organism Clostridium botulinum, *commonly known as botulism. This assumption was made by a veterinarian because the dingoes still had access to alternative water through a fence, and because they were still in good condition at the time of death.* *Damian McGreevy*

population in a restricted area of Australia; it is likely to spread, both geographically and among domestic dogs.

Mange

Mange is probably one of the diseases that was introduced with the first dingoes as it has been widely reported among wild dingoes. Both sarcoptic mange (*Sarcoptes scabei*) and demodectic mange (*Demodex canis*) can cause the disease. It generally causes death only when it leads to severe secondary bacterial infection that gains entry through the continual rubbing and scratching in response to the mange mite. Extremely emaciated dingoes with mange are common in central Australia and it is assumed that such susceptible individuals often die, either because their hunting ability is impaired or because they cannot compete with healthy individuals for a home range or territory.

THE DINGO AS A CARRIER OF DISEASE

Hydatids

The evolution of the wild canids has been entwined with herbivores because of their close relationship as predator and prey. Humans have kept this association alive by using dogs as an aid in managing livestock and rewarding their canine workers with food cut from the animals they herded. Wherever humans domesticated livestock for food and fibre they also tended to domesticate dogs. It is not surprising, then, that dogs, livestock and humans share some parasites and diseases. The main cause of concern in Australia is the potential for the wild dog population to frustrate attempts to control a disease known as hydatidosis.

In Australia, hydatidosis is caused by an internal parasite called *Echinococcus granulosus*, or more simply, the hydatid tapeworm. Several strains of *E. granulosus* are found in various parts of the world. Canids such as the wolf and the dog are always the definitive host; that is, they are essential for the tapeworm to complete its life cycle. However, it also requires an intermediate host where the eggs that are passed out in dog faeces can hatch in the stomach and then enter the bloodstream which transports them to a suitable site for a cyst to develop. Infective larvae, or protoscoleces, develop inside these cysts and are ingested by canids when they eat the carcase, so completing the cycle.

The hydatid tapeworm depends entirely on canids as the definitive host but many other animals, including humans, can act as an intermediate host. The most important intermediate host in Australia is the sheep. However, not all species that are infected as intermediate hosts will develop fertile cysts. Hydatid cysts are commonly found in cattle although most of the cysts do not contain protoscoleces. Hydatids is very rarely fatal in the canids although death may occur if the host is carrying a very heavy infestation or if it is old or weakened by poor seasonal conditions and lack of food. It is not known how often the disease causes death in intermediate hosts other than humans.

The major economic and social cost of hydatids lies in its capacity to infect humans. People infected with the disease may develop large cysts on internal organs such as lungs, liver and brain. New South Wales has the highest incidence of human hydatids on the mainland where overall one person per 100,000 is infected. However, up to 27 people per 100,000 are infected in parts of the Southern Tablelands of New South Wales. There was one major hydatid operation on a human every week in Tasmania before the eradication program took effect.[5]

A common source of infestation among humans is through the domestic dog–sheep cycle. Dogs eat sheep offal and pick up larvae which develop into adult tapeworms in the digestive tract. Here they lay eggs that pass out in the dogs' faeces and become attached to their coats or lodge around the kennel area. Humans can easily ingest the eggs if they touch their mouths or eat after handling an infested dog. The recognised system of breaking this cycle is to drench dogs regularly, restrain them from eating sheep offal and maintain strict hygiene after handling dogs.

Hydatids is not regarded as a very important disease of livestock. The most apparent loss is through the condemnation of parts of carcases that carry cysts. The site most commonly contaminated is the liver which, fortunately, is not a prime component of the carcase. A survey carried out in 1960 estimated that the total loss to the livestock industry through carcase condemnation was then around $1,200,000 per annum.[6]

The loss caused to farmers through reduced production by animals carrying cysts is unknown, although there is some evidence from overseas that a reduction in milk, growth rate and fertility may follow infestation with hydatid cysts. The cost of controlling the disease through government education and control programs, and the cost to farmers of having to treat their dogs regularly and feed them correctly, is another aspect of the economic importance of hydatids.[6]

Interest in the dingo as a carrier of hydatids emerged at least as far back as 1886 when it was accused of being the chief transmitter of the disease "in inland Australia where man and beast depended on the same waterholes".[7] More recent research has confirmed that dingoes do carry *E. granulosis* and that very heavy infestations are common in the wetter climatic conditions required by the disease.[8,9]

A high level of infestation occurs in dingoes that do not have access to sheep and cattle or where the main part of their diet comprises native game. The search for intermediate hosts directly led to kangaroos and wallabies, particularly the latter. In south-eastern

Australia, where swamp wallaby (*Wallabia bicolor*) is the main prey species, the dingo carries the highest number of hydatid tapeworms.[10]

The continuing interest in hydatids as an important disease in humans led to a fascinating piece of biological detective work that has identified three separate strains or variants of *E. granulosis* in Australia.[11] This tells us a lot about the disease, and it also tells us something about the dingo.

One strain is found on the mainland and occurs in the domestic dog livestock cycle. Although it has been found in a wide range of livestock, including camels, pigs, goats and horses, the principal intermediate host is the sheep. A second strain has been identified in Tasmania that is also dependent on the domestic dog–livestock cycle but it appears to have evolved in response to unintended selection pressure exerted by the chemical treatment of dogs in the 20-year-old government hydatid control program. These two strains are believed to be the main cause of cysts in humans and control measures are aimed at breaking the dog–livestock cycle by educating the public on the need for hygiene and preventing dogs gaining access to sheep offal.

The third distinct strain occurs only on the mainland and is found in the dingo–macropod cycle. This strain is referred to as the sylvatic cycle, or wildlife strain. Research has shown that it develops much faster in dingoes than in domestic dogs. When domestic dogs are infected with this strain its development is greatly retarded in comparison to its development among dingoes. There are inherent differences between the domestic strains and the wildlife strain that reinforce the assertion that they arrived in Australia independently. The wildlife strain is very well developed among dingoes and wallabies, suggesting that it came to Australia with the first dingoes.[6]

The wildlife strain is not found in Tasmania, which also supports the view that it arrived with the dingo over 3500 years ago. Dingoes did not reach Tasmania because of Bass Strait so they could not carry the strain to the kangaroos and wallabies there, which are just as suitable as intermediate hosts as their counterparts on the mainland. If the wildlife strain had been introduced since European settlement, it would have been taken across to Tasmania along with dogs and sheep. It is not known whether the thylacine, a marsupial carnivore quite unrelated to the dog, could have carried the parasite even if it were present in Tasmania. It seems unlikely because the Tasmanian devil (*Sarcophilus harrisi*), which still exists in Tasmania and was once found on the mainland, does not carry any strain of hydatids.[6]

The failure of the wildlife strain to reach Tasmania, even since European settlement, indicates that the dingo–macropod cycle remains somewhat isolated from the dog–livestock cycle. If there were a high rate of interchange between them, it would be unusual for the wildlife strain not to have reached Tasmania by now, given the number of domestic dogs and livestock that have been imported from the mainland. The degree of interchange between the two mainland cycles continues to be a vexed question and is the subject of continuing research.

The wildlife strain does infect cattle but it may not go any further because only 0.7 per cent of the cysts were fertile in the 28 per cent of cattle found to carry them in the coastal belt of Queensland north of the Tropic of Capricorn.[12] Moreover, a closer study of a 3000 sq km area within this region found that while most of the 21 dingoes that were trapped and examined carried infestations, none of the 21 domestic dogs that were examined showed any trace of the parasite. In this case the wildlife cycle was perpetuated through the predator–prey relationship of the dingo and the black-striped wallaby (*Macropus dorsalis*). It is supposed that cattle picked up the parasite through flies that had previously alighted on dingo faeces. The cysts do cause some economic loss through condemnation of parts of badly affected carcases but the $500,000 loss to the Queensland export meat industry does not rank hydatids among the most important livestock diseases of the state.[12]

More recent research in south-eastern Queensland found that on 40 cattle properties that had a high incidence of bovine hydatidosis, at least two domestic dogs carried the wildlife strain of the disease. This is the first time that the wildlife strain has been isolated in domestic dogs and indicates that it is capable of infecting farm dogs when they are fed kangaroo or wallaby meat or are given the opportunity to scavenge their carcases. Such an interchange poses human health problems where domestic dogs are given access to macropods.[13] There is also evidence, from the case of a nine-year-old boy, that the sylvatic strain of hydatids is dangerous to humans.[14]

An awareness that there was a wildlife strain of hydatidosis in Australia before European settlement and that it was introduced by the dingo or, more accurately, the people who brought the dingo, raises the question of whether it infected Aborigines and caused deaths among them. Denied the surgery necessary to remove cysts, a certain mortality rate would have been inevitable among Aborigines if the wildlife strain infects humans. There is a high incidence of hydatids among Aborigines in Western Australia today but it is not known whether they are infected with the domestic dog–sheep strain or the wildlife strain.[6]

Farmers whose properties border national parks or rugged forest country where there are dingoes or feral dogs should be cautious about feeding their dogs kangaroo and wallaby.[15] The cheap dog food supplied by the readily shot kangaroo may be better foregone in the interests of personal health, even if all the other arguments against the practice have failed. There is evidence to suggest that the wildlife strain of hydatids is dangerous to human health from the high incidence of hydatids among dingo trappers in Victoria.[9] The following macropods have all been found to be intermediate hosts for the wildlife strain

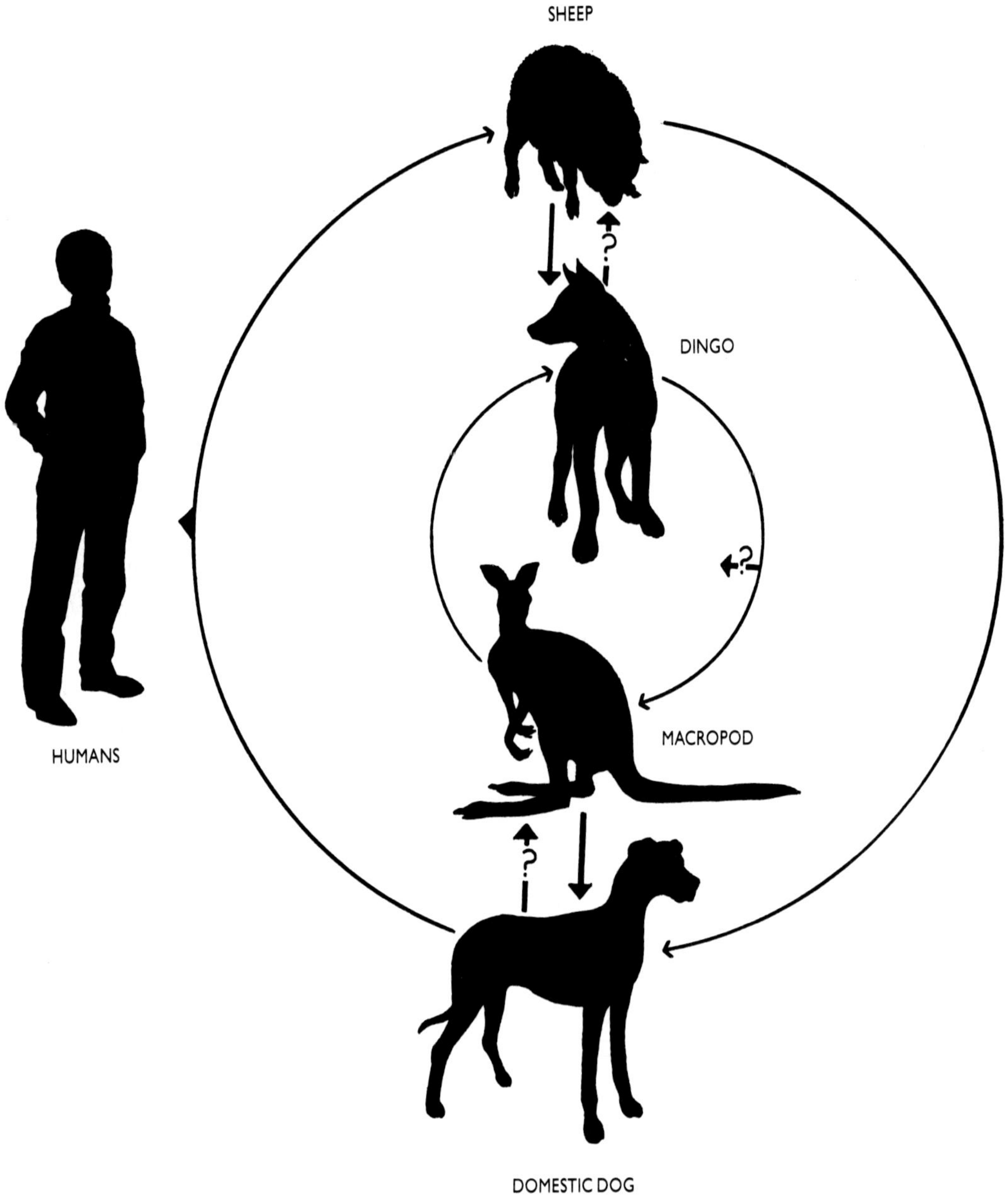

The domestic dog-sheep and the dingo-macropod hydatid cycles. The broken arrow with question mark indicates that the degree of interchange between the two cycles remains uncertain. After Parasitology Today. *Elsevier, 1987.*

of *E. granulosis* and should be handled with care:

Eastern grey kangaroo ...... *Macropus giganteus*
Western grey kangaroo ...... *Macropus fulignosis*
Wallaroo .... *Macropus robustus*
Whiptail wallaby..... *Macropus parryi*
Black-striped wallaby .... *Macropus dorsalis*
Swamp wallaby ..... *Wallabia bicolor*
Godman's rock wallaby .... *Petrogale godmani*

EXOTIC DISEASES

Fortunately, Australia remains free of some of the major livestock diseases found in other countries. The most damaging of these is foot-and-mouth disease and strenuous efforts are made to keep it out of Australia. It is carried only by cloven-hoofed animals and the dingo is not implicated in any contingency plans should it enter the country. Indeed, the dingo could play a positive role in preventing the disease gaining a foothold in the feral pig population by preying on pigs, particularly in remote regions such as Cape York Peninsula.

There are some exotic diseases that could be harboured by the dingo should they gain entry into Australia. An expert committee established by the Standing Committee on Agriculture listed the exotic diseases that could be carried by wildlife.[16] This committee suggested that the dingo is a potential carrier of the following diseases:

Rabies
African horse sickness
Aujeszky's disease
Canine brucellosis
Nairobi sheep disease
Rift Valley fever
Surra
Trichinosis

The economic impact of most of the above diseases is not known; nor is it known to what extent the dingo would carry them — it is merely suspected that it would be implicated because such diseases are carried by dogs in other countries. There is no certainty that they would be carried by dingoes under the conditions that prevail in Australia. One of the above diseases warrants a fuller exposition — rabies has been feared since time immemorial.

RABIES

Rabies is present in Indonesia and other South-East Asian countries close to northern Australia so there is always a danger that it will gain entry. It is primarily a disease of canids but can also affect humans and livestock. Rabies destroys the nervous system and results in death through general paralysis. Before the terminal stage of the disease, the animal may go through a "furious

TABLE 12:
The most serious canine diseases and parasites found on dingoes. Adapted from Corbett, 1974, with amendments by Sabine, 1986.

Type of disease	Organism involved	Severity
Internal parasites		
Heartworm	*Dirofilaria immitis*	Serious; fatal with heavy infestations.
Lungworm	*Filaroides osleri*	Serious; fatal in pups with heavy infestations.
Whipworm	*Trichuris vulpis*	Rarely fatal except in pups with heavy infestations.
Spiruroids	*Cyathospirura dasyuridis*	Unknown.
Tapeworms	*Echinococcus granulosis* *Taenia ovis* *Taenia hydatigena* *Taenia pisiformis* *Taenia serialis* *Spirometra erinacei*	Does not cause disease in dogs but heavy infestations of *E. granulosis* can cause diarrhoea and loss of weight.
External parasites		
Coastal scrub tick	*Ixodes holocyclus*	Can be fatal.
Sarcoptic mange Demodectic mange	*Sarcoptes scabiei* *Demodex canis*	Can be fatal when accompanied by secondary bacterial infection.
Virus		
Canine distemper	*Paramyxovirus*	Serious, usually fatal.
Canine hepatitis	*Adenovirus*	Serious, often fatal.
Canine myocarditis and enteritis	*Parvovirus*	Serious, usually fatal.

stage" marked by hyperactivity and muscle spasms. It is at this time that the rabid dog is likely to bite a human or another animal and spread the disease.

Even though human deaths are few, particularly in the developed countries, a vivid folklore fuels the fear of rabies through the ugly death it causes in humans. The cost to the livestock industry of vaccinating cattle against rabies caused through the bites of either canids or vampire bats can be significant: in France, the annual cost of cattle vaccinations is around $30 million.[17]

Rabies occurs on all continents except Australia and it has not yet entered New Zealand, Cyprus and Hawaii. Wild carnivores are the main transmitters of rabies. Infected animals eventually die from the disease but it has a long incubation period. The virus is excreted in the saliva and is readily transmitted to any animal bitten by a carrier.

Rabies is usually carried by one or two main host species which are responsible for perpetuating the disease even though other susceptible carnivores may be present. In central and western Europe the red fox (*Vulpes vulpes*) is the main carrier whereas in eastern Europe the red fox and raccoon dog (*Nyctereutes procyonoides*) are the main carriers. In North America there are more or less independent epidemics maintained in different parts of the country by foxes (*Vulpes vulpes* and *Urocyon cinereoargenteus*), skunks (*Mephitis mephitis*) and raccoons (*Procyon lotor*). Wolves, jackals, stray dogs and mongooses are all carriers of rabies in some parts of the world. The introduction of the Indian mongoose (*Herpestes auropunctatus*) to the Caribbean resulted in the spread of the disease, causing a major health problem because it bites domestic animals and humans when infected.[17]

Two cycles of infection are recognised. The urban cycle is spread through domestic dogs. A second wildlife cycle is perpetuated through animals such as the fox and raccoon. It is possible that both cycles could be perpetuated by dingoes in Australia. If the wildlife cycle were introduced, it could also possibly be carried by the fox and feral cat.

The most likely avenue for the introduction of rabies is the illegal importation of a dog that is carrying the disease in its incubation stage and is therefore not yet showing any symptoms. This dog would also have to bite a number of other dogs for the disease to be transmitted. Thus the chance of dingoes becoming a reservoir for rabies is not high. Moreover, outbreaks of rabies in Europe coincide with high population densities of susceptible animals. Whether the extensive range conditions of Australia and the relatively low numbers of canids it supports could lead to outbreaks of rabies is yet another unknown.

A possible avenue for the introduction of the wildlife strains of rabies to Australia is through bats. The vampire bat of middle and South America transmits rabies and causes a few human infections each year as well as the death of many livestock. Cattle are vaccinated against rabies in many parts of South America to protect them against infection from bats. Nevertheless, if the bats of the Australian region were able to spread rabies, the disease would probably already exist on the continent.

Vaccinating wild populations of foxes against rabies has been attempted in Europe. Chicken heads were inoculated with vaccine and distributed so that they were available to foxes. An area of 1600 sq km was treated in the Federal Republic of Germany in 1983; this helped to contain a rabies epidemic.[18]

Contingency plans exist in the Australian Bureau of Animal Health for the eradication of dingoes, foxes and feral cats in a certain zone around a suspected outbreak of rabies. Given the elusive nature of these three species, the chances of containment could not be rated very highly. Under these circumstances the best approach to rabies remains a vigilant quarantine presence and rigid enforcement of the regulations covering the importation of all canids and exotic species of wildlife that may carry the disease.

PART FOUR

The Barrier Fences

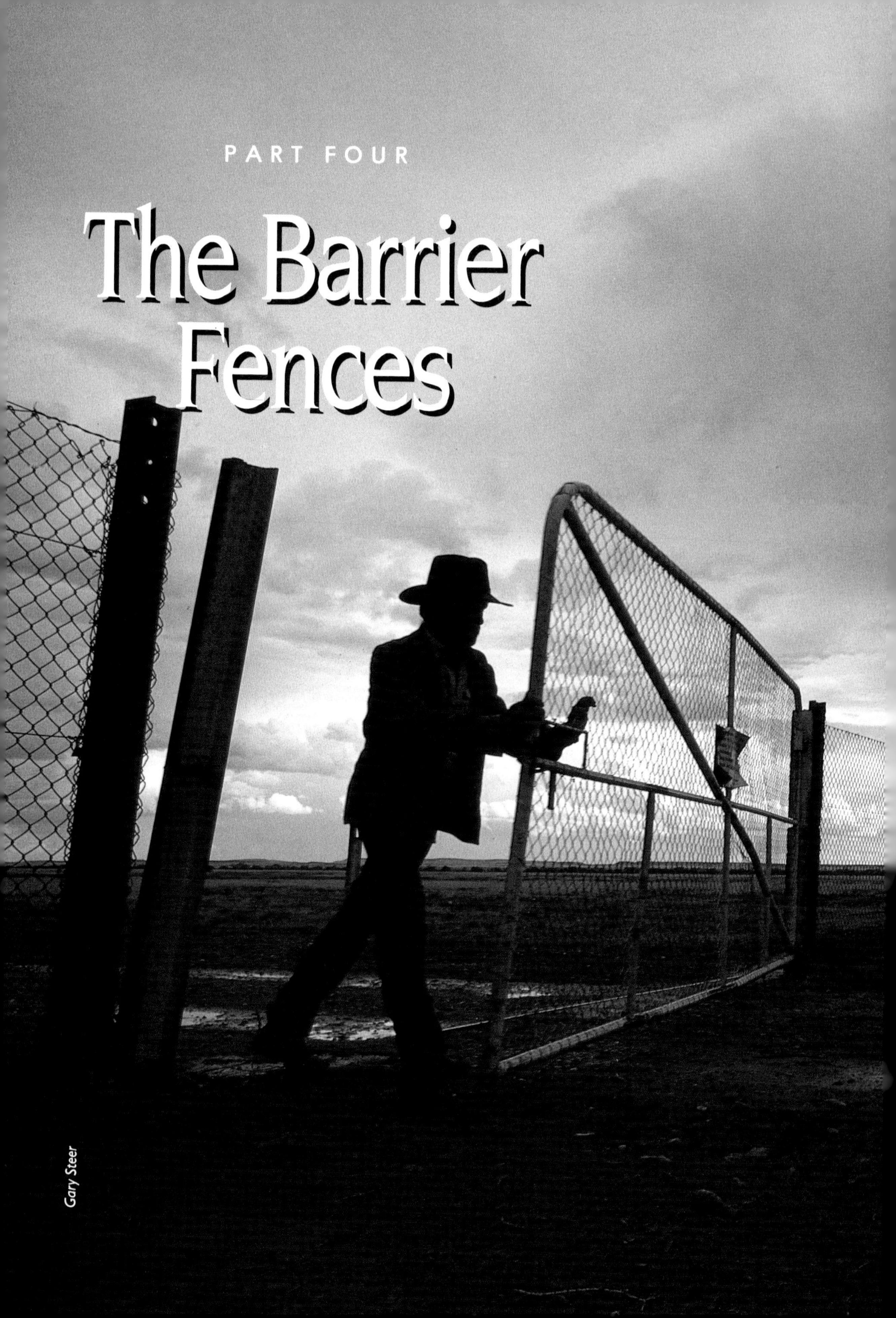

Gary Steer

Fenced into a corner

An iron curtain stretches across Australia. It starts on the Darling Downs behind the warm waters of the Queensland coast and finishes where the land meets the cold southern waters of the Great Australian Bight in South Australia. This iron curtain is made up of the three state dingo barrier fences that are linked to form the longest fence in the world. The total length is now 5614 km, making it 3374 km longer than the Great Wall of China. Until 1980, when the original Queensland barrier fence was shortened, the total length of the barrier fences was an incredible 8614 km.

The fences were built against all the odds of a hostile environment, high costs, shortages of materials and labour during two world wars and the Great Depression, and all the human foibles that can tumble grand schemes. The fences had to traverse country where shifting dunes in the dry times could obliterate all trace of the fence, or floods in the wet could flatten it. Acid soils ate away the wire that had to be anchored underground to prevent the wily dingo getting through. Animals that ranged in size from white ants to brumbies damaged the fence and rendered it useless if maintenance lagged over the years. But unless sheep were protected from the dingo, there was little hope for the flourishing wool industry in a land where the only advantage people had was an eternal optimism.

Once fencing materials became readily available, graziers began constructing barriers to keep the dingo away from their sheep, thereby changing the nature of the industry. This photo from the collection of John Gerritson shows dingo netting being carried into a remote area by packhorses.

THE FIRST BARRIER FENCE

Privately constructed and owned dingo fences were built as soon as netting fence materials became available late last century but the first government dingo fence had its beginnings in the Corner Country of north-western New South Wales. It is hard to know where Corner Country begins because there is no precise boundary to its eastern edge; since its inhabitants take some pride in being "Corner People", that edge is inclined to sneak east at least as far as the Darling River. No such flexible sense of place can alter the northern or western boundaries — Corner Country ends precisely at the dingo fence. This fence runs along the border with South Australia in the west and Queensland in the north to where they meet at Camerons Corner.

This is the land of Burke and Wills, dreams of gold, and a place where those unconnected with the landed gentry could still find country to settle and seek prosperity on the sheep's back. It was also the land of the Aborigine and the dingo. For a while it looked as if the dingo would be the only one to prosper from sheep, but that was changed by the dingo fence.

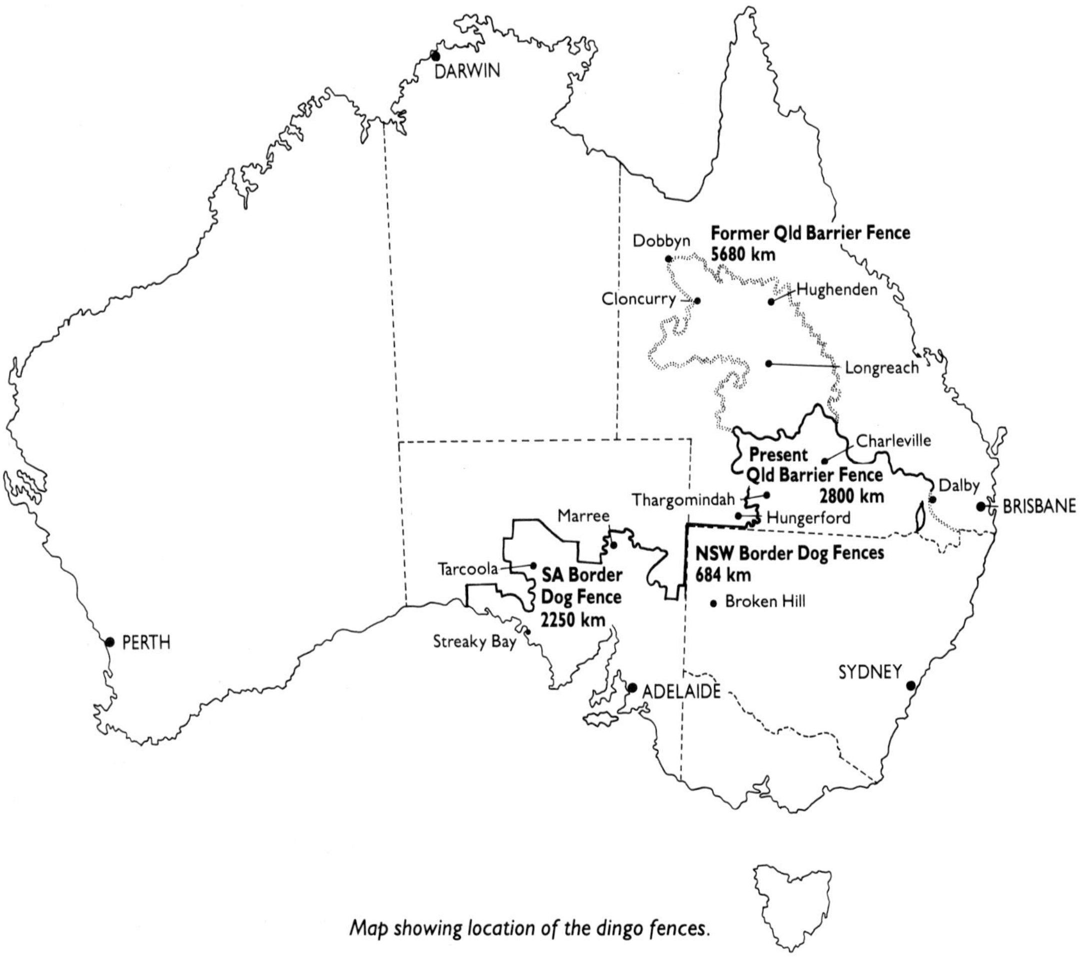

Map showing location of the dingo fences.

THE SOUTH AUSTRALIAN LEG

The dingo barrier fence along the New South Wales border started its life as a futile impediment to the spread of the rabbit. When the rabbit fence between South Australia and New South Wales was first suggested in 1884 there were already plenty of rabbits in both states so it is not clear what a fence between them was meant to achieve. The idea belonged to New South Wales, which accused South Australia of allowing rabbits to breed with such fecundity that they continuously spilled over the border. It was more a consequence of jealous parochialism between the two states than a considered attempt at using scarce resources to control the rabbit in the best ways available at the time.[1] With a rabbit-proof fence between them, each state could pursue its own form of rabbit control without being sniped at by the other. It seems an expensive way to avoid a conference.

By 1890 a rabbit fence ran along the South Australian border from the Murray River to the corner of New South Wales and Queensland, a distance of 556 km. The fence cost £23,150, which was paid in full by the New South Wales government.[2] To build that fence today would cost $2 million so it might have been a reasonable investment if the invincible combination of environmental vagaries and human foibles had not prevailed.

Maintenance of the fence was the responsibility of adjoining landowners who were directed by an inspector to undertake maintenance work should their own diligence fail, which it did within less than five years. The fence was kept in good order until 1893 and then rapidly fell into disrepair. Wind blowing against a "sail" of grass caught against the fence, acid sand, fire, rust, flood, shifting dune, kangaroos and disillusionment all took their toll. By 1910 it was useless and long stretches had literally disappeared.

Parts of the fence remained where the adjoining landowner and the environment were more benign. As closer settlement took more and more sheep into dingo country the notion took hold that the fence that had failed to stop the rabbit should be rehabilitated, and modified, to stop the new enemy. Private dingo fences protected sheep from dingoes and this encouraged the governments of New South Wales and South Australia to co-operate on the dingo where they had failed with the rabbit.

The two states agreed on a new dingo fence on 8 April 1914. The remoter country to the north was seen as the refuge of the dingo so the new fence was to be much shorter than its failed predecessor. The tender documents specified a fence of 225 km running south from "The Corner" to Lake Charles pastoral holding in South Australia, finishing at the old 205-mile post on the rabbit fence, measured from the Murray River.

The tender documents also specified the work to be carried out and the dimensions of the new fence. The old rabbit fence was to be repaired. Wherever it was less than 91.5 cm in height the sand that had blown against it had to be scraped away. A band of

The dog fence boundary rider, Edward Illies (centre), with his family outside the boundary rider's cottage at the Wompah Depot on the Queensland border, circa 1915.
Collection of John Gerritson

marsupial netting above the old fence had to be secured to topping posts every 9 m to raise the height of the fence to 182 cm. A new strand of barbed wire was fixed in place 70 cm above the ground and two strands of barbed wire were added at 12 cm intervals above the marsupial netting.

Work on the fence began late in 1914 and was complete by 1917 at a cost of £13,800, which was shared between the two states. South Australia actually contributed the equivalent of 22 cents more than New South Wales and, although insignificant, this discrepancy could have been a portent of things to come. South Australia undertook the physical task of maintaining the fence on the condition that New South Wales contributed to the cost.

Six full-time boundary riders each patrolled and maintained an average of 35 km of fence with inspectors to oversee them. Each boundary rider was supplied with two camels, one for riding and one for carrying equipment. Two tents were also supplied: a large one to establish a more luxurious base camp near water and a small one to pitch near a job on the fence that had to be finished before moving on. Camels held out against motor vehicles on this section of the fence until the early 1940s.

Things started out reasonably well, with New South Wales making its first contribution in 1916. But, like an irresponsible absent parent, New South Wales neglected paying maintenance. By July 1934 it had managed to mail only £16,238 across the border while South Australia had spent just over £500,000. Annoyed by the discrepancy,

A camel train passing through Tibooburra, circa 1915, loaded with equipment and stores for the dog fence boundary riders based at the Smithfield and Wompah Depots.
Collection of John Gerritson

South Australia promptly terminated the arrangement.[3]

Once again, both states went their separate ways on the dingo, as they had with the rabbit. South Australia relinquished any claims to the fence and handed over all plant and equipment to New South Wales. Under a special arrangement, South Australia continued to maintain the fence for a short period, but this time, New South Wales paid £898 towards the cost. On 24 August 1934 the New South Wales parliament assented to the Western Lands (Amendment) Act, finally formalising its ownership of the South Australian border dog fence.

THE QUEENSLAND BORDER FENCE

Meanwhile, the outrage felt at the rabbits swarming across southern Australia and heading north convinced Queenslanders to build a rabbit fence of their own. They made sure it was *their* fence by building it one chain into Queensland rather than precisely along the border. There were wooden markers on the fence with the number 29 on them that obviously signified the 29th parallel, which is the border between New South Wales and Queensland. It is therefore possible that the fence was intended to be on the border and the contractors made an error.[2] Nevertheless, the consistent placement of the fence inside Queensland points to a deliberate decision to secure its possession.

New South Wales, already covered in rabbits, saw no advantage in contributing to the cost of a fence that could protect only Queensland's interests. It thus avoided sharing responsibility for a valiant failure. There were rabbits in Queensland around the Bulloo, Paroo and Ballon rivers in 1890, the year in which this ambitious fence was completed. That year saw a rabbit fence running over 1060 km from Mungindi in the east across to Camerons Corner and then turning towards the Simpson Desert to the north, following the South Australian border, crossing Coopers Creek and almost reaching the north-east corner of South Australia.[3,4]

Although there were rabbits in Queensland by the time the fence was completed, it was regarded as a success because it halted the plague proportions of rabbits that seemed to swarm north in search of feed. The annual report of the Queensland Lands Department of 1907 stated: "The fact of enormous numbers [of rabbits] perishing against the netting fences evidenced again the value of the fences, not only as checks to the general migration of the pest, but as contributing agents to its destruction."

There is a note of self-congratulation in the words of a grazier in the Thargomindah district who could look south over the fence and report: "The country on the Queensland side is luxuriant with vegetation after this fine season while on the New South Wales side of the line it is a desert of red sand relieved only by rabbits and the black stumps of dead bushes."[5]

Apparently the Queensland government maintained the fence in good order but the rabbit headed north regardless. Rabbiters had to make a living and carried rabbits to new country to boost the stocks of those that got through the fence by themselves. The futility of trying to halt the rabbit induced a widespread apathy among those who had started out with such fervour to fence the vermin out. The many miles of rabbit fencing built throughout Queensland under the direction of Rabbit Boards established under *The Rabbit Boards Act of* 1891 gradually suffered the consequences of bad planning. Some Rabbit Boards actually went bankrupt while trying to maintain the fence and it soon fell into such disrepair that commentators noted that rabbits could be seen happily cavorting and breeding under it and on both sides of it.[6]

All the while, the dingo was becoming a greater concern to the pastoralists in the Corner Country, who had by now accepted the inevitability of the rabbit. The emergence of the dingo as enemy number one had to do with closer settlement, which made the settlers more dependent on sheep, from which they could derive a higher income than from cattle. It was also said that the dingo increased in numbers following the introduction of the rabbit. This would have been fine had the dingo

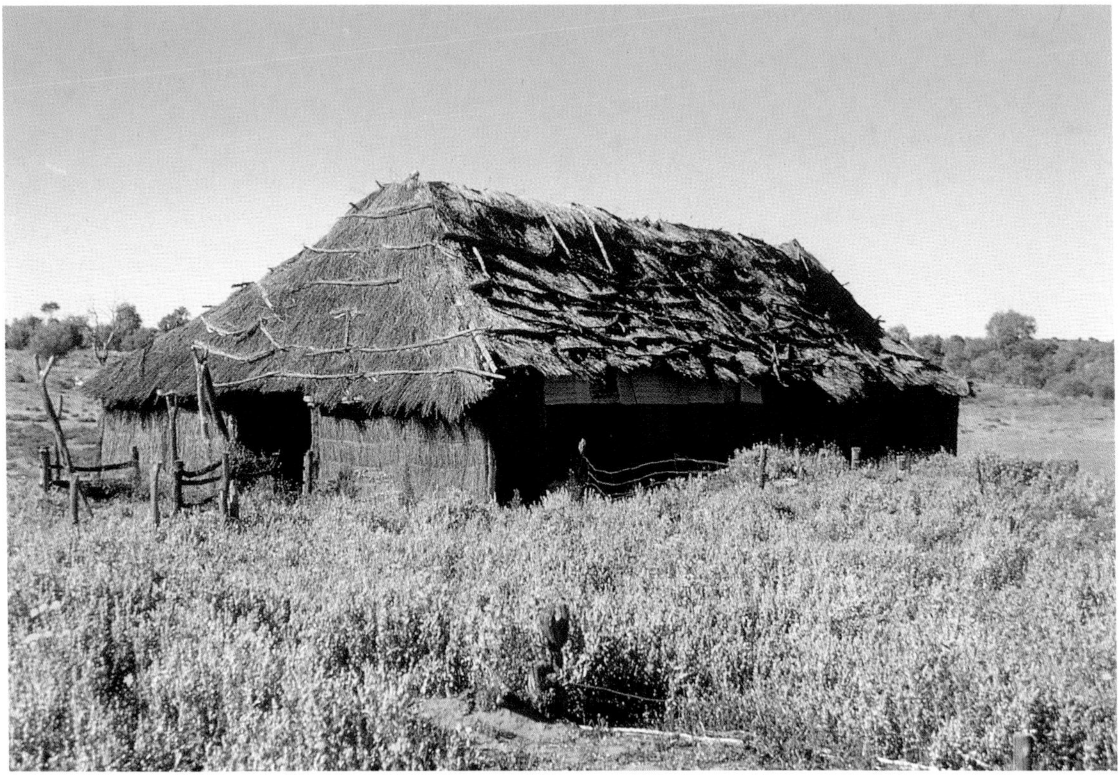

A tribute to the determination of the early pastoralists — a cane grass shearing shed built on Waka Station in the Corner Country in 1927.
Photograph taken in 1974 by John Gerritson

stuck to a rabbit diet — unfortunately it did not, and took to harassing sheep.

Attempts to establish sheep over the border in south-western Queensland were often abandoned because of dingoes and these properties remained large cattle runs, as many still do today. South of the border, the sheepmen were starting to rally around the efforts of a station manager named Frank Little. Something of Little's commitment and determination can be discerned from a letter that he sent to the directors of Mount Wood Pastoral Company in 1910, soon after he was appointed as manager of Mount Wood Station near Tibooburra in the Corner Country:

> Gentlemen
> In accepting the position of manager I wish to thank you for your confidence in myself. I will at all times work to and for the company. I am only sorry that things are in such a critical stage but am hopefully looking forward to relief in the shape of rain until such time comes I will do all in my power to save as many stock as possible.
> I am dear sirs, yours faithfully, Frank K. Little.

After trying to save sheep from drought, Little turned his considerable talents to saving them from dingoes. Other voices may have been equally strong but Little committed his convictions to paper. His correspondence shows that he would not approve of Sidney Kidman's knighthood or his elevation to folk hero as "the cattle king". Kidman responded to the dingo simply by getting out of sheep whenever the dingoes caused problems and depending entirely on large cattle runs. Little saw this as irresponsible and disloyal to the settlers struggling to survive on their small blocks, totally dependent on sheep. It was an Australian version of the conflict between the ranchers and the homesteaders in the "Wild West" of the United States.

In 1912, only two years after his appointment as manager of Mount Wood Station, Little began organising local landholders into lobbying for a dingo fence between Queensland and New South Wales. He cited the case of six large stations across the border that had run 227,000 sheep at the turn of the century but by 1913 had been forced to run cattle. To Little it was the domino theory — a yellow peril in the form of the dingo would see all the adjoining sheep stations in New South Wales fail and fall into the hands of the large cattle companies. His deeply felt concern was expressed in another letter to the directors in Adelaide: "The rot stopped at the border fence for a considerable time and then Connulpie went and now we are right up against the dingo infested country."[7]

Pastoralists in the Corner Country saw their future threatened and rallied around Frank Little. They formed a Border Fence Trust and agreed on a self-imposed levy according to the size of their holding to raise funds for the purpose of converting the border rabbit fence into one that would stop dingoes coming across from the cattle country on the other side.

Kidman refused to make any commitment to the proposed fence, which led many of the settlers to believe that he was waiting for their failure at the jaws of the dingo so that he could buy them out cheaply at forced sales. It was with some bitterness that Little wrote to his directors in Adelaide during April 1913:

> The dingo question grows more serious each year. The Pastoralists Union and the Pastures Protection Boards have endeavoured to do something but unfortunately their scheme failed on account of Kidman to aid the Trust, this man seems to be always against true progress and is always on the alert to benefit from others misfortunes. All the pastoralists of the Milparinka District and many right out of the district who would not get any direct benefit out of a vermin proof fence signed the bond and were willing to pay towards the erection and maintenance of the fence but Kidman who has three stations which would receive direct protection refused to assist but simply says that if the dogs beat him he will put cattle on.[7]

Little saw Kidman only as a selfish opportunist. Another view might be to respect his understanding of the Australian environment. Kidman wanted to drought-proof himself with a string of stations in different climatic regions so that he could move stock to southern markets and be assured of fattening them on the way. By the time the dingo became a threat to the frontiers of the sheep industry, Kidman's cattle empire was so well established that he did not have to worry about either sheep or dingoes.

The interests of the sheepman and the cattleman at the frontline of dingo country remain at issue to this day. The dingo story is not without its insights into social stratification. The disdain Frank Little had for Sidney Kidman was similar to that felt by the soldier settlers in the marginal blocks along the edge of the New England Tableland who felt that they controlled the dingo for the benefit of the established graziers on the better country.[8]

Frank Little was a prodigious correspondent but his letters do not indicate whether he and Kidman settled their differences. Success often mellows enmity and Frank Little did get his dingo fence.

A Fenced-in Corner

In 1913 the Queensland government gave the Border Fence Trust permission to convert the rabbit fence into a dingo fence. The trust began work immediately and completed the task the following year. In tribute to Frank Little's leadership, the fence became known as "Little's fence" and it ran from Hungerford to Camerons Corner, a distance of 359 km. It still stands and operates effectively to this day but it faced some uncertain times.

Frank Little retained his interest in the fence and, through his position as chairman of the Milparinka Pastures Protection Board, saw to it that it was maintained. The Border Fence Trust had agreed to pay the Queensland government to maintain the fence with the boundary riders who had been employed on the rabbit fence.

The awesome drought of 1916–20 brought this happy arrangement to an end. Drifting sand and shrivelled finances made it hard for the trust to honour its commitment and in 1919 the Queensland government abruptly terminated the agreement and refused to allow the trust to maintain the fence in any way.

The trust, anxious to keep the fence, made representations to the New South Wales government who despatched the Minister for Lands, the Hon. P. F. Loughlin, out to inspect the fence. With his help the state government was able to reach an agreement with Queensland, which handed over the fence free of any capital liability. With bureaucratic blindness to the failure of the original scheme, the Queensland government stipulated that the fence must always be kept rabbit-proof. Even today, the Queensland rabbits are kept apart from the New South Wales rabbits except for events such as floods that temporarily breach the barrier and allow some miscegenation.

The New South Wales government passed the Wild Dog Destruction Act,

1921, which made the Western Lands Board responsible for the control and maintenance of both the South Australian and the Queensland border fences. Hereafter, the fences would be the state government's responsibility, but funded for the most part by a special "dog rate" on all landholders in the Western Division. The state government agreed to contribute an amount equal to one-quarter of the rates collected.[2,4]

The greater, and more reliable, funding that followed state government intervention made possible changes in the management of the fence. One of the first changes was the improvement of facilities for the boundary riders. This allowed them to devote more time to maintaining the fence. Before this, one commentator was moved to write that he was "assured on excellent authority that on both fences the men spend three-fourths of their time in going for water and rations, and the remaining fourth on the fence".[9]

Soon after assuming responsibility for the two fences, the Western Lands Board increased the dingo bounty to £2 per scalp for any dingo caught in the Western Division. This generous bounty lured quite a few scalps across the border and it must have been a trying task to determine the difference between a Queensland, South Australian and New South Wales dingo. The bounty paid by Wild Dog Destruction Boards in 1987 was only $8. Back then, in addition to the official bounty, graziers also offered considerable private bounties to further speed the eradication of dingoes in the fenced-in corner.

The wire fences became the basis of the social and economic fabric of the Corner Country. There were brief periods when gold fever gripped places such as Tibooburra but the cornerstone industry of the area remained wool. The two border dingo fences cossetted the sheep from the dingoes that lurked outside, awaiting any sandstorm, flood or flagging enthusiasm for maintenance to come back through.

The border fences were also used to help prevent the spread of livestock diseases such as pleuropneumonia into New South Wales by cattle passing through the Corner from Queensland

Dingoes do get through the fence into the Corner Country when sand drift or flood makes access easier. Here, I am not far inside the fence, inspecting an emu that was probably killed by dingoes and, by the many tracks around it, was certainly eaten by them. Gary Steer

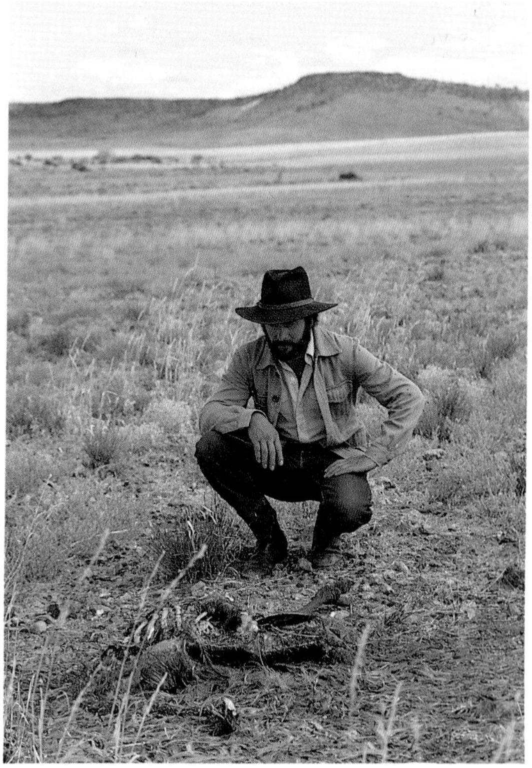

on the way to Adelaide. Special gates were put in the fence and cattle had to be inspected by a stock inspector as they passed through.[10] It was at one of these gates that Percy Bates, a boundary rider on the dingo fence, committed suicide. Mick Kennewell, a former resident of Tibooburra, does not give any date for the happenings he describes. The mention of "roo chillers" puts it in the age of mechanisation on the fence:

> Percy Bates committed suicide at Adelaide Gate, Bill O'Connor found him three days later, unfortunately by then he was a bit high. "Springheel Jack" was the copper then and he had to take him to Broken Hill in his landrover but by the time he got to Thompsons Creek, the smell from behind was too much for him so he ran back to Tibooburra and rang his O.I.C. and claimed his vehicle had broken down. So they put Percy into one of Paech's roo chillers and waited for the police from Broken Hill to come up and get him.[11]

The fences continued to perform their function, with interruption of course, by floods and drifting sand. Dingoes always get into New South Wales when the muddy Bulloo floods and spills down to fill the waiting giant saucer that is Bulloo Lake, right on the border. Sometimes that section of the fence is down for months and dingoes can wade, swim or even walk through mud and shallow water to new pastures. But apart from such events, the fence continued to work until after the Second World War.

That war drained the Australian countryside of fit men. Many of them never returned and, if they did, they had no materials with which to work. The shortage of basic building materials following the war lasted well into the next decade. I can still remember my father trying to obtain corrugated iron and fibro to build our first house in 1949 and 1950, and that was on the outskirts of Sydney. Imagine what it was like getting fencing materials at Tibooburra!

There had always been some animosity by the Corner people towards the administrators of the fence who were based so far away in Sydney. The old Western Lands Board had by now been changed to the Western Lands Commission and while it did have representatives from Western Division landholders, the local people felt that the fence was still administered and managed from Sydney. The antipathy towards the Western Lands Commission was heightened by the problems that faced the fence following the war. By 1950 it had, once again, fallen into such a state of disrepair that many locals regarded it as useless.

The conflict came to a head when the then Commissioner for Western Lands, Mr Cronin, who had the support of his Minister for Lands, the Hon. Roger Nott, responded to criticism of failure to maintain the fence by suggesting that a new dingo fence be built about 50 km east of the existing border fences to dodge the difficult sand dune and flood country.

Maintenance of the fences had always been a problem because they rigidly adhered to the state borders rather than taking a route through the country that was easier to fence and maintain. In the intervening years, both Queensland and South Australia had built their own dingo fences, but because they ran within their own borders they had been able to choose the most suitable terrain to carry the fences. No country out there is easy to fence; some is just a bit better than the other. This had not escaped Cronin and Nott but they first had to sell the idea to the Corner.

The Cronin Plan, as it came to be known, still incorporated the existing border fences. These would become buffer fences and would have to be maintained by the adjoining landowners who would receive a small rebate of their dog tax to help cover the cost of materials. The new fence would convert existing rabbit-proof boundary fences into dingo fences and build new fences where there were no suitable existing ones. The actual construction was to be carried out by the landholders who would receive what the Pastoralists Association of West Darling described as a token payment of £50 a mile for new fencing and £20 for converting existing fences. Thereafter, the landholder through whose property the dingo fence ran would receive £8 per mile per annum as a contribution to maintenance.[12] This was similar to the administration of the South Australian dingo fence and it is quite likely that Cronin modelled his plan on that state.

According to the Cronin Plan, the border fences were still in good order and could be maintained by the pastoralists at little cost. It was this insistence that the fences were in good repair that really drew the ire of the western pastoralists. A letter to the editor of the Broken Hill newspaper the *Barrier Miner* of 3 November 1955 was signed "Dingo". Dingo was not happy about Cronin's scheme:

> The appalling condition of the present border fence is a direct consequence of the fact that the Western Division is administered from Sydney. It is the height of absurdity to accept Mr. Cronin's new buffer fence proposal. Is it too much to ask that our coastal pork choppers should be transferred to the division which they serve.

Perhaps it was mistrust of the bureaucrats in Sydney that prevented people putting their names to their feelings. Another letter to the *Barrier Miner* on 4 April 1957 is signed "Far north grazier":

> The wild dogs are really bad in our area, and it is because the Border Fence is not good at all. It is far from good; in fact it is very bad. We recently had a graziers' inspection committee and it is easy to find stretches of the fence up to 40 yards in length not even in the ground. At other places the mesh was so far out of the ground that the biggest man in the party could get through without any effort whatsoever. So much for the fence reported to be in good condition. We pay dog tax and are entitled to government protection. We cannot receive this proection from a moth-eaten fence, especially when it is declared so good that nobody in Sydney would think of doing anything.

Boundary riders Edward Illies and Albert White pose with White's wife in their 'town' cars, circa 1915.
Collection of John Gerritson

"Roger the dodger" was also moved to write to the *Barrier Miner* and on 8 May 1957 the editor printed his letter voicing concern for those employed on the border fences. Roger pointed out that there were 87 people dependent on the fence, including women and children, and that the Cronin Plan would "boot them all into the discard, and turn the key in their homes. Everyone in Sydney would keep their jobs. Only the families along the fence will get the big boot of Cronin and Nott".

The Pastoralists Association of West Darling convened a general meeting of Western Division graziers and led the voices against the Cronin Plan. The graziers put forward an alternative proposal that the fences be administered by a board located in Broken Hill. Anxious to end the conflict, the New South Wales parliament amended the Wild Dog Destruction Act in 1957 to create a Wild Dog Destruction Board that would take over responsibility for the fences. Moreover, the board would be located in Broken Hill and its membership comprise Western Division pastoralists. From then on, the only "insider", on the board would be the Commissioner for Western Lands as its chairman. The new board enthusiastically set about restoring the fence.

The Wild Dog Destruction Board at Broken Hill continues to manage the two border fences. Today tractors, graders and four-wheel-drive vehicles are employed to keep the fences up. There are even boats with outboard motors for when the Bulloo comes down. Technology has provided plastic-coated netting to guard against the acid sand that can rust wire within a year and see it disintegrate not long after. There are still natural and man-made

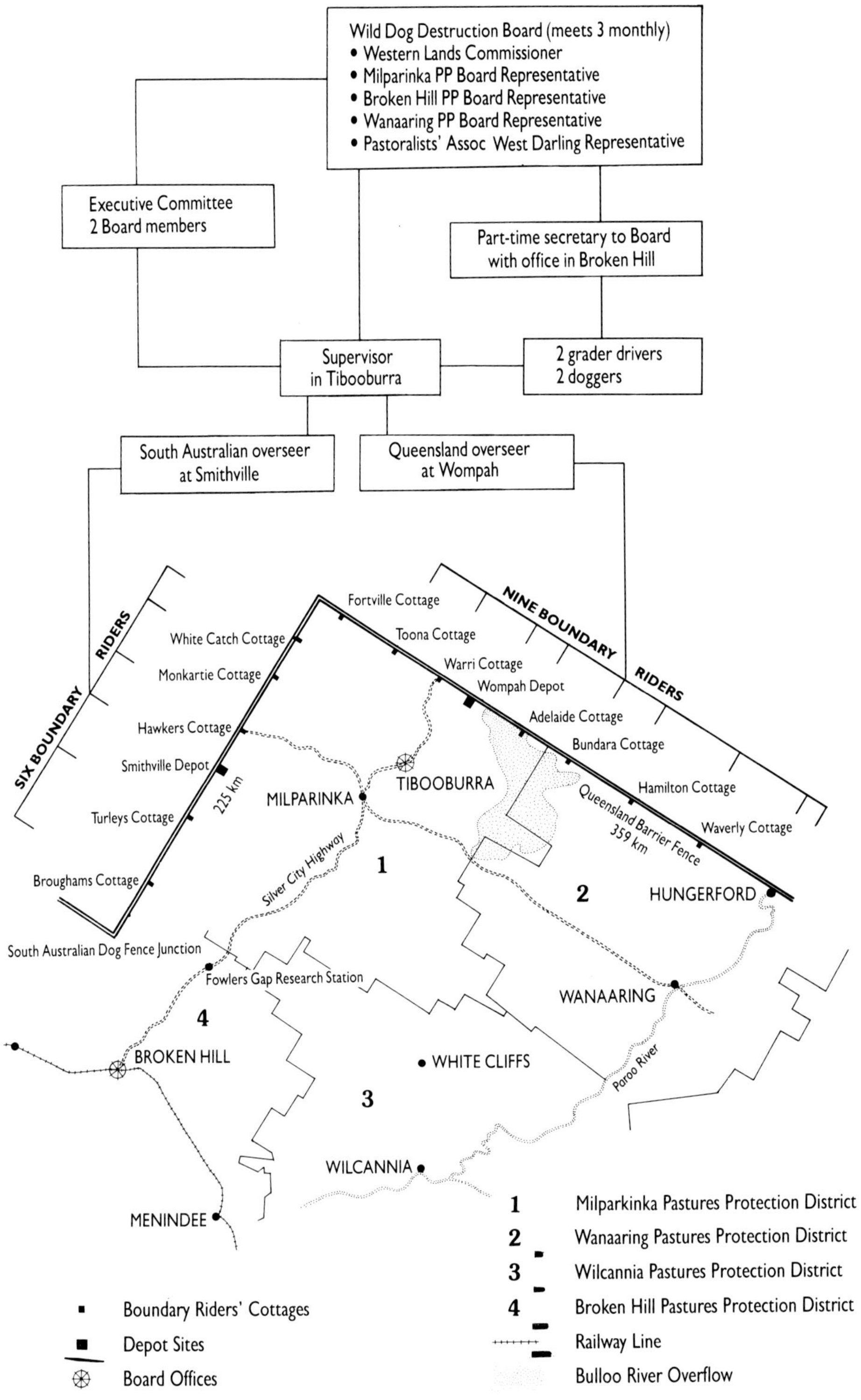

Map showing location and administration of the New South Wales border dingo fences. Department of Agriculture, New South Wales, 1987.

catastrophes along the fences that threaten to remove the wire curtain. Floods of the magnitude that swept parts of the Corner in 1974 are hard to imagine in this arid land. Two cottages at Wompah Gate were simply washed away. Trucks, tractors and plant also disappeared, along with many kilometres of fence. The Bulloo Overflow country was a 32 km wide sea of muddy water that flattened or drowned a fence.[4]

Dingoes always get through the fence when the Bulloo comes down. The records of the Milparinka Pastures Protection Board show that there is always a dramatic increase in the number of dingo scalps in the years that follow a major flood. A robust population of dingoes still lives inside the fence as a result of the 1974 floods and they are said to cause significant sheep losses from time to time. There were 223 dingo scalps handed in to the Wanaaring Pastures Protection Board during 1985–86 it was the largest user of the poison 1080 in the state during that period, having laid 17,325 baits.[13]

The continuing presence of dingoes inside the fence was addressed in 1984 by a Parliamentary Inquiry into the Western Division of New South Wales.[14,15] It reactivated the notion that the adherence to the border line meant that the dingo fence traversed the most difficult terrain in the region. Indeed, the inquiry recommended that the fence be relocated to the south where it could skirt the Bulloo Overflow and to the east on the South Australian leg where it could miss the sand dunes.

The delicate matter of Sturt National Park, which occupies the extreme Corner, also came under scrutiny in this inquiry. The dingo fence is kept intact around the park so that dingoes do not become established there and trouble the surrounding sheep. Any dingoes that do get into the park are ostensibly controlled by the National Parks and Wildlife Service staff or doggers who are allowed to operate within it. However, many of the local pastoralists say that the service lacks the degree of enthusiasm necessary to keep the park "clean".

One consequence of not allowing dingoes in the region is that kangaroos, euros and emus have increased in number. The red kangaroo has now replaced the dingo as the main enemy of the pastoral industry. The Parliamentary Inquiry was aware of this dilemma, noting that there were ten times as many red kangaroos on the New South Wales side of the dingo fence as in the dingo country across the border. The proliferation of other wildlife, particularly macropods, following the eradication of dingoes has been noted by numerous observers ever since strychnine poisoning dealt the dingo its first serious blow. The ability of dingoes to control the number of kangaroos and emus on the other side of the dingo fence has also been confirmed in a more thorough survey.[16] No longer can the high numbers of kangaroos in Sturt National Park be considered a natural event. The early settlers obliterated Aborigines and dingoes, the two main predators of the red kangaroo, and they also provided extra water for the kangaroos to drink.

To its great credit, the inquiry did not ignore this difficult issue of nature conservation and sound land use management. It even went so far as to recommend that the dingo fence be realigned to run south of Sturt National Park, thereby allowing dingoes in and avoiding the difficult terrain along the borderline. How to pay for the new route was altogether another issue and one that the state government did not feel comfortable with. Alas, there has been no move to put this recommendation into effect and it is certain to lapse for want of funding.

The greatest problem facing the border dingo fences is money. The high cost of wages, plant and materials will always compromise the fence and make sheep protection an expensive business. It has to be said that most of the cost is borne by the Western Division pastoralists through the Wild Dog Rate, a levy set at 1.85 cents per hectare in 1983. However, some pastoralists feel that a uniform rate across all Western Division lands is inequitable and that those adjoining the fence should pay more as they need the protection. This hardly seems fair since those further inside the fence get the added benefit of the adjoining pastoralists controlling dingoes that happen to get through. Equity in dingo control is as controversial as any other issue involving this animal and conflicts arise even among those whose interests would seem to coincide.

Every taxpayer in New South Wales also has a small investment in the dingo fence. The state government contributes about $100,000 to its maintenance each year and this may be bolstered by a special grant from time to time such as the National Disasters Flood Relief Grant of $200,000 given after the 1974 floods. The 1984 inquiry into the Western Division was critical of the amount spent by the Wild Dog Destruction Board on maintenance, saying that it spent $300 per kilometre each year whereas South Australia could do it for $130. It did not, however, point out that the maintenance of the South Australian dog fence was carried out by the adjoining landowners on a subsidy that hardly covered the full cost of maintenance.

The border dingo fences have had a precarious existence and have remained in good condition only for relatively short periods. The longest time they have remained dingo-proof has been the 30 years since the establishment of the current board. Modern plant and equipment, improved fencing technology and materials, all moderate the impact of the environment and will help ensure that the Corner Country dingo fence will not be as difficult to maintain as in the past. There are, however, two enemies of more recent origin — the high cost of materials and labour. Maintaining and rebuilding old sections of the fence is very expensive and should the widespread use of 1080 reduce the number of dingoes to a degree where the fence is seen as no longer necessary, it could easily be abandoned to be greedily consumed by sand dunes and floodwaters with only a post here and there and some rusty wire as a tribute to determined people, and to the dingo.

To the Gulf and back

Queensland also created obstacles for the dingo. *The Marsupials Destruction Act of* 1881 established Marsupial Boards and Districts enabling local representatives to levy landholders, thus raising funds to pay for bounties on the wide variety of native and introduced animals that were regarded as enemies of Queensland's two great industries — wool and beef. As the name of the Act implies, kangaroos and wallabies were seen as the main offenders. But to correct what some saw as a dreadful oversight, the Act was amended in 1885 to ensure that the dingo came within its ambit. A dead dingo then became worth five shillings. Only another two years passed before the Act was amended once again to allow the Marsupial Boards to also turn their efforts against the rabbit.

The extra responsibility of rabbit control was too great a burden for the Marsupial Boards, and *The Rabbit Boards Act of* 1891 established Rabbit Boards and Districts whose sole function was to enclose their area with rabbit fences and ensure the destruction of the rabbits therein. This legislation was blessed with the insight that the bounty system was flawed and must not be used in any circumstances for rabbit control. The boards had to ensure that no one got rich by breeding rabbits and harvesting them.

The Marsupial Boards administered the destruction of a wide range of native fauna. Between 1881 and 1918 they paid bounties on almost eight million kangaroos and wallaroos, almost 18 million wallabies, over one million bandicoots, pademelons and kangaroo rats, and over one million dingoes.[1] The exact species are not given in any reports, nor is it likely that a clerk in, say, Thargomindah at the turn of the century would have distinguished between common and rare and endangered species. How many of the then common species are now extinct or endangered as a result of the Marsupial Boards is another issue.

In 1918 the Marsupial Boards were renamed Dingo Boards and they administered Dingo Districts under the provisions of *The Dingo and Marsupials Destruction Act* of that year. Bounties were still paid on a variety of kangaroos and wallabies as well as foxes but the new boards focused on the dingo. The dingo bounty had been fixed at five shillings per head back in 1905 whereas the benign marsupials warranted only a lowly two pennies per head.

Thirty-six Dingo Boards covered Queensland, with not even the remotest corner being exempt. While not bereft of territory, the boards were lacking effective means of carrying out their brief. Not realising the weakness of the bounty system, the legislators amended the Act in 1923 to set the bounty on dingo scalps at 15 shillings. They obviously believed that financial incentive was the key to controlling the dingo and it seemed justified when in the five years between 1925 and 1929 the Dingo Boards paid a bounty on 198,460 dingoes.[1]

Paying a bounty on an endless supply of dingoes in the vast cattle country of south-western Queensland sent the Bulloo Dingo Board bankrupt. So many dingo scalps were being presented that the Bulloo Board could no longer pay the bounty in cash and had to issue vouchers that would be converted to cash as a first priority after the annual rates were collected from stockowners. By 1930 this board was in arrears for 4469 dingoes and 69 foxes.

Other boards fared similarly and also responded by issuing vouchers that could be redeemed for cash at a later date. This spawned an active trade in vouchers that became a form of currency among the townsfolk. The vouchers could be swapped for cash or traded for services but the dogger would have to accept less than they were actually worth. The holder of the voucher would then make a profit when the board was able to pay.

The dependence on the bounty system encouraged widespread abuses that did not go unnoticed by a Royal Commission appointed in 1930 to examine the question of rabbit and dingo control.[2] The Report of the Royal Commission addressed itself to the administration of noxious animal control but its rhetoric may sound similar to political exhortations of today:

> This Inquiry, comparatively limited though it may be, yet illuminates the heavy cost borne by the community in maintaining some governmental and semi-governmental institutions. Such bodies are called into being for some specific purpose: organisations are framed and staffs are appointed. When the circumstances which justified their creation alter, the bodies often

> continue to function, to levy taxation and generally exercise their statutory powers irrespective of any public service rendered. The public, immersed in its own affairs, is indifferent and so the matter runs on.

These good intentions were applied to the Dingo Boards and the dingo bounty. The Royal Commission found that the bounty had encouraged trappers always to leave a core of breeding animals, deliberately to release female dingoes so that they could trap their pups later on, and to breed their own dingoes for the purposes of claiming bounty or bonus. At least doggers weren't short of enterprise and economic strategic planning skills! But the commissioners did not appreciate their talents and found that "Fifty years of Dingo Board administration have left us with as many dogs as ever there were in Queensland's history. It therefore becomes necessary to try methods entirely new".

The Report of this Royal Commission was the first official recognition that different methods of dingo control would be required for different areas. It was a significant step in a chain of events that would eventually lead to the longest individual dingo barrier fence in Australia, and the longest fence in the world. Commenting on the failure of the bounty system, the Report stated:

> The whole matter shows strikingly what a farce it is to attempt to impose a uniform system of dingo administration on every district in Queensland. Cattle and sheep districts, grazing and mixed farming areas, western and coastal lands, dairying and agricultural country—each requires different treatment, and rigid legislation applying to all districts is futile.

The Report also criticised cattle graziers for not meeting their obligations in helping to control the dingo and thus protect the sheep industry, and recommended changes to the administration of dingo control that would force them to show "a little effort and a little consideration for the welfare of the sheep men, and for the general interests of the country".

The most important recommendation made by the Royal Commission was to abolish both the Rabbit Boards and Dingo Boards and replace them with District Improvement Boards. The proposed new boards would also administer stock routes but their main role was to select and apply methods of dingo and rabbit control appropriate to the economy and terrain of the region. In a rallying cry for talented people to serve on the boards, the commissioners invoked that:

> No more honourable or important position in a district will be in the gift of graziers. Election to no other post will confer on a man the opportunity and power of moulding and shaping the development and progress of his particular grazing district to the same extent as his selection on a District Improvement Board. All Districts owe it to themselves, therefore, to elect only experienced, energetic, sound, and honourable men. Will each district rise to the occasion?

The Queensland government acted on the recommendations of the Royal Commission within the year its report was released. *The Grazing Districts Improvement Act of* 1930 replaced all the Dingo Boards and most of the Rabbit Boards with District Improvement Boards. In each district two graziers and a Land Commissioner then set about "moulding and shaping" their area to free it of dingoes. The promise was more than what was realistically possible and within three years yet another Act was passed to hand the boards over to local government shire councils. Then followed a period when there were so many Acts passed relating to dingoes, rabbits and other noxious animals, as well as noxious plants and the control and management of stock routes, that Queenslanders laboured under legislation which few understood.

A decade later, an attempt was made to untangle the ensuing confusion. *The Stock Routes and Rural Lands Protection Act of* 1944 was passed to try to standardise the control of dingoes and other "district improvement" issues which had lapsed as a result of the Second World War. The Act established a coordinating board to ensure that all local authorities carried out their responsibilities in a uniform manner. This Act, with various amendments, is still in operation although since 1978 it has been administered by the Stock Routes and Rural Lands Protection Board.

In its first annual report the new coordinating board emphasised that the only way to stop dingoes eating Queensland's sheep was for existing private dingo fences to be linked up as a "front line of defence".[3] The military terminology reflects the attitude to the enemy dingo. In 1945, only a year after its inception, the board was actively pursuing the concept of fencing in the state's sheep.

The cattlemen were once again regarded as a problem. Dingoes in the cattle country were seen as a threat to the marginal sheeplands. And as each marginal sheep grazier gave up and turned to cattle the threat became greater to those on the best sheep country of western Queensland. To the sheep people, the managers of the vast cattle runs were in partnership with the dingo. The only form of dingo control on these runs was often that undertaken by stationhands to augment their wages. Elsewhere, the country was so remote and inaccessible that it was difficult enough to get there for an annual cattle muster let alone to trap dingoes. The cattle people accepted the loss of a certain proportion of their calves as a normal part of management. That proportion was small enough not to put dingo control high among the priorities competing for scarce labour and resources.

By 1948 the board reported on "the dingo menace" and proposed that a dingo fence should be constructed along the external boundaries of the sheep areas of the state that would enclose an area 350 km wide, running from the New South Wales border to the Cloncurry River in the Gulf Country. The board argued that the Commonwealth government ought rightly to pay for this fence out of the Wool Industry

Fund. The Queensland cabinet agreed with both the proposed fence and the novel source of funding. However, the Commonwealth government refused to allocate any funds, saying that this was a state matter.

The proposed fence was welcomed by the United Graziers Association and the Local Authorities Association and, since there was no other source of funds, they agreed that the fence should be paid for by both the state government and the landowners whose properties were protected, as prevailed in New South Wales and South Australia. By the formula that was soon approved, the government paid for all materials and also agreed to fence some of the more difficult sections, such as near major rivers and floodways, and to employ inspectors to issue notices for maintenance and repair on tardy or recalcitrant landowners. If that landowner still refused to co-operate, the board was empowered to undertake the work and recover the cost through the courts.

The landowners whose property the fence traversed or bounded were obliged to build and maintain the fence with a subsidy of £8 per annum for every 1.6 km of fence. This subsidy had only risen to $20 per km by 1976. The greater proportion of this maintenance fee was obtained by levying a rate on all stock owners within the fence according to the number of head they ran. The rate could be varied according to the needs of the different local government areas but the minimum rate was 0.0014 cents per animal and the maximum was 1.25 cents. The only shire to charge the maximum rate was Boulia in the south-west.[3]

The completed fence was 5680 km long and enclosed over 16 million sheep and 640,000 cattle. It included some of the best sheep rangelands in Australia but to achieve all this it had to cross barriers such as endless mulga scrub, rocky ranges and blacksoil plains that became slippery bogs during the wet. Of course, some forbidding country could be avoided because the fence did not have to follow a rigid line such as a state border, and it was designed to take advantage of existing dingo fences wherever possible. But rivers had to be crossed and major roads intersected where special gates or dingo-proof grids had to be installed. There were even dingo grids across railway lines.

The first fencing materials landed on far-flung outback properties soon after *The Barrier Fences Act of* 1954 was passed and the area it encompassed was proclaimed a Vermin District so that the necessary rates could be levied and collected by local government authorities. The route of the fence was varied here and there after consultation with landowners. Some who were left outside the fence requested to be included and this was done where possible.

Some could foresee the problems that would eventually emerge because the barrier fence had to be maintained by so many different landowners with varying levels of commitment. One cattleman urged his fellow beef producers to do their share in maintaining the fence where it went through their country.[4] He believed that dingoes did cost the cattle industry a lot of money and that it was foolish to regard it as a pest only to sheep. He did not share the fence administrator's faith in individual responsibility for fence maintenance: "But will these be enforced? Past experience says, No. Perhaps the government is right, and there is wisdom in the multitude of owners. However, I believe the adage about cooks could well be applied here."

Another grazier whose pastoral company in the Longreach area owned 144 km of the dingo barrier fence saw the cattlemen as the weakest link in the chain.[5] He listed them along with the brumbies, rogue cattle, kangaroos, emus, pigs, foxes and goannas as the enemies of the fence. Apparently, goannas would burrow under the fence and dingoes would enlarge the hole after them. Cattlemen, with no overriding need to maintain the fence, could not be relied upon to carry out the weekly inspection that this grazier believed was essential to keep the fence in order in the face of nature's battery.

Despite some cynicism, almost all the fence had been completed by 1959. Six inspectors were stationed around the fence and their initial reports on the landowners' attitude towards maintenance were optimistic. However, the board's annual report for 1959 finishes on a foreboding note:

> . . . apathy has been displayed by a few landholders towards the maintenance of their fences and either they have not carried out their maintenance obligations in a satisfactory manner or have only done so under pressure. These few cases are being watched closely, and unless these landholders face up to their responsibility, the Co-ordinating Board will have no alternative than to cause the fences to be maintained at the cost of the landholders.

They were not watched closely enough, nor was the law employed to make landowners maintain the fence. Although it was completed by September 1963, the fence quickly deteriorated and the dingo remained an enemy of the wool industry.

The dingo and the fence received sufficient attention to place them among the priorities of yet another investigation. In 1975 the Queensland government saw fit to hold an inquiry into the pests that plagued its agricultural ambitions.[3] This inquiry showed that the fence was too long, that it could not be maintained and that its route had incorporated too many existing fences that were near the end of their life. Queensland had a dingo fence that was falling apart less than ten years after its completion. Moreover, the inquiry reported that there were as many dingoes inside the fence as there were on the outside.

By this time, the poison 1080 had come into use and landholders were using it on dingoes to great effect, both inside and outside the fence. The inquiry suggested that had this poison been available in 1954, the fence would never have been built. It also appears that the fence inspectors had abandoned the fence as their major project and were now almost fully engaged in mixing 1080 on behalf of landowners well inside, and well outside, the fence.

1080 or the fence? This would become one of the most controversial issues ever raised concerning the Queensland dingo barrier fence. It took a couple of years for this controversy to emerge because, as a result of the inquiry's recommendations, the future of the fence was left in the hands of a restructured board. This was the Stock Routes and Rural Lands Protection Board, constituted as the single pest control authority in the state.

The inquiry had concluded that the larger proportion of the fence was in good enough condition to be regarded as a valuable asset that would be very expensive to replace. It also recommended that, until the new board had assessed the situation, all funds paid to landholders for maintaining the fence should be stopped and instead be paid into a general account used to get the inspectors back on the fence as a full-time occupation. It was felt that the landowners should maintain the fence at their own cost and at best receive some materials free of charge, at the inspector's discretion.

The new board assessed the condition of the fence and concluded that repairing it and bringing it up to a standard that was worthy of maintenance would cost at least $4 million. And there was still the problem of who would pay for the maintenance. While wrestling with these financial and practical issues, the board was under considerable pressure from the south-western sheepbreeders who wanted the fence to be rehabilitated. Elsewhere in the state it was firmly believed that 1080 could bring about the same result at far less cost.

In responding to the increasing pressure from sections of the south-western Queensland sheep industry to restore the fence, the board took the stance that the old system of placing the burden of maintenance upon landowners was a failure and should not be contemplated in any future dingo fence. Various means were suggested to overcome this problem. For example, the Warrego Graziers Association wanted a much-shortened fence only going around Tambo, Murweh and Booringa shires. This association wanted the landholders to bring the existing fence up to working condition and construct any new sections. Thereafter, all maintenance should be carried out and paid for by the board from funds raised from a levy as high as 8.7 cents per sheep. This prompted the board to investigate the possibility of restoring most of the 5635-km existing fence on the same basis but an estimate of the annual cost of maintenance came to around $1 million, which would require a levy of 10 cents per sheep.

On 12 June 1980 the board reached a compromise between the voices for and against restoration of the fence. This policy was for the dingo fence north of the 23rd parallel to be abandoned and "a concentrated vermin control campaign" carried out in this area. However, the sheep country south of the 23rd parallel would be enclosed by using the existing fence and constructing a new fence from east to west. Any restoration and construction was to be carried out by the landholders with all future maintenance the responsibility of the board, financed by both a levy on stock and an annual state government contribution.[6] Once again, the landholders against the inside of the fence were singled out to bear a greater burden by the imposition of a higher levy on them than on other landowners inside the fence.

There was enough controversy about this proposal for the Minister for Lands and Forests to instruct the board to re-examine its policy. In a good exercise of public participation, the board sent a copy of its policy to the major rural industry groups and the Local Government Association of Queensland, asking them to comment on it. The Cattleman's Union responded by saying that the dingo fence was of no concern to them and if the sheepmen wanted it then they should pay for it themselves. The United Graziers Association wanted the state government to pay for the entire restoration of any new fence and said that it should also be maintained by the board from funds raised by a levy on stock. The Queensland Graingrowers Association was inclined to leave the matter in the hands of the board. The Local Government Association said that it was really up to the rural industry groups to sort it out among themselves. Faced with these conflicting viewpoints, the board concluded that it was in a no-win situation but would nevertheless come up with another proposal for a dingo barrier fence in Queensland.

The debate about the future of the fence was embellished by argument in the letters columns of both the rural and urban media. Bill McCormack, a member of the executive of the Maranoa Graziers Association wrote to the editor of the *Queensland Country Life*, saying: "The old fence did not stop dingoes and especially did not stop pigs and kangaroos making holes in it. Yet, we are about to embark on a new, massively expensive exercise with no change in the fence concept."

The voices of dissent from those cattlemen who would either border the fence in the east, or be trapped just inside it and have to help pay for it, may have influenced the route chosen for the fence but they could not change the notion that the only way to protect the sheep was to put a dingo fence around them. The next proposal put to the Minister for Lands and Forestry, Mr W. H. Glasson, at an extraordinary meeting of the board on 13 March 1981 was accepted.

The future dingo barrier fence would be 2800 kilometres long — half the length of the original fence — and it would attempt to keep dingoes out of the major sheepbelt only. It would embrace seven million sheep, instead of the former 16 million, and about one and a half million cattle. The state government would contribute up to a third of the annual maintenance cost, the remainder being raised by a levy on stock inside the fence.

The government would also contribute towards constructing the 732 km fence running east to west across what had become known as "the gap" as well as fencing any new sections that had to be realigned, such as a section around the Bulloo, or where the landholder faced genuine hardship. Elsewhere the landholders were to repair the existing fence. It was emphasised that once the fence was in place, all maintenance would be carried out by board staff but provision was made for shire councils or groups of landholders to take on this task as contractors to the board. Effective management was seen as the key to the success of the new fence.

It looked as if the entire plan would founder on the rocky shoals of a Cabinet that could not be convinced of the value of the fence. Memories of the failure of the former fence also haunted the new proposal. The Queensland Cabinet decided in favour of abandoning the fence entirely and making 1080 poison the mainstay of dingo control.

The eruption that followed this decision sent shock waves as far as the Sydney press. On Tuesday 24 November 1981 the *Sydney Morning Herald* ran an article under the heading "Baiting Replaces Dingo Fence". The article described how the Queensland Cabinet faced a rural revolt over its decision to abandon the fence. Many conservation groups also felt that the decision left the way open for Queensland to be saturated with 1080.

The threat of a rural revolt and some intense lobbying in favour of the fence managed to change the vote within Cabinet. On 20 July 1982 the Deputy Premier and State Treasurer, Dr Llew Edwards, and the Minister for Lands, Mr Bill Glasson, released a media statement saying that the Queensland government would spend $2.7 million over the next three years to rebuild and realign the dingo fence. The length of the fence would be 2800 kilometres. The cost of maintenance would be met by the state government and all landowners inside the fence who would be levied at a rate of five cents per head of livestock, to be collected by the relevant shire council. There was provision for some shires to undertake the maintenance of the fence themselves and so avoid the collection of an extra rate.

Work on the fence began the same year. The overseer, or "key man" as he had been described by the board, chosen for the job was Ron McCullagh, otherwise known as "Rocky" because his ability with his fists was likened to Rocky Marciano. I travelled a long section of the fence in the Thargomindah area with Ron during 1984 when it was almost completed. He was inspecting the work being done by contractors and his absolute commitment to the success of the fence was respected as much as his formidable reputation.

The fence was completed in 1985. There are still disputes about its effectiveness and whether or not this fence will go the way of its predecessor.[7] The critics, like Rod Henzell, president of the Maranoa Graziers Association in 1985, said that it was impossible to stop dingoes getting through the fence and impossible to eradicate all those inside the fence when it was completed. Then there are supporters such as Errol Brumpton, owner of one of the largest

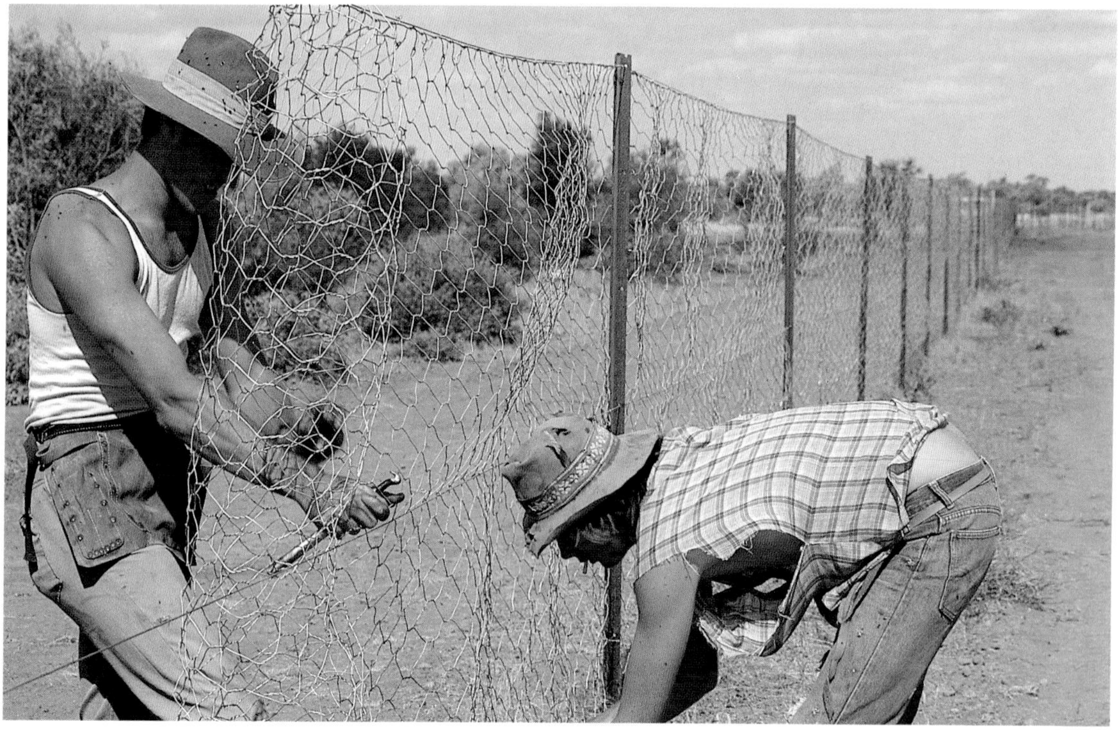

sheep studs in Queensland, who believes that the success of the sheep industry in Australia can be attributed to the barrier fences. It was probably the strong voice of the established sheep men and women that got the fence back in working order. Albeit a shortened fence, it nevertheless protects seven million sheep which represents a lot of voters — no disrespectful comparison between voters and sheep intended.

Both New South Wales and South Australia have kept extensive dingo fences in good working order for a long time now and this more manageable Queensland fence should fare no differently. The universal threat to all the fences is the cost of maintenance. Should the number of dingoes and wild dogs be diminished in the future through years of consistent poisoning then perhaps this fence could be neglected again and go the way of its giant parent. For the moment the fence is new, in good shape, and there is plenty of optimism about its future on the part of the board that manages it.

Top: *A section of the old Queensland Barrier Fence near Thargomindah, which has recently been repaired, and is now patrolled by inspectors with all the modern equipment necessary to maintain it.* *Gary Steer*

Bottom: *Parts of the old fence were beyond repair, so other sections were realigned to make the new, shortened Queensland Barrier Fence. The last sections were built as recently as 1985, when this photograph was taken near Thargomindah.* *Roland Breckwoldt*

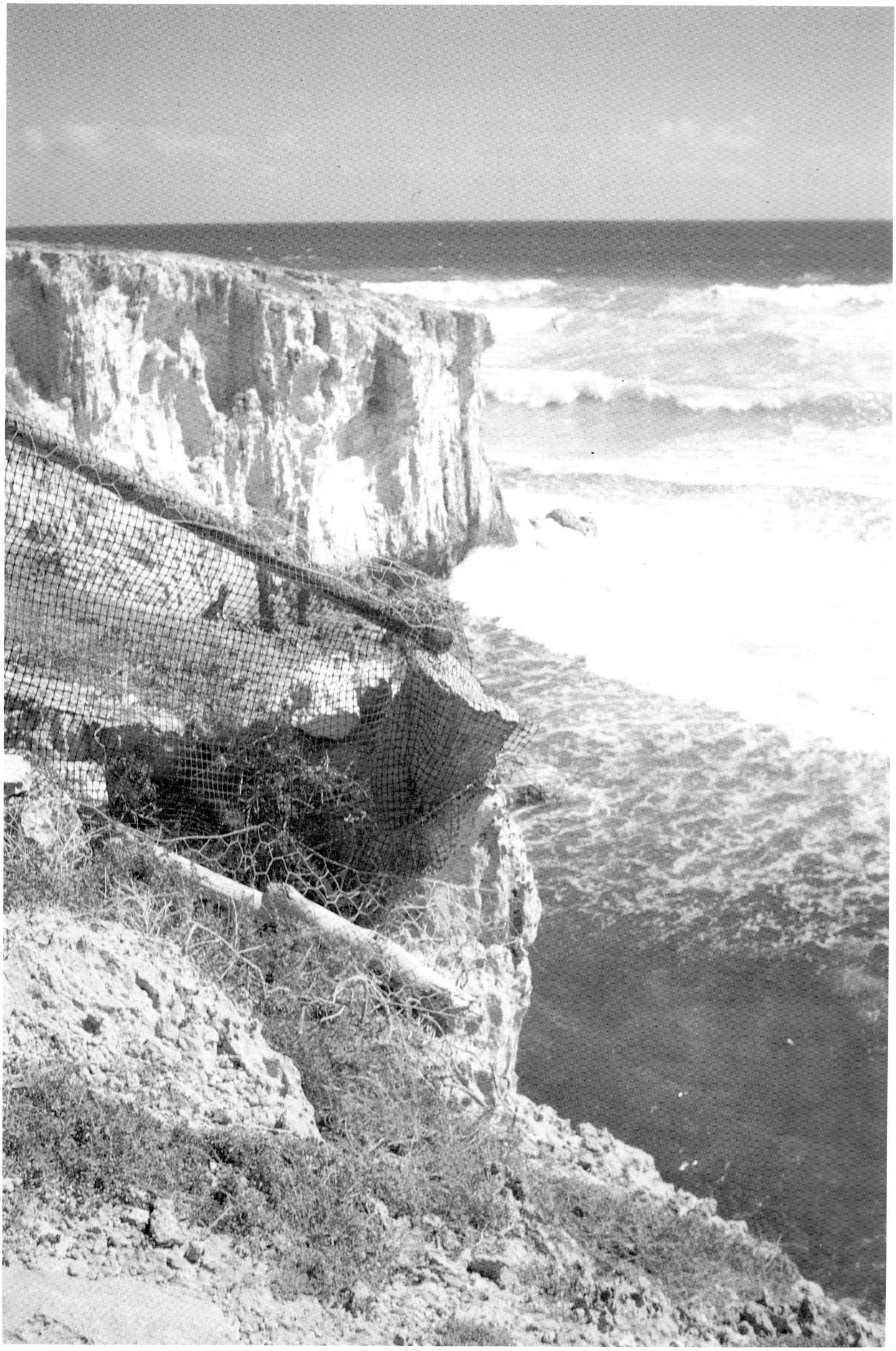

From border to Bight

A glance at the map showing the South Australian dog fence, as it is called, reveals that the dingo is now denied about one-third of that state and all the sheep that graze there. The history of the fence can be traced right back to the early days of South Australia when it was a colonial province. A local Dog Act was passed in 1852 in order "to abate the Nuisance and Damage to Property occasioned by the Great Number of Dogs which are loose in the Province of South Australia".[1] The bounty on dingo scalps was set at seven shillings and sixpence whereas the bounty on unregistered domestic dogs was only two shillings and sixpence. The dingo bounty was incredibly high and therefore it could make being a dogger a very lucrative occupation.

The South Australian dog fence meets the cold waters of the Southern Ocean at the Great Australian Bright.
Kathleen Fourie

As pastoralism spread north, shepherds were employed to guard the flocks against the Aborigines, dingoes and the lack of fences. However, the greatest enemy came from within. The early settlers misjudged the carrying capacity of the arid lands. At first they could coast on the abundance of feed available on land that had never before felt the imprint of a cloven hoof. Then they had a run of good seasons. But overstocking and a crippling drought in the 1880s put an end to closer settlement. The holdings were amalgamated into large pastoral runs and the shepherds were gradually replaced by fences.[2]

Those early fences were designed only to restrain wandering sheep and not to exclude dingoes, so the absence of shepherds introduced a phase in the pastoral history of South Australia when the dingo had a feast. The result was that many pastoralists abandoned sheep and turned to cattle. Other leases were simply abandoned due to the combination of dingoes and drought.

Some of the more affluent and innovative pastoralists started building dingo-proof fences. At first these were only around individual paddocks where particularly vulnerable stock such as lambing ewes could be run when they needed the most protection. Gradually more and more land was being fenced out of reach of the dingo.

The bounty on feral dogs and dingoes was made equal in 1882 and two years later Vermin Boards were established to collect scalps and pay bounties. A bounty was also paid on other species of wildlife that were declared vermin. A wedge-tailed eagle brought one shilling, kangaroos paid sixpence, wallabies (including the now extinct toolache wallaby) brought fourpence, and rabbits were worth tuppence each. Ironically, neither the wedge-tailed eagle nor the dingo was protected by the law of the time which forbade the destruction of any creature that preyed on the rabbit.

All these bounties cost a fortune to pay. Between 1880 and 1889 the bounty payments just on rabbits amounted to £300,000. In 1885, 3800 dingoes were killed on Paratoo Station alone.[1] The cost of the bounty system and its failure to reduce the incidence of complaints about damage caused by vermin, particularly rabbits and dingoes, was voiced during the parliamentary debate over the Wild Dog Destruction Bill, 1889. This criticism and the exorbitant cost of the system led directly to the Fences Act, 1892. This Act included a provision that enabled the Commissioner of Crown Lands to declare an area rabbit-infested so that when a landholder erected a rabbit-proof boundary fence the neighbour was obliged to pay half the cost.

Although these first official fencing programs dealt with the rabbit, it was not long before the idea of separating dingoes from sheep was promoted and a Royal Commission was appointed in 1892 to examine the value of barrier fences in vermin control. It found that a great area of potential sheep country in the north of the colony was running cattle because of the dingo, and that many former sheep runs had been abandoned.

Governments appear to have adopted the recommendations of their Royal Commissions in those days, and this was no exception. A Vermin Districts Act was in force by the end of 1894. This allowed an area to be proclaimed a Vermin-Proofed District if over half the landowners gave their consent. The district was then administered by a board elected by landholders and a government representative. They received fencing materials to erect rabbit- and dingo-proof fences on concessional loans. Landholders outside Vermin Districts could gain access to these loans if six or more of them with a combined area of over one hundred acres were prepared to form a Wire Netting Trust.

The scheme to erect barrier fences to fight rabbits and dingoes under the Vermin Districts Act received a boost with the support given to it in the findings of a Royal Commission into the decline of the pastoral industry which were handed down in 1898. By the turn of the century a Vermin Branch was established in the Crown Lands Department to cope with the increasing demand for cheap loans to build netting fences.

By 1907 there were 30 Vermin Districts throughout South Australia, building and maintaining thousands of kilometres of rabbit- and dingo-proof fencing. The Vermin Boards had become a force in local affairs and flexed their muscles in sending representatives to Adelaide to form a statewide Vermin Districts Association. It was established to promote the interests of landholders within Vermin Districts and one of its activities was to lobby for a change in the Vermin Act to secure better control of dingoes. Consequently, a separate Wild Dogs Act was passed in 1912 which set a differential rating system for fenced and unfenced land. The dog rate of three pennies per square mile for fenced land as against six pennies for unfenced country was designed to encourage landholders to put up dog fences.

This they did and by 1931 there were 34,154 miles of dog fence and 56 proclaimed Vermin Districts in South Australia. Some years earlier, in 1922, the Vermin Districts Association had put forward the idea that many thousands of miles of fencing could be saved if there was just one fence that ran from the New South Wales border across the Nullarbor to the waters of the Great Australian Bight.

Such a fence would pose a barrier to dingoes coming south from the northern cattle country and it would render obsolete all the thousands of miles of private dingo fences within the area and save those fortunate landholders a great deal of time and money. The proposal had merit because dingoes were becoming very scarce in the southern parts of the state. The problem was that the cost of linking up the existing outer fences to form a continuous barrier was estimated to be £100,000 and this was too much for the government of the day.

The number of dingoes within the fenced Vermin Districts of the southern sheep country continued to decline. This was open country, heavily settled in the better regions, where persistent dingo control in concert with all the fences could really make an impact. As a result, the inside fences began to fall into disrepair. Quite unlike the Queensland situation, where the first fence was abandoned largely out of a sense of hopelessness, the lacework of fences inside South Australia fell by the wayside partly because there were no dingoes left.

The decline in wool prices in the 1930s forced the sheep farmers to stop spending on anything but basic necessities. Many who may have wanted to maintain their dingo fences found it difficult to do so and several Vermin Districts were not held to any interest payments for up to three years during this decade.[3]

Those who wanted to run sheep in the north of the state still had to maintain their fences and so it became recognised that they now carried the burden of protecting the sheep belonging to all the farmers further south. The first organisation to take up the cause of the outer landholders was the Stockowners Association, which in 1938 suggested that these people should receive financial assistance. The Vermin Districts Association took up the cause and pressed for low-interest loans for the outer landholders and suggested that additional funds for maintenance should be raised by a tax on all protected lands. The Pastoral Board of the Lands Department proposed that the great number of Vermin Districts be reduced so that the state was divided into seven such districts based on existing fences.

Eventually, the Vermin Districts Association succeeded in getting the government to appoint a committee to inquire into the feasibility of a single outside buffer fence. The membership of the committee reflected the influence of private landholders in the management of dog fences in South Australia. It included delegates from the Vermin Districts Association, the Stockowners Association and the Stock Salesmans Association. The Surveyor General represented the state government.[3]

The recommendations made by this committee resulted in the Dog Fence Act, 1946 which provided for a continuous dog fence across South Australia. The Act also established a Dog Fence Board with a chairman drawn from the Pastoral Board and two members nominated by the Stockowners Association and another nominated by the Vermin Districts Association.

The membership of the Dog Fence Board that controls the fence to this day reflects the high degree of private pastoralist involvement. Indeed, the fence itself is part of the pastoral lease and the pastoralist on the inside of the fence is legally obliged to maintain it in dog-proof condition. Failure to do so can result in the board undertaking the work and then recovering the full cost from the pastoralist concerned.

The Vermin Districts and the thousands of miles of dog fence that went with them were abandoned for the outer fence which was proclaimed in the *Government Gazette* on 3 July 1947. Some of the Vermin District Boards continued to operate and they were not officially abolished until 1975. The Vermin Districts Association continues as a forum for concerned pastoralists to protect their interests in the management of the dog fence, but it has no regulatory powers.

There are now 800 lessees of pastoral land within the South Australian dog fence and each must pay an annual dog rate of 61 cents per square kilometre of land they lease as a pastoral holding. An upper limit of $1 per square kilometre was set by an amendment to the Dog Fences Act in 1982. The amount raised through this levy was $124,000 in 1983–84, for which there is a dollar-for-dollar subsidy from the state government, bringing the total operating funds for that year to $248,000. Of this amount, 94 per cent went straight back to the fence owners as a subsidy of $105 for every kilometre of fence they maintain.[2,3]

Only 30 pastoralists own the 2230 km of dog fence. At least ten of them own and maintain over 100 kilometres of fence each. The longest stretch of the fence owned and maintained by a single lessee is an incredible 191 km.[1] For this onerous responsibility that lessee would receive only $20,000 per annum, just about enough to pay the wages and support a full-time boundary rider. It would certainly not cover the cost of materials for maintenance or rebuilding old sections of the fence. The average length of fence owned is 74 km and it is the smaller properties that are most disadvantaged because they are less able to pay wages for boundary riders and buy materials for maintenance.

Not all sheep country in South Australia is held as pastoral lease. There are many sheepfarmers in South Australia who farm in the higher rainfall areas outside the Pastoral Zone and benefit from the dog fence without paying anything for it. However, they could argue that it is extremely unlikely that dingoes would now be a problem in the more settled areas of the state.

The pastoralists who have had the responsibility of maintaining the dog fence forced upon them by legislation are inclined to the view that the financial arrangements are inequitable. Their cause is taken up from time to time by people such as Bert Kelly, "the modest farmer", who wrote a column in the *Bulletin* for many years. Kelly aired their concerns to a national readership and even felt that the cattlemen outside the fence to the north received some benefit from it by impeding the movement of dingoes and that they too should contribute to the cost of its maintenance.[4]

The cost of erecting just 1 km of 152-cm-high dingo-proof wire netting fence is currently about $5000. Much of the South Australian dog fence is now old and needs renewal and neither pastoralist nor state government is able or willing to spend this amount of money on fencing out the dingo.

Electric fencing is one way of providing a much cheaper dog fence and it has the added advantage of withstanding the hairy-nosed wombat (*Vombatus hirsutus*) which damages the old netting fences around the edge of the Nullarbor Plain. Already two sections of the fence are electrified. One section consists of a 90 km special wombat fence near Fowlers Bay that has four wires and reaches a height of only 46 cm. It is designed to protect the main netting fence from the pushy wombat.

Elsewhere, electric fencing has been erected specifically for dingo control and replaces the old netting fence. Over 266 km of the dog fence is now a seven-wire electric fence. The arid environment helps ensure that vegetation does not grow rapidly against the fence and cause power leakages. The flat topography also makes it easier to get even wire spacings without having to use too many extra posts. Provided an efficient earthing system is used to overcome the dry soils, this environment is ideal for electric fencing. It will be interesting to monitor the development of electric fencing and see if it completely replaces wire netting on the dog fence. Either way, there remains an effective barrier to the dingo extending from the dry western border of New South Wales to the cold waters of the Great Australian Bight.

Roland Breckwoldt

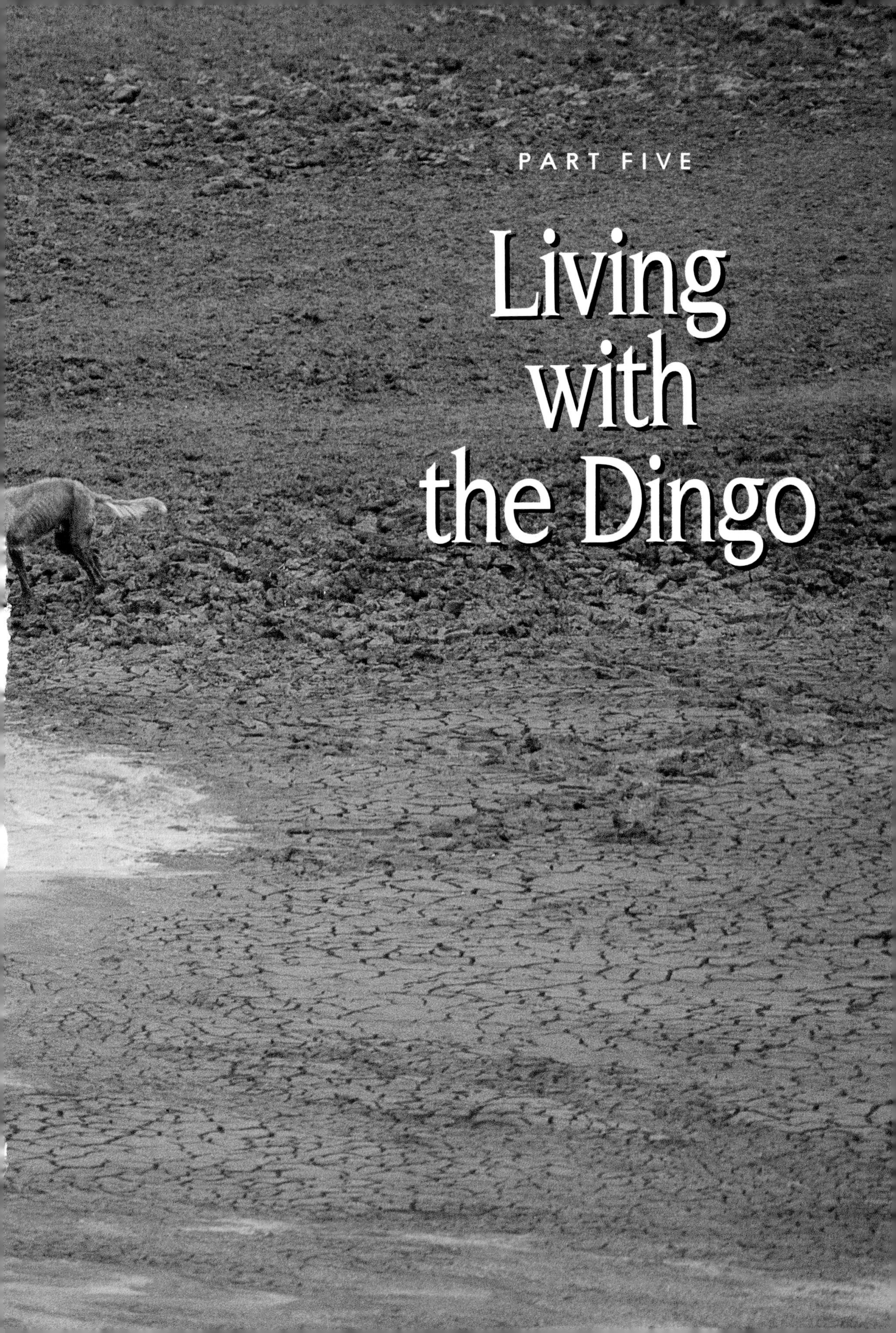

PART FIVE

Living with the Dingo

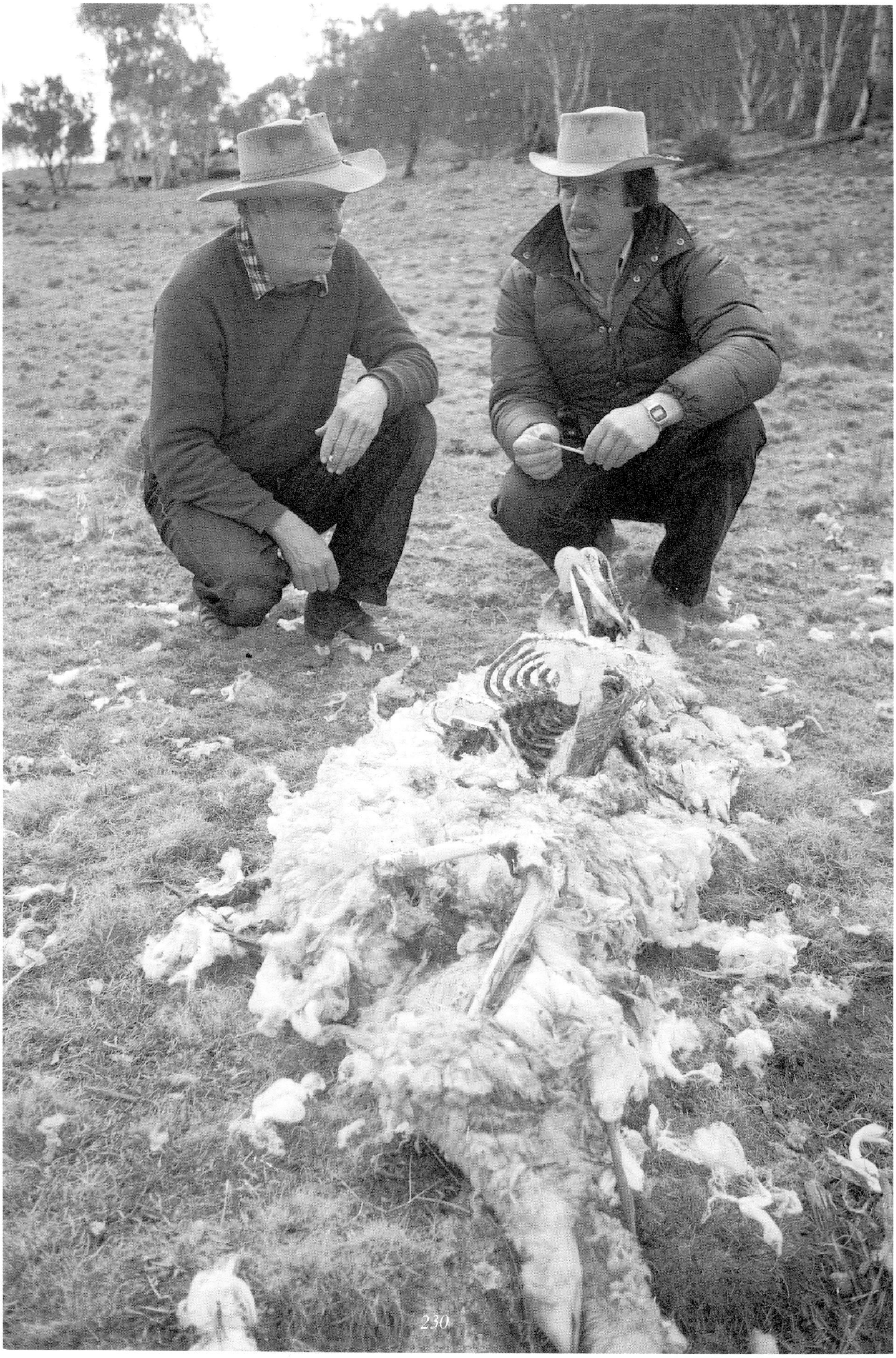

Dingoes, sheep and cattle

Few Australian animals have been caught up in the European settlement of Australia quite like the dingo. Some native animals quietly take whatever space we are now prepared to set aside for them. Others have slipped even more quietly into extinction. The dingo bites back to remind us that there are conflicts to resolve between what we demand from the environment and what we have to compromise to accommodate its wild plants and animals.

The vast majority of Australians live in towns and cities far removed from the haunts of the dingo and only a small proportion of all farmers and pastoralists now experience dingo problems. The dingo touches few people directly and it becomes easy to see the "dingo problem" in simplistic terms. People ask whether you are for the dingo or against it, as if the dingo were either all good or all bad. However, labels of good and bad are useless in dealing with the dingo — good for one can be evil for another. The time, the place, the perspective of the observer all bear weight on attitudes to the dingo.

THE SHEEP INDUSTRY

It is hard to imagine anyone in Australia who does not gain some benefit from the wool industry. It is not necessary to eat lamb or mutton, wear wool or sleep beneath woollen blankets to benefit from the sheep. The advantages can be more indirect through the export income earned by the wool industry and

On the right is Rick Haine of Moles Station, near Kybean, New South Wales, who is showing John Coman, the dingo trapper based at nearby Delegate, one of the 70 sheep killed by dingoes and/or feral dogs in one night during a long period of 'dog troubles' in 1985 and 1986. Roland Breckwoldt

this involves all Australians in the management of the dingo.

Because there are now fewer dingoes in the sheep lands, there is a tendency to dismiss claims that dingoes kill sheep. Farmers are said to use the dingo as a scapegoat for poor management such as overstocking or as an excuse for any dead sheep found in a paddock. There is also an understandable tendency to attribute sheep killing to feral domestic dogs rather than to dingoes. Furthermore, farmers troubled by wild dogs, be they dingoes, feral dogs or hybrids, have been quick to seize the political advantages of labelling them all as feral dogs and must share the blame if sections of the community now take the view that the pure dingo is much maligned and would never harm a sheep.

The history of the sheep industry shows that dingoes killed sheep long before there was any reduction in its native game through land clearance and closer settlement. Dingoes did kill sheep in the past and there are plenty of remote sheep lands in Australia that are still exposed to pure dingoes. A long-term study in the Fortescue River area of northern Western Australia included research into the behaviour of dingoes on sheep country at Mardie Station, 490 km north of Carnarvon.[1]

A total of 48 dingoes were studied, 26 of which were fitted with radio collars so that they could be closely observed. Intensive monitoring of those wearing the collars showed that 22 out of the 26 were involved in killing or injuring sheep over a two-year period. The study showed that if dingoes were exposed to sheep over a prolonged period they would invariably start attacking them. Many individual dingoes had to be destroyed before the study was completed because they caused too much damage. The only notable exception was one dingo that was implicated in harassing sheep only once over a one-year period.

Not all sheep attacked by dingoes are killed immediately. Some will recover from their wounds, but others, such as this sheep attacked in 1977 at Lake Stewart, Tibooburra, by dingoes that had broached the Border Dog Fence in 1974, will die. Stan Hotchin

The Mardie Station study also confirmed what every sheep person knows — that dingoes will kill sheep well in excess of their food requirements. Of the 166 sheep killed by dingoes, 39 per cent were not eaten at all. Another 25 per cent of the sheep carcases had less than half a kilogram eaten, while only 34 per cent had more than this amount consumed. One pair of dingoes killed five sheep in one night. Sheep people often assert that if dingoes only killed sheep to eat then they would not be a major problem.

While the dingoes in this study readily killed sheep, and sheep were more easily killed than native game, they still preferred to eat kangaroo and euro (*Macropus robustus*). This finding is consistent with the historical record showing that it is not necessarily a reduction in native prey that makes dingoes attack sheep.

It was not the old, weak or diseased sheep that fell prey to dingoes. The sheep killed had all been strong and healthy and it may well be that a strong and fast sheep helps to provoke a dingo into attacking it. Weak sheep could easily fall over or refuse to run but a mob of panicky sheep seems to incite dingoes into attacking so that some are killed immediately and others die from wounds they receive as dingoes move from one sheep to another. Many farmers also report heavy losses when sheep mill into the corner of a paddock and smother when they are panicked by dingoes.

A survey of 212 graziers who belonged to a dingo or wild dog control association on the New England Tableland in 1963 revealed that a total of 4132 sheep had been killed by dingoes in the previous year.[2] This loss represented only 1.33 per cent of their sheep and about 19 head per property. The fact that graziers themselves reported such a small proportion of sheep killed should help allay fears that they exaggerate losses attributed to dingoes. However, the number of sheep killed was kept so low partly because these graziers spent an average of 39.3 days each year on dingo control.

A more recent survey that examined the losses suffered by members of wild dog control associations in the same region shows that the level of predation has decreased slightly to about 14 sheep per property per year but the number of days spent on dingo and wild dog control has been reduced by two-thirds.[3] The reason for the decline in the amount of labour spent on control is believed to be the increased use of 1080 poison since the 1963 survey. Labour-intensive methods of dingo control such as organised dingo drives are now rarely used

The former Southern Tablelands Wild Dog Control Board, which was based at Cooma on the Monaro Tableland of New South Wales, reported that sheep losses were increasing and had reached a new peak of 4683 sheep in 1983.[4] The Pastures Protection Boards that made up this particular Wild Dog Control Board were responsible for over six million sheep. This means that the number of sheep killed by dingoes and wild dogs in that year, when the board was making vociferous representations for a continuation of aerial baiting in national parks, was only 0.078 per cent of the area's total sheep population. This tiny proportion, coming from the graziers' own reports, also shows that they do not exaggerate losses simply to condemn the dingo. Other surveys confirm that the overall loss of sheep to dingoes is small with the current level of control.[5]

Landholders in eastern Victoria calculated the total annual loss of livestock in the region to be worth $480,000 at 1986 values. A further $380,000 was spent by them on wild dog and dingo control. However, the formal stock reporting system established by the Department of Conservation, Forests and Lands had only received reports of stock lost to the value of $60,232 during 1984–85.[6] This may simply indicate that many landholders do not bother to formally report losses. Even so, the figure reported in the direct survey is still not high when measured on an individual property basis and in comparison to the total number of livestock in the region.

The number of sheep killed by dingoes each year in Australia is only a small proportion of the total sheep population. However, one reason the number of sheep killed is low is because of the amount of dingo control that is exercised. Furthermore, even though only a very small proportion of the total sheep population is being killed at any one time, it is no consolation if most of them are your sheep! A case study of one grazier who was badly affected by wild dogs or dingoes on the New England Tableland revealed that their predation cost him $12,770 during September 1984.[3] Admittedly, the major portion of this was spent on an exclusion fence to prevent further attacks and this was a capital investment that would be of benefit for future protection.

A cost imposed by the dingo on some graziers is the potential income lost by not being able to run sheep in what is otherwise good sheep country. It is difficult to calculate this cost because the land is used for beef production which can be more profitable than sheep in some years but bring a lower return in others. Such graziers argue that the dingo denies a choice of enterprise.

It is interesting to contemplate whether the dingo could also have a hand in keeping up the price of wool. If there were no dingoes, there could be a lot more sheep in Australia. For example, the New South Wales border dingo fence divides sheep from the cattle of northern South Australia yet the country on either side is similar because the fence follows state borders and not environmental zones. Presumably, there could be a lot more sheep in South Australia if it were not for the dingo. A study of the attempts to raise sheep in the Northern Territory may also reveal that it was the dingo that closed this vast area off to the wool industry.

In summary, the following costs to the sheep industry are attributed to the dingo:

- Direct loss of stock and the value of the wool on them.
- Loss of production through harassment by dingoes.
- Cost to individual landholders in carrying out dingo control. This includes labour, fencing materials and money that is tied up in private dingo fences.
- Rates paid to dingo control authorities such as those that maintain the barrier fences and employ doggers.

• The "opportunity cost" of not being able to run sheep on what is otherwise sheep country.

There is a bone of contention between sheep people and some animal welfare groups about who should take responsibility for cruelty when sheep are attacked by dingoes. It is common for sheep farmers to curse the dingo and wild dog as a cruel and vicious killer that does so for amusement more than necessity. Farmers will show photographs of sheep that would have died slowly and painfully with horrific wounds. However, it is quite logical to argue that it is the farmers who are to blame for cruelty because they knowingly run sheep in country where they are likely to be exposed to attack by dingoes and wild dogs.

Equity in the cost of dingo control also causes conflict wherever dingoes are a problem. Those people with properties adjoining dingo country may control dingoes while others benefit from their efforts. One response is to say that those who choose to run sheep near dingo country do so out of their own free will. Another is that we do not compensate a farmer who has a property with poor soil because that is the nature of the environment and a similar situation applies to dingoes and wild dogs — their presence is part of the cost of production. Both these answers, while possessing a certain logic, overlook the fact that dingoes and wild dogs can move. If a landholder at the front gives up dingo control and changes to cattle then the problem may simply shift on to the next sheep farmer.

There are ways to spread the burden of dingo and wild dog control beyond the parties caught in a feud over dogs that are killing. On the Monaro Tableland, for example, it is quite within the scope of Pasture Protection Boards to establish a dingo and wild dog fund raised from the general rate upon all landholders and used to assist people in trouble spots. This would mean that all landholders would contribute to dingo and wild dog management and ease the tension that often develops in this area between a few sheep graziers and the National Parks and Wildlife Service.

Another method of achieving equity in dingo control is to provide landholders in areas with chronic wild dog or dingo problems with a financial incentive to undertake exclusion fencing. With proper record-keeping and surveys over a period of years it is possible to determine if there is a pattern of livestock predation. In some cases, it might be fairly judged that the weight of responsibility lies with the landholder but in others it might be equitable for a state government to make a direct grant because the wider community requires a different response to dog problems. This type of incentive is being given already when fencing materials and/or labour are provided by governments for electric fencing in areas adjoining national parks.

Better ways must be found to ensure that dingoes and sheep do not mix. An open acknowledgement that dingoes will kill sheep is by no means sealing the fate of the dingo. Indeed, it is the very beginning of its conservation. Before it is possible to develop a management policy for any species it is necessary to have a full understanding of its ecology and relationship to humans.

THE CATTLE INDUSTRY

The beef industry has far more flexibility in its relationship to dingoes and wild dogs than does the sheep industry because cattle have ways of beating them. Killing cattle is harder work for a dingo and it usually takes more than one dingo to do it, except for very young calves. Cattle can defend themselves and their calves with a well-aimed kick or powerful butt.

Cows usually leave the main herd to calve quietly by themselves and the newborn calf is often left alone for long periods while the mother grazes or walks to water. The calf need not necessarily be deliberately hidden but it does receive some protection by lying low, particularly when the herbage is long.

Young calves are vulnerable at this time, particularly if they become separated from their mothers and go looking for them. As the calves grow older they tend to congregate in groups accompanied by one or two cows, often referred to as "nursemaids". These cows are able to give the calves some protection and the bellowing that results from a dingo attack will bring any cattle within earshot running over and frighten the dingoes off. It is this type of behaviour that results in many calves surviving a dingo attack. One survey in a north Queensland herd showed that as many calves were bitten and survived as were killed.[7]

The incidence of dingoes killing in excess of food requirements does not appear to occur with cattle as with sheep. However, young cattle that are suddenly removed from the herd and left alone can be at great risk from heavy dingo attack. I worked on Camboon Station in the central highlands of Queensland in 1962 when dingoes were abundant in the area. The number of calves lost to dingoes could never be estimated and was probably a fairly insignificant proportion of the losses normally associated with extensive pastoral management. Indeed, the greatest loss of production was caused by the cattle tick. Notwithstanding, at weaning time when young cattle between eight and ten months of age were separated from their mothers and put out in the "weaning paddock", there could be heavy losses and considerable carcase damage. Even though weaners are fairly large compared to young calves, the dingoes obviously knew that they were disoriented, unprotected and vulnerable.

The productivity of cattle herds in the pastoral zones is overwhelmingly influenced by climate and management. Calving rates in northern Australia are commonly as low as 46 per cent and do not often reach beyond 75 per cent due to poor conception rates.[7] Under these circumstances, it is unjust to lay sole blame on the dingo for curtailed economic returns. However, poor conception rates do mean that healthy calves are valued and northern cattle graziers are understandably angry if they are killed by dingoes.

While the number of cattle killed or damaged by dingoes is much lower than sheep, the economic impact on an individual grazier can be high. The survey of landholders on the New England Tableland showed that although the number of cattle losses was low, the cost was high because of the greater value of cattle compared to sheep.[3] Indeed, the value of cattle lost approximated the value of the sheep.

Research into the level of dingo predation upon cattle under different management regimes is imperative and should also compare the effect of the dingo on British breed cattle as well as those derived from *Bos indicus* breeds. It is widely believed that the latter Brahman types and their crosses are able to defend themselves better against dingoes because of their superior agility and fitness in northern Australian conditions. In the absence of research findings, it is only possible to present the general consensus among cattle people in dingo country. Majority opinion seems to be that if dingoes are present and no control is practised, the number of calves killed in a normal season can reach between 10 and 20 per cent of all calves born.

Augustus Downs station in the Gulf of Carpentaria, where I worked during 1960–61, allowed an annual loss to dingoes of 10 per cent of all live calves. It was impossible to substantiate this figure or know if it was influenced by poor management practices such as insufficient time being spent on keeping the cattle together after branding. If cattle aren't "tailed" by people on horseback or confined in a holding paddock once they have been let out of the yards then cows that have been separated from their calves often fail to find them. As many as 4 per cent of calves can be lost on large northern cattle stations because of the disruption caused by mustering.[7]

My experience on northern cattle properties was before 1080 was being used in the extensive pastoral zones of Australia. Now many stations have their own aeroplane so that meat baits poisoned with 1080 can be more readily distributed. It costs money, and there is plenty to do besides aerial baiting of dingoes, but an annual baiting program shared between neighbouring properties is not expensive or too difficult to organise. This has in large part removed the dingo as a problem in cattle country.

Conflicts do arise when a cattle grazier refuses to join a neighbourhood 1080 baiting program. A common reason for such a refusal is that more and more cattle people are using working cattle dogs in an effort to reduce the amount of hired labour. Cheap labour is no longer available and this, together with the difficulty in getting good stockmen, has seen more cattle dogs being used in places where they were once very few. Cattle dogs can pick up a bait that was intended for a dingo and die just as quickly. Baits also last longer in the north where rainfall is seasonal so cattle people using dogs are often fearful they will lose a valuable asset.

Other cattle people see a place for a few dingoes on their property. They may wish to retain the right to reduce the dingo population by strategic poisoning from time to time, to shoot one if they happen to see it, or to lay some traps if the need arises, but they do not want to reduce it to such a level that there are none about to keep the emus and kangaroos down. Whether dingoes actually help control such species and others, such as the feral pig, has not been satisfactorily resolved and requires urgent research.

The strongest evidence that the dingo is no longer widely regarded as a serious pest of the cattle industry comes from the representations made by the Cattlemens Union of Australia to the Queensland government when it was considering the rehabilitation and realignment of the dingo barrier fence in 1980.[8] In three separate submissions the Cattlemens Union maintained a firm stance against any compulsion for cattle producers to contribute to its cost because it was for the protection of sheep not cattle. Similarly, a review of wild dog control in eastern New South Wales by the Department of Agriculture and the National Parks and Wildlife Service invited submissions from interested parties. The Cattlemens Union declined to make a submission because not one of its members had complained about wild dogs or dingoes in recent years.[9]

Dingo management

Dingo control has relied heavily on the traditional methods of trapping, poisoning and shooting. Even the exclusion fences depend on the same methods because the idea is to eradicate the dingoes inside the fence and keep their numbers down on the outside so they do not get through when the vagaries of the elements prevail against the barrier. A curious and demanding public is now asking whether the level of dingo control that has occurred in the past is always warranted and whether the methods used fit comfortably with the increasing concern for animal welfare and wildlife conservation.

Alternatives in dingo control are being developed, as are better ways of applying the traditional methods. Only an informed public can judge the issues and help choose the most equitable policies. The discussion that follows is aimed to assist that debate. It cannot be a manual on dingo control — it is neither appropriate nor is there sufficent space. It is, however, possible to present the various alternatives and the principles that should dictate their use.

POISONING

The first great assault upon the dingo occurred when strychnine was introduced. It reached its peak sometime after 1946 when aerial baiting was first used. Pieces of brisket fat containing strychnine were dropped from aeroplanes in Western Australia and Queensland. The technique was refined into the quaintly named "Queensland Minty" which consisted of a 2.5 cm cube of brisket fat containing 32 mg of strychnine, all neatly wrapped in green paper. The purpose of the green paper was to deter birds and to protect the bait from the elements for as long as possible.[1]

The Queensland Minty was dropped throughout northern and central Australia for a number of years but was discontinued because it was not particularly successful. Then 1080 came along. An assessment of aerial baiting with manufactured strychnine baits was carried out by the CSIRO in 1968 in central Australia. It did not reduce the number of dingoes, partly because there was abundant game at the time. Ants, undeterred by the poison or the wrapping, ate most of the baits.[2] Another trial a few years later found that fresh meat baits using strychnine or 1080 were effective in reducing the number of dingoes in this part of Australia, particularly during dry times when game is scarce.[3]

1080 is a code name for the chemical monofluoroacetate that was synthesised in Belgium as early as 1896. It was first used in Australia for rabbit control in 1956 where it was shown to be highly effective in killing both rabbits and farm dogs that happened to eat any poisoned rabbit. Being resourceful people, some landowners around the New England Tableland of New South Wales began throwing dead rabbits poisoned by 1080 from an aeroplane that gave them access to the rugged gorge country that adjoined their sheep holdings.[4]

These aerial poisoning campaigns were regarded as a success by the landholders and the Wild Dog Boards and before too long the first sorties using meat baits were being flown. A newsreel film of the day shows baits being shovelled out of a DC-3 accompanied by an earnest voice reading a dramatic script on the farmer's fight against the killer warrigal.

1080 has now almost entirely replaced strychnine in dingo control although the regulations governing its use vary between the states and territories. Only Western Australia and Queensland widely use aerial baiting from fixed-wing aircraft in dingo and wild dog control. Aerial baiting is banned in South Australia but ground baiting is allowed. New South Wales has recently confined all aerial baiting to the use of helicopters to ensure accurate laying of baits. The Northern Territory allows baiting from fixed-wing aircraft under particular circumstances if approval is first obtained from the Conservation Commission. Neither the Australian Capital Territory nor Victoria allows aerial baiting for dingoes and wild dogs.

Poisoning should always be viewed as a weapon of last resort. If a poison is to be used, 1080 has numerous advantages. It is the ideal poison for introduced pests because of their extreme susceptibility. Most Australian marsupials have varying levels of tolerance to 1080 because the compound occurs naturally in some native plants, particularly in the west. The introduced placental mammals, which comprise all our feral animal pests, have no such resistance.

The toxicity of a poison is expressed as the lethal dose (LD) and is presented in the standard form of milligrams of the poison per kilogram weight of the animal species referred to. The most common LD used is the LD50. This means that if a posion is used at that dose rate it will kill 50 per cent of the individuals under test. The LD50 for dingoes and wild dogs is only 0.11 mg per kilogram of body weight which amounts to a mere 1.79 mg for an average-sized dingo or wild dog. In contrast, an eastern quoll (*Dasyurus viverrinus*) has an LD50 of 5.41 mg which is over three times higher than that of the dingo. The brown antechinus (*Antechinus stuartii*), a marsupial mouse, is 17 times more tolerant to 1080 than the dingo.[5]

When 1080 is ingested it is converted into fluorocitric acid which blocks the conversion of food into energy. The animal dies as its energy reserves are depleted and cellular functions are impaired. Carnivores show symptoms associated with disorder of the central nervous system such as hyperactivity, vomiting, biting, convulsions and defecation. It takes between five and 14 hours for a dingo to show symptoms, and death follows between five and ten hours after the onset of symptoms.[5] Humans who have recovered from accidental 1080 poisoning report that there is no pain associated with what appear to be very distressing symptoms. Lack of pain is consistent with the depression of the central nervous system and, unlike strychnine which causes severe pain and distress, 1080 is regarded as a relatively painless poison.

A further advantage of 1080 is that it is not persistent in the environment because it is rapidly broken down by soil bacteria. Most baits are rendered harmless by 50 mm of rain and the poison does not accumulate in water. All this is starting to build a picture of the perfect poison — the answer to the sheep and cattle person's prayers. And so it is, but like all weapons it has a dark side and that emerges in concern about the effect of 1080 on non-target native wildlife. A related issue is what areas should remain free of poisoning campaigns because they are rightful places for the dingo.

The image of the countryside being saturated with planeloads of meat liberally laced with 1080 has forced a change in policy towards 1080 in most parts of Australia. Aerial baiting over national parks and other Crown lands was prohibited in New South Wales in 1976. The size of the bait has been increased in New South Wales while the dose rate of 1080 has been reduced to 6 mg per 230 g meat bait. This state also requires that all baits have the poison injected into them so that the concentrated poison is not so readily available to small native animals that may nibble at the outside of the bait.

Unfortunately, not all states have such strict limitations on the size of the bait and the amount of 1080 it may carry. Queensland allows baits as small as 130 g to carry 10 mg of poison which is about half the bait size and double the poison allowed south of the border. Most states have now changed over to injecting the poison into the centre of the bait but Queensland still allows tumble application in a cement mixer.

Several factors should be taken into account when considering the impact of 1080 poisoning on non-target native animals. Many native animals do not find a piece of raw meat a favourable dietary item and will totally ignore it. Native animals have a degree of tolerance to 1080. Mammals are the least tolerant, birds are moderately tolerant and reptiles are the most tolerant. It is unlikely that 1080-poisoned meat baits could ever be distributed widely enough to kill the entire population of a species of native wildlife. Traps set for dingoes and wild dogs probably kill more non-target species than 1080. Part of the public concern about 1080 may arise from a more general fear about poisons, the sinister uses they have been put to and the unintended consequences of persistent chemicals such as DDT.

The research carried out by the CSIRO Division of Wildlife and Rangelands Research suggests that few species of Australian native wildlife (other than the dingo!) are at risk from 1080 poisoning provided baits are kept large and dose rates are kept small.[6] There is still need for concern over species of rare and endangered native animals such as the native quolls and tiger quolls, commonly known as "native cats". The eastern quoll (*Dasyurus viverrinus*) is probably already extinct on the mainland and 1080 could have lent a hand in its demise. It is the unintended consequences of 1080 that necessitate special care in its use. The Victorian Department of Conservation, Forests and Lands reduces the impact of 1080 on non-target species by burying meat a few centimetres under the ground where it can be readily found by a dingo or wild dog. Not until it is certain that one of these animals is taking the meat is a poisoned bait buried at the site.[7]

Research in the Pilbara region of Western Australia shows that in this area the use of strategic aerial baiting using 1080 every two or three years around the perimeter of sheep country can give a high degree of protection to the sheep therein.[8] It was also shown that it was only necessary to poison a buffer area 10–15 km wide, this being the combined width of about two home ranges of dingoes in this area. Keeping the number of dingoes down in the buffer zone around the sheep country meant that there was always vacant territory to absorb any dingoes that were forced out of an adjoining home range because of population pressures and territorial disputes.[9] An understanding of the ecology of the dingo in this area has allowed an approach that saves sheep people the cost of flying long sorties out into dingo country to drop baits on dingoes that pose no threat.

What is appropriate for the vast, open Pilbara may not be successful for the cold, rugged highlands of Australia's south-east. Research on the use of 1080 in Kosciusko National Park has given some pessimistic results on its ability to kill dingoes and wild dogs in that type of country.[10] Baits were quickly taken by foxes and birds and soon lost their toxicity due to wet weather. Either the dingoes and wild dogs don't find them, or perhaps native game is too abundant and more attractive.

TRAPPING

Trapping has always been a very successful method of catching dingoes and wild dogs. It is, however, very labour-intensive and baiting programs can cover more country faster and more economically. But trappers get results and they can lay their traps where dingoes are killing sheep and aim to eradicate particularly troublesome individuals.

A trial that compared the effectiveness of hand-laid 1080 meat bait and trapping in Kosciusko National Park found that trapping was much more successful than the baiting.[10] The baits killed only two of the nine dogs (22 per cent) fitted with radio transmitters after they were caught in padded traps. In comparison, traps caught 15 out of the 27 dogs known to be in the area (56 per cent). This is not to say that 1080 is not more effective under other circumstances, particularly in inland Australia where baits last longer and there is less water so that they can be laid at regular watering points where dingoes or wild dogs will be more likely to find them. This trial does show the very high success rate that is possible with traps, especially in areas where dingoes and wild dogs don't seem to come across baits so readily, or are less willing to consume them.

An analysis of methods used to obtain the 10,710 dingo scalps presented to the Lower North Coast and Tablelands Dingo Destruction Board in New South Wales between 1961 and 1972 shows that trapping contributed the most scalps.[1] The percentage killed by poisoning would be underestimated because few dingoes killed by 1080 are ever found. The following table shows the high proportion of dingoes killed by the two traditional methods of trapping and shooting.

Steel jaw traps are cruel and they catch other animals besides dingoes and wild dogs. Even the most hard-bitten dogger will not deny the cruelty of the steel jaw trap. The leg is often broken in more than one place — first where the jaws have fastened on to the leg, secondly higher up on the leg as a result of the animal's violent struggles against pain and fear.

Many argue that poison wads on traps should be made compulsory so that the dingo dies soon after it bites at the trap to free itself. Another way to reduce the cruelty is for a daily inspection of traps. This is not always possible with the areas that individual trappers have to cover and it is not uncommon for a dingo to die in a trap. These things vary, because some trappers pride themselves on getting around their traps at least

Above: *Dingoes caught by John Coman will be scalped so that he can claim the bounty. Gary Steer*

Left: *Dingo trapper John Coman setting a trap near Rockton on the Monaro, south-eastern New South Wales. Gary Steer*

TABLE 13:
Proportion of dingoes killed by different methods of control in the New England Tablelands region of New South Wales. From Harden, 1980.

Method of destruction	Percentage of total scalps
Trapped	46.7
Shot	30.7
Ground poison	11.3
Run over by vehicle	1.4
Killed after being run down in vehicle or on horseback	5.3
Unknown	4.6

every two days. Still, five seconds in a steel jaw trap would be too long for me.

Various alternatives to the steel jaw trap are being proposed. Trappers employed by the Victorian government are no longer allowed to use these traps, unless under exceptional circumstances.[7] The new traps release a snare around the leg instead of steel jaws. This "treadle snare trap" catches dingoes without inflicting the same wounds as the traditional steel jaw trap.[11] Experiments are also being conducted in New South Wales and Queensland with "Victor soft catch traps". These have offset jaws of tough rubber instead of steel and are fitted with swivels and springs to absorb the sudden movements of a trapped animal. The plates are also smaller and appear to catch fewer non-target species.[12,13]

We are through the harsh frontier phase of Australia's history and more humane traps must be developed and used. Animal Liberation points out that there is really no humane way of killing another animal because we are exercising power over species that have no control over their fate.[14] If some dingoes are to be killed then it behoves us to reduce their suffering as much as possible. There are many possibilities — for example, radio-transmitters could be fitted to traps so that a signal is sent to the trapper the moment an animal is caught. Sedative pads can be fitted to traps so that animals such as dingoes and wild dogs that bite at the object that is holding them receive a dose of sedative. More stringent codes of practice need to be developed and implemented

TABLE 14:
Target and non-target species caught in dingo traps in south-eastern Australia. From Newsome et al, *1983.*

Species	"Lane" traps	"Oneida" traps
Mammals		
Short-beaked echidna (*Tachyglossus aculeatus*)	1	0
Bandicoot (*Parameles nasuta* or *Isodon obesulus*)	3	0
Common brushtail possum (*Trichosurus vulpecula*)	49	1
Common wombat (*Vombatus ursinus*)	69	0
Swamp wallaby (*Wallabia bicolor*)	92	2
Eastern grey kangaroo (*Macropus giganteus*)	8	0
European rabbit (*Oryctolagus cuniculus*)	21	1
Pig (*Sus scrofa*)	6	1
European cattle (*Bos taurus*)	1	0
Dingo (*Canis familiaris dingo*)	95	51
Farm dog (*Canis familiaris familiaris*)	1	0
Fox (*Vulpes vulpes*)	118	25
Cat (*Felis catus*)	36	4
Birds		
Emu (*Dromaius novaehollandiae*)	9	0
Whistling kite (*Haliastur sphenurus*)	0	1
Wedge-tailed eagle (*Aquila audax*)	1	1
Hawk (Fam. *Accipitridae*)	0	3
Wonga pigeon (*Leucosarcia melanoleuca*)	7	0
Tawny frogmouth (*Podargus strigoides*)	1	0
Superb lyrebird (*Menura novaehollandiae*)	16	0
Spotted quail-thrush (*Cinclosoma punctatum*)	1	0
White-winged chough (*Corcorax melanorhamphus*)	4	0
Australian magpie (*Gymnorhina tibicen*)	1	0
Raven (*Corvus* sp.)	7	6
Reptiles		
Goanna (*Varanus varius*)	2	2
Blue-tongued lizard (*Tiliqua* sp.)	1	0
No. of trap-nights	16464	2692
Total non-target species (number per 100 trap-nights)	455 (2.76)	47 (1.59)
Total dingoes (number per 100 trap-nights)	95 (0.58)	51 (1.72)

Australia-wide. The large steel jaw traps should be phased out, as in Victoria, and replaced by the treadle snare and the Victor soft catch traps.

The non-target species most commonly caught in dingo traps is the fox, and a significant number of feral cats are also trapped. Both are introduced animals with few friends. However, the common brushtail possum, eastern grey kangaroo, swamp wallaby and the lyrebird are frequently caught in dingo traps set in eastern Australia.[15] No surveys of the impact of traps on native non-target species in other parts of Australia have been published.

The attitude of trappers to non-target species varies according to individual foibles. Most badly injured animals are destroyed. Other animals are given a "bush amputation" and released to fend as best they can. It is a very fortunate wombat that is released alive from a trap even if it is uninjured, as is often the case with these tough creatures. Wombats are territorial; consequently, if one is caught and released it is just as likely to get caught again the next night so they are usually shot with the rationalisation that "you have to trap the rubbish away first before you can get your dog".

In one trial, CSIRO researchers used the smaller "Oneida" steel jaw traps and deliberately set them so that they would catch less non-target native wildlife.[15] This was achieved by setting them just to the side of fauna trails and roads and away from trees used by possums. They caught just as many dingoes and wild dogs, but half the amount of native wildlife caught by the trappers using the larger "Lane" traps who made no deliberate attempt to avoid catching non-target species.

Unless there is some remarkable breakthrough in technology, trapping is likely to remain a very big part of dingo control. This does not mean that methods of trapping cannot be improved. First, trappers must be bound to release all non-target species except those that are too badly injured. Second, traps should be checked daily. Third, traps and methods of trapping that do not injure non-target species must be devised and used.

SHOOTING

Shooting accounts for a lot of dingoes but it is not a reliable method of dingo control. If a hunter deliberately went out to hunt dingoes, he or she would often return home empty-handed. Most dingoes are shot on an opportunistic basis by farmers out checking the fences or the waters, or engaged in other management routines. They happen across a dingo and get a bead on it with the rifle that sits as a permanent feature behind the driver's seat. A dingo trotting along the track that pauses in a moment of curiosity is shot.

There are variations on this hit-or-miss theme, and many a sheep person has staked out a mob of sheep night after night, finally getting a shot at the dingo that has been causing havoc. Doggers, who are out and about in dingo country all the time, also shoot some dingoes. A few people who are wise to the ways of the dingo have been known to "howl up" a dingo to within shooting distance. But night-long vigils to stake out a dingo, individual stalking, or big drives involving riders on horseback and shooters in hides, were never the main form of dingo control. They are frequently a desperate last resort. Throughout central and northern Australia there is too much country to cover, while in eastern Australia there are too many trees, mountains and valleys for shooting to be a reliable method of dingo control.

EXCLUSION FENCING

So far, this chapter has been about us living and the dingo dying. Mark Twain was right: "The world was made for the white man." If some dingoes are to be killed, it should be done with minimal cruelty and impact on native non-target species. Trapping, shooting and poisoning are not methods that those involved in dingo "management" would choose if there were suitable alternatives. There *are* alternatives and they offer hope, but not for all dingoes everywhere in Australia.

The oldest form of exclusion fence, the complete wire netting barrier, is now too expensive for all but a very few landowners in exceptional circumstances. It costs around $8000 per kilometre to build a conventional dog-proof fence. This cannot be passed on to the consumer of wool and so this form of fencing is rapidly disappearing from private properties. Some private and co-operatively owned fences are still maintained and their life is being extended by the use of offset electrified wires. Even these costly fences do not eliminate the use of traps and poison to kill dingoes that get through and those waiting for an opportunity to do so. Wanaaring Pastures Protection Board, inside the dingo fence in north-western New South Wales, was the largest user of 1080 in the state during 1985.[12] This shows that even this barrier fence, maintained by full-time boundary riders only 20 km apart, cannot keep out all dingoes.

ELECTRIC FENCING

The great advantage of electric fencing is its low cost. A dingo is deterred from going through the fence by the fear of receiving an electric shock of up to 8000 volts. Obviously, a dingo must first get a shock to initiate the learning process; this is achieved by putting the earth and live wires close together near the ground so that a dingo cannot squeeze through without coming in direct contact with two such wires.

An accidental shock from an electric fence operating at full efficiency is an experience to be avoided. A farm dog that tries to pass through a new electric fence runs yelping across the paddock

A great hope is that electric fencing will continue to be as successful in controlling dingoes and wild dogs in the long term as it has been thus far. This fence was built by John Alcock of 'Greenlands', near Kybean, in response to dingo and wild dog problems. Roland Breckwoldt

in an extreme state of anxiety. However, that dog will soon learn ways of getting under, around or over the fence. Since dingoes are just as smart as farm dogs, if not a bit smarter, there is some concern in the bush that they too will soon learn how to avoid a shock.

Nevertheless, electric fencing for dingo and wild dog control is becoming very widely used. As long as the dingoes have alternative areas, electric fences are capable of keeping a high enough proportion of them out of sheep country to make the cost of the fence worthwile. At only about $2000 per km for a high-quality electric fence, it becomes a very attractive method of dingo and wild dog control, particularly when the fence is also used in normal stock management. A fence is a permanent asset whereas money spent on poisoning and trapping is lost.

Giving pest animals an alternative is one of the basic tenets in keeping them away from the product to be protected. While there are large national parks and state forest areas near grazing country, there is a good chance that electric fencing will keep dingoes away from sheep. When dingo or wild dog populations build up in those areas, and their native game becomes scarce, they may be more tempted to get through such fences. However, technology and equipment are constantly being improved and, coupled with a better understanding of dingo and wild dog behaviour, it will soon be possible to design and build highly efficient electric dog fences for all terrain and conditions.

Electric fencing is still at a stage where it is unlikely to stop all dingoes getting among sheep and it is usually supplemented by other methods of control. Notwithstanding this fact, most people who build them are well satisfied with the result and swear to a reduction in sheep losses. More research is essential; for example, some dingo country needs to be divided by an electric fence and the movements of radio-collared dingoes followed to see whether they cross it or how it otherwise affects their behaviour.

Electric fencing can also have an impact on non-target species. Fences carrying high voltages with the wires close together at ground level do kill echidnas. The echidna is either immobilised by the shock or bunches itself up and gets jammed between the wires by its spines and soon dies. This must be most unpleasant for the poor echidna and it also shorts out the fence, rendering it useless until the dead animal is removed. This problem is being overcome by using energisers that send out faster pulses so that any small animal receives a shock and is deterred before it gets caught between the wires.

The future of larger fauna such as kangaroos, wallabies and emus that are in areas surrounded by an electric fence also requires consideration. An efficient electric fence could perhaps prevent the recruitment of new genetic material to what may become isolated populations of wildlife. At present, the imperfections of electric fencing mitigate against such consequences. Nevertheless, we are meddling with nature without understanding all the ramifications of our actions.

AVERSION THERAPY!

Some people who want to overcome bad habits or anti-social behaviour submit themselves to an electric shock when a picture of the offending activity is flashed before them. The activity which once gave pleasure becomes associated with pain and is stopped. This powerful theory has been applied for a long time in the relationship between human and domestic dog. Rover recieves a well-aimed rock when he chases the fowls. This is extremely effective and both Rover and the fowls live in harmony. But how can this be applied to a dingo or coyote that has free run of the range and remains well out of stone's throw?

Research in the United States has attempted to overcome this problem. Meat baits cut from sheep killed by coyotes are laced with lithium chloride or thiabendazole and left lying around for the coyotes to eat.[16,17] They become violently ill but recover and from then on they are supposed to associate sheep with the most unpleasant gastro-intestinal disorders. The benefits would flow to both farmer and coyote. First, it means that coyotes do not have to be killed. Secondly, it is felt that stable populations of "educated" coyotes will defend their territory against "uneducated" invaders so that farmers do not have to get on the treadmill of repeated lethal control measures. Thirdly, the coyotes can keep on doing their good work of keeping the "varmints" down.

There is no agreement that aversive conditioning protects sheep even in the United States where flocks are much smaller and more intensively managed than in Australia. Some speak highly of it but others consider that the results are inconclusive and that much more research is necessary to determine its potential.[18,19] It may find some application in parts of the more settled regions in Australia but is hardly likely to replace other methods on the vast sheep properties of central and northern Australia or around the rugged ranges of the east where native prey is abundant. It would simply be too difficult to "train" all the dingoes to a level that gave sheep sufficient protection.

TOXIC COLLARS

It would be convenient if there was a sure way of destroying only those dingoes that killed sheep. One way of achieving this would be to fit sheep with a lethal defence system that was only released upon an attacking dingo. Trials with toxic collars have been carried out in the United States, Canada, Mexico and South Africa.[20] A collar carrying 1080 is fitted to the sheep so that a coyote or wolf that takes it by the throat gets more than it bargained for.

Apparently toxic collars have afforded some protection to small flocks in these countries, but the process would be far too expensive and impossible to manage under most Australian conditions. The collars are expensive to fit — imagine the cost when even a modest sheep station in this country carries 6000 sheep. The poison collars could also dislodge and lie about for working dogs to chew. In addition, there is no pattern to the way dingoes kill sheep and they are as likely to run off with a ram's testicles as take him by the throat.

DOG AGAINST DOG

Special breeds of dogs were developed in Central Europe and Asia to guard sheep and goats against predators and they have been used for this purpose for as long as dogs have been domesticated. These dogs spend their puppyhood in close proximity to one or two sheep or goats so that they become conditioned to them instead of other dogs or humans. They are gradually allowed to run with the flock during the day until they can be trusted to run with it all the time. From then on the dog fends off any enemy of the sheep or goats under its care.[21]

Perhaps Australia's cultural isolation prevented the acceptance of guard dogs for its sheep. On the other hand, it is highly likely that attempts were made to use guard dogs from among the breeds that were available and that they failed because of the vast areas of land and the huge flocks in the Australian sheep industry. But it remains possible that the most appropriate breeds from overseas were unavailable and an opportunity for them still remains to be exploited.

Correct training and a reliable temperament are two important aspects of a potential guard dog, even under European and Asian conditions where flocks are small. To train sufficient reliable guard dogs for even a single large sheep station in Australia would be extremely difficult, and expensive. Under Australia's extensive range conditions sheep must disperse and forage over large areas. A dog would be required for every 10 or 20 sheep for them to remain under constant supervision. A small property would need numerous dogs to guard one paddock. Even if it were possible to train sufficient dogs, they would need to be fed while living among the sheep — a hungry guard dog could be tempted to covet the sheep under its care! It certainly could not guard livestock if it had to spend its time hunting.

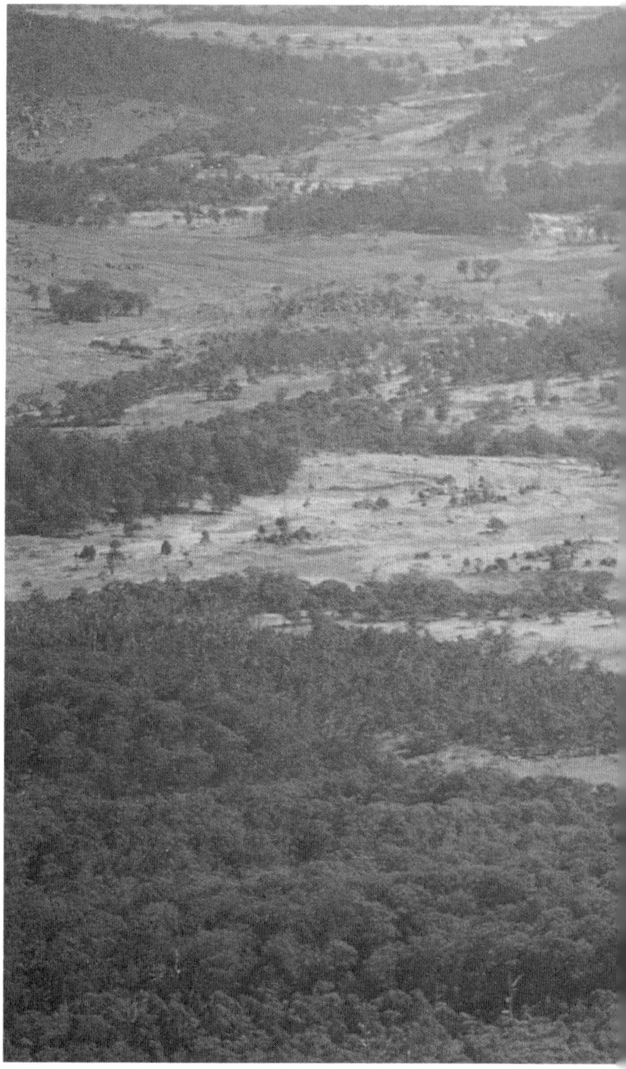

When sheep are run in partly timbered country near the habitat of wild dogs and dingoes, as happens on the edge of the Monaro, conflict arises as to who is responsible for the resultant sheep losses. The solution to the problem becomes as much a social issue as an ecological one, and the best methods of resolving the conflict remain to be found.
Gary Steer

Still, there are a few places in Australia where guard dogs could find a role in protecting sheep against dingoes. Many of the cattle properties on the coastal side of the Great Dividing Range run a few sheep to diversify the economic base. More of them are also turning to mohair production. These properties frequently extend up coastal valleys where some paddocks adjoin forest that is dingo habitat. When these dingoes come out and kill sheep, there is usually an outcry against the conservation or

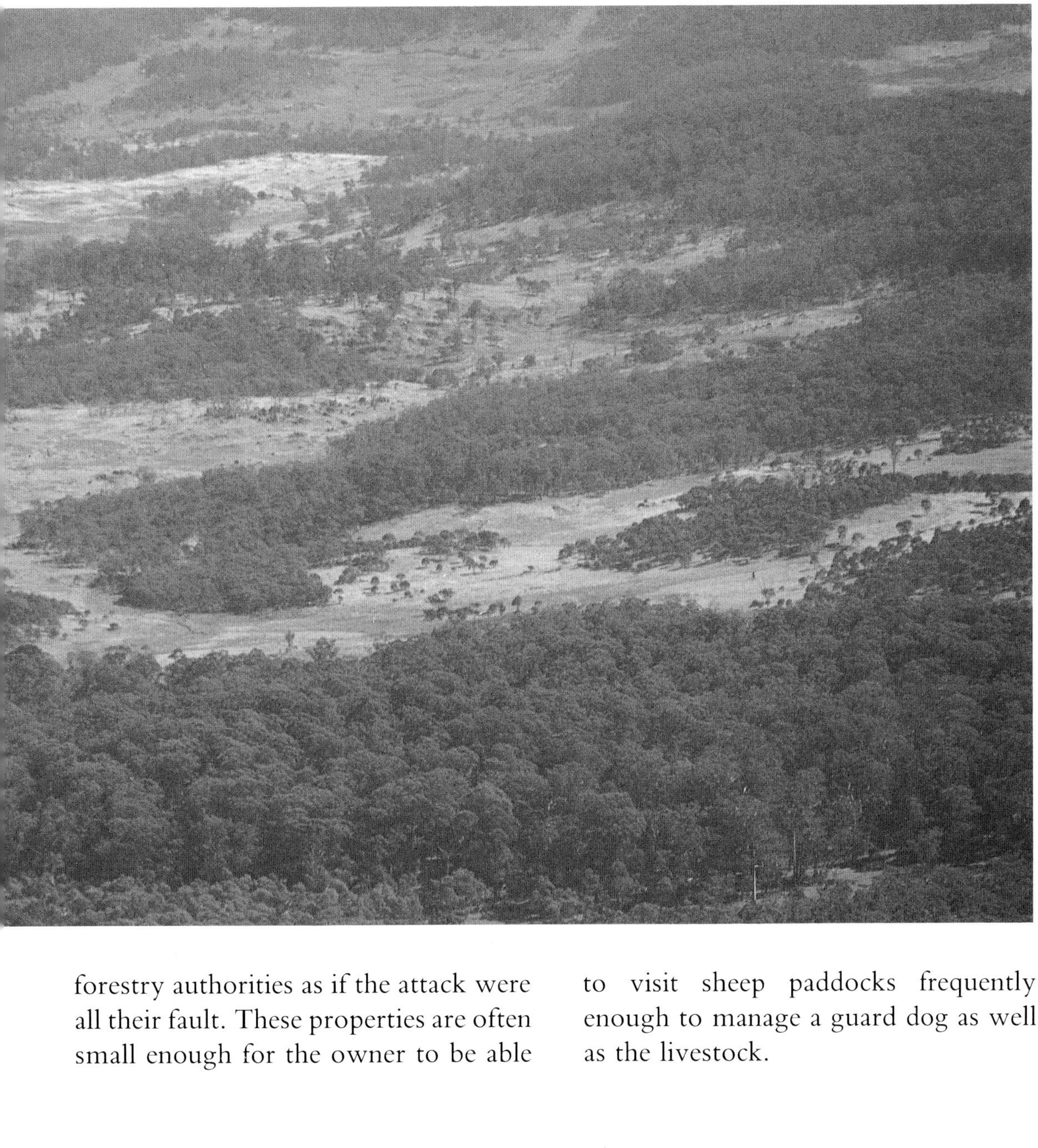

forestry authorities as if the attack were all their fault. These properties are often small enough for the owner to be able to visit sheep paddocks frequently enough to manage a guard dog as well as the livestock.

LAND USE PLANNING

Australian agriculture grew like Topsy. And like Topsy, it is not all neat and tidy. Land was cleared that directly adjoined rugged mountain ranges. Coastal valleys that snaked up between forested hills were cleared so that paddocks intrude on dingo territories. Some places should never have been cleared and there sheep will always fall prey to dingo or wild dog unless land use is changed.

Because agriculture held such a commanding position during the settlement of Australia, it was always the dingo that was in the wrong, not the settlers. Now, after 200 years, it is almost impossible to correct some of the decisions that were made because there was no grand plan for the white man in Australia.

Whenever an opportunity arises for land use planning to help separate sheep from dingoes, it should be exercised. In Chapter One I described how dingoes in Nadgee Nature Reserve are rarely troubled by accusations of killing livestock because the reserve is surrounded by state forest which in turn adjoins cattle country. If this configuration of land use can be achieved more often then it will gradually help ease the tension that arises in some rural communities when sheep are run next to dingoes. Again, it is not the answer to all dingo problems but it does have an important role in some areas.

CHANGING THE SHEEP INDUSTRY

It is hard to imagine any situation where dingoes and wild dogs would not have to be controlled to keep them from scavenging in town and city and becoming a hazard to human health and safety. A certain level of dog control will always be necessary. However, by far the greatest influence on the level of dingo and wild dog control, and the methods used, is the sheep industry.

One option is to change the sheep industry rather than exert the level of dingo control that has been necessary to protect it as it is now. That suggestion will not carry any favour with most farmers — but it is an alternative. The size and extent of the sheep industry are negotiable. So are husbandry practices. The economic fabric of society is based on value judgements of what is good and bad, right and wrong, and any industry can be changed or discontinued if enough people want it that way and are willing to accept the consequences.

IN CONCLUSION

There have been suggestions that one effect of dingo control is to disrupt stable social groups and allow subordinate females to breed and thereby cause an increase in both the dingo population and the problems of attacking livestock.[22] To date, however, the practical result of dingo control has been to eradicate dingoes from a large part of Australia. This indicates that the dingo did not respond to most control programs with a sufficient increase in breeding to remain in the area. This is supported by the findings of recent research in the Fortescue River region and on the Nullarbor Plain in Western Australia, which showed that 1080 poison suppressed the dingo population for a number of years and that there was no increase in breeding in response to control.[23]

The overwhelming evidence is that dingo control is very efficient wherever it is carried out on a serious and sustained basis. Given further research, finance and willpower, it may not be long before it is possible to remove the dingo from its remaining haunts. Fortunately, at least two of the ingredients are likely to be missing — the money and the willpower. There is still plenty of country where no one is likely to pursue the dingo. Nevertheless, it is sobering to consider that it may soon be possible to eradicate the dingo. There is, of course, an alternative scenario — a concern for the dingo could result in control being lifted and it could increase in numbers and regain some of its former range.

Landholders directly involved with dingo or wild dog problems are unlikely to see the choices as clearly as that because government control programs and policies are not always clearly articulated and money is never in unlimited supply. However, there is now a wide range of options in dingo management and all those organisations involved can, together with landholders, develop management plans based on the most appropriate methods for each area. Two recent initiatives have been taken in this regard. A South-East Feral Animal Control Task Force was established in Cooma as a result of a Search Conference that tried to resolve the conflict that has developed on the Monaro Tableland over dingo and wild dog control. This task force was made up of members from government departments, landholder organisations and conservation groups. In this forum each group can present its policies and work towards resolving differences. The second important initiative is the way the Victorian government has developed a wild dog control plan for the state that clearly presents it programs and policies so that they can be considered by landholders and the public.[7]

No one method of dingo control will suit all situations. Australia is vast, with many different environments reflected in different livestock management systems. What is appropriate for the arid centre may not be at all suitable for the wetter, rugged, forested ranges of the south-east. The danger to non-target species from any method of control may be high in one area but completely absent in another. These variations in the effectiveness of dingo control and its wider implications make it impossible to provide guidelines that are suited to all Australia. Each landholder and government authority must make a responsible choice from among the methods that are available and apply them with a similar sense of responsibility.

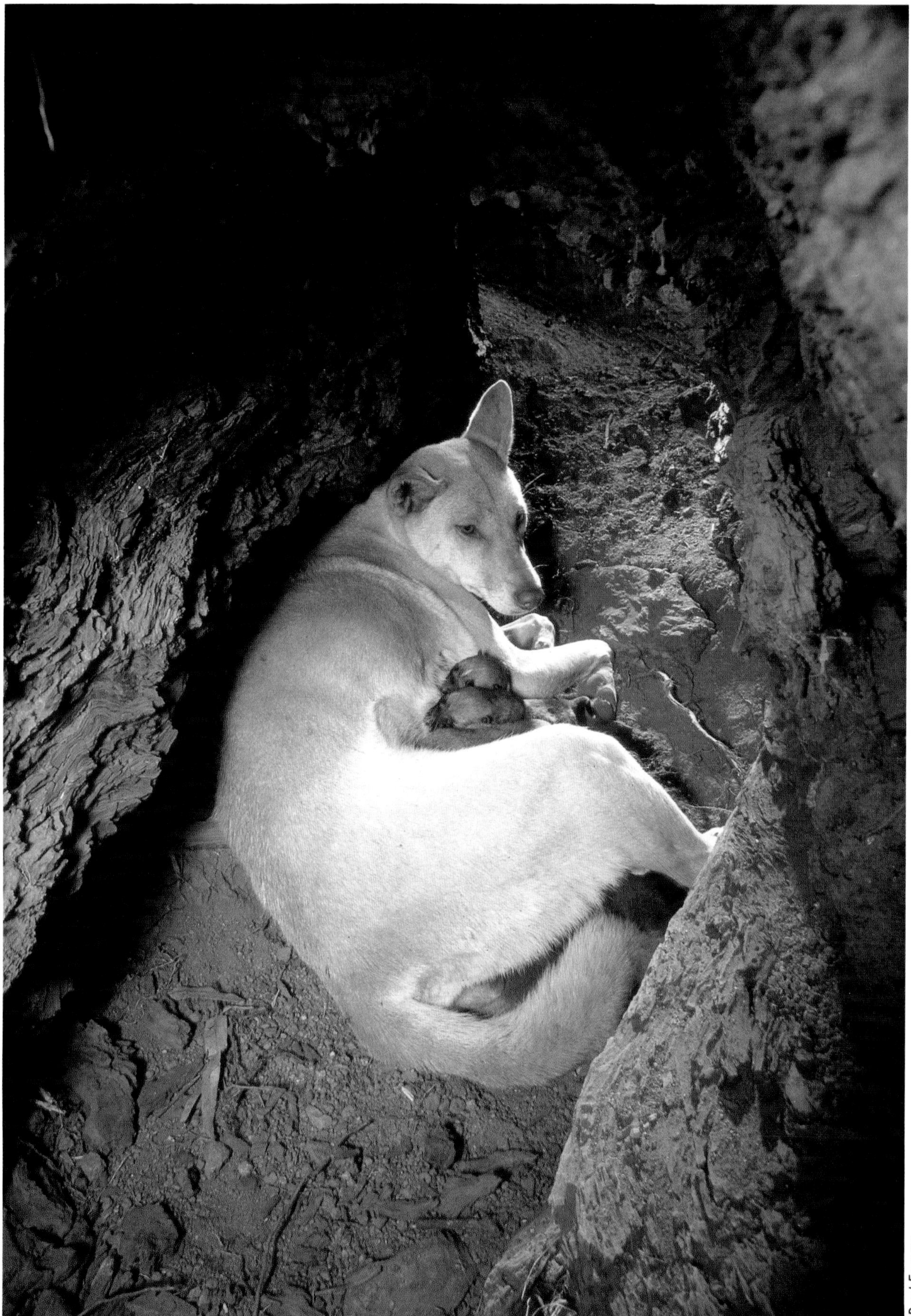

Jean-Paul Ferrero

Conservation of the dingo

It is easy to disregard any concern about the future of the dingo on the grounds that it has withstood two centuries of European settlement. While it has been edged out of much of its former habitat, it is still common in central and northern Australia. There are also enough dingoes left in the forested east for some to argue that the dingo will survive everything that can be thrown at it. A historical perspective, together with the factors that influence its distribution today, shows the need for a conservation-orientated management strategy for the dingo.

Labelling a species a pest while assuming its capacity to withstand all control measures has been an ingredient in the extinction of other species of Australian wildlife. So went the thylacine, the toolache wallaby and the brush-tailed rat-kangaroo. True, their extinction was helped by changes in land use but that is also occurring with the dingo as settlement and technology close in on it. Indeed, we may be witnessing the latter period of the dingo in Australia, unaware of its decline.

Although they are totally unrelated, the dingo and the thylacine make good comparison because of their size, carnivorous habits and the dog-like nature of the thylacine. The extinction of the thylacine must be regarded as our greatest wildlife tragedy. It is certain that future generations will feel the same if the dingo too becomes extinct in Australia.

One reason for the commonly held cavalier attitude towards the dingo is that it breeds so readily — in the wild, in captivity, or in association with people. Elaborate schemes to get the last of the species to breed in captivity have been devised for such well-known endangered species as the panda and lesser known but equally important species such as the numbat in Australia. The problem with keeping dingoes in captivity is to find homes for their offspring or perfect the art of canine contraception. However complacency is dangerous and there are dozens of examples throughout the world where species that were abundant suddenly became rare or extinct where no one thought it possible.

IS THE DINGO AN ENDANGERED SPECIES?

To make an issue of whether the dingo will become an endangered animal seems unwarranted because it is still abundant enough. It does not meet any of the criteria used to define a rare or endangered species. Sensational newspaper articles stating that the dingo is in imminent danger of extinction because "hundreds of thousands" of pelts are being exported overseas every year are figments of someone's vivid imagination given that it is quite impossible to shoot or trap dingoes on that scale.[1] A whole range of species of Australian wildlife *is* in immediate danger of extinction and warrants concerted efforts and financial commitment. However, the dingo does have two serious enemies which, when they operate in concert, have the capacity to reduce its numbers to the point where a concern about its future in Australia is not misplaced.

COMBINED ENEMIES — WHITE PEOPLE AND THEIR DOGS

The dingo has joined the ranks of many other species of Australian wildlife whose former range has been greatly reduced since European settlement. Fortunately, a proportion of these species is now conserved in national parks and equivalent reserves and they are secure. Similarly, there are places where no one would want to control dingoes in the foreseeable future. The dingo could be assumed safe forever in the rugged forests of the Great Dividing Range and the remote central and northern regions of Australia.

In the case of the dingo, a reduced distribution is not in itself a major cause for concern about its future. A problem emerges only when the reduction in its number and range renders it vulnerable to an additional threat. One such threat has emerged. It is the potential for the dingo to be bred out of existence by the domestic dog.

SWAMPED BY DOMESTIC GENES

Research indicates that feral dogs are swamping the dingo in eastern Australia. This is where the greatest number of domestic dogs find their way into the wild and there is no biological reason why this trend will not gradually continue across Australia. There may be anthropological reasons, such as the much sparser human population and the fewer domestic dogs in the northern cattle country, but these barriers between domestic dog and dingo are rapidly being removed. Mining camps and towns, tourism, an increased use of dogs in cattle work, the adoption of the domestic dog by Aborigines — all these changes are putting domestic genes among the last stronghold of the dingo.

The dingo will not be hybridised out of existence overnight. There is also hope that it will prove too resilient and that its fitness to the Australian bush will hold out against the feral domestic dog. However, the evidence indicates otherwise — that gradually more and more pure dingoes will give way to hybrids until eventually there are no pure dingoes left.

The case of the red wolf (*Canis rufus*) in the United States shows that we have no reason for complacency. Today the red wolf is the most endangered mammal in the United States yet it was once widely distributed across seven southern states. It has now been reduced to a small remnant population ranging over a mere 600,000 hectares.[2] The main reason why the red wolf is in grave danger of extinction is that it has been swamped by the coyote (*Canis latrans*). The coyote followed the farmers and their livestock into the range of the red wolf and then started interbreeding with it. The changes brought about by humans favoured the coyote and so the red wolf could never recover.[3]

The decline of the red wolf by hybridisation with the coyote is so clear that the European settlement of the region can be traced through the fossil remains of coyote–red wolf hybrids. The older fossils show that there were two distinct species, the more recent ones indicate that the process of hybridisation had begun, and finally there are only coyotes.

Is this, then, the fate of the dingo in Australia — to be bred out of existence by the domestic dog? Will what the white man began with trap and poison be finished by his lusty dog? Of course it is too early to predict if and when the last pure dingo will mate with a feral domestic dog to end the sub-species in Australia but it is a very likely occurrence and steps must be taken now to avoid the possibility.

THE DINGO AS PART OF THE AUSTRALIAN ECOSYSTEM

Wildlife conservation is concerned with more than the protection of individual species. It is vital to protect entire ecosystems with their full complement of plants and animals. Every species of plant and animal is important and the entire ecosystem can be diminished if one is removed.

The dingo has taken a niche in the Australian ecosystem and has been on the continent long enough to be regarded as a native animal, as important as any others with which it shares the bush. It is therefore not unreasonable to assert that a national park or equivalent reserve cannot be a "natural" ecosystem if it is devoid of one of its major predators, the dingo. An area set aside for wildlife conservation can hardly represent the Australian environment if it is brimming with kangaroos because the dingoes were eradicated. Predators are an essential part of the food chain.

I am not suggesting that every national park or equivalent reserve now devoid of dingoes must suddenly have them replaced. Obviously, some reserves are far too small and are so surrounded by sheep that the potential problems outweigh any rigid adherence to principle. However, the dingo has a place in the Australian scene and it will be to the country's detriment if it is entirely removed.

DINGOES OR WILD DOGS?

The issue of whether the canids in a national park or on pastoral land are pure dingoes or feral dogs still needs to be addressed. From a biological or ecological point of view it may make very little difference. To a kangaroo or wallaby being eaten it doesn't really matter whether the diner is dingo or feral dog. It would, of course, matter very much if the feral dog ate more kangaroos and wallabies than the dingo and this should be the subject of some serious research.

At the heart of the problem is the question of what to do about feral dogs in national parks and reserves. If they have become part of the ecosystem by replacing dingoes, they could simply be ignored unless there are steps being taken to reduce their numbers in order to protect pure dingoes. But how to tell the difference between dingoes, feral dogs and hybrids in the bush remains a difficult problem. It comes to the fore when conservation authorities are accused of harbouring wild dogs in national parks and reserves that are implicated in killing livestock.

Calls for unlimited control of wild dogs in national parks because they are all feral dogs and not dingoes should be treated with caution. The word "feral" immediately conjures up the image of goats, pigs and buffaloes and all the havoc they have wreaked upon the Australian environment. The use of this image to gain control over the dingo is deliberately misleading.

THE DINGO IN THE KENNEL

There have always been people who have kept dingoes as pets and there probably always will be, even though it is illegal to do so because they are declared vermin in most states. Some states have strict laws but do not enforce them; others enforce them with a rigid adherence to the fine print.

Individuals keep dingoes for a variety of reasons. If people really want a dingo, they can usually find ways of obtaining one. From my observation, only a very small proportion of the people who would like to keep a dingo, or who actually get to do so, are suited to what can become an onerous responsibility. Like lion cubs, small dingo puppies are quite endearing — they also grow big and have needs of their own that can be difficult to accommodate. The success stories of people keeping their dingo pet long into adulthood and caring for it properly are few. Most infatuations founder with the dingo being dumped, shot or spending a miserable existence on a short chain or in a pen. The reason for the high failure rate is that the dingo is not like the domestic dog. Once they reach adulthood, dingoes can be difficult to control when they are let free. While it is quite easy to train domestic dogs to come to a call and respond to simple commands, the dingo does not necessarily focus on its owner's needs at important moments — such as when the neighbours' cat appears or their prize muscovy ducks are out for an afternoon pick on the lawn. Give me a reason for having a dog and I will suggest any number of suitable domestic breeds before a dingo.

The ability of people to train dogs varies, as does the degree to which they are prepared to modify their lifestyle to keep their pet. My experience and observation leads me to the belief that dingoes are not suitable domestic pets. They should be regarded as native animals and have similar restrictions placed on keeping them as apply to other native animals. Keeping dingoes would thus remain illegal except under unusual circumstances. It would be illegal, not because dingoes are declared vermin, but because they are now protected native animals.

A less favoured option, if people insist on keeping dingoes, is to accredit a suitable private organisation established for the sole purpose of allowing its members to keep dingoes. Ownership of dingoes should then be restricted to members of the organisation. Such an organisation would require a constitution that ensures election of all office bearers by the membership to help guarantee that factions with idiosyncratic notions about dingoes do not gain control. The organisation should also have a code of conduct that binds all members. Moreover, it, rather than the individual member, should retain legal ownership of the dingo.

It is unlikely that the keeping of dingoes as pets will assist in conserving the subspecies. Selection pressure for certain traits can easily take place, either intentionally or inadvertently, by which dingoes kept in domestic situations are changed. This may not eventuate as a problem because domestic dogs adapt to life in the wild and the same would apply to dingoes. The appeal of the dingo is that it is a semi-wild dog that has not been modified by heavy selection pressure and it should remain that way, in the bush, from a wildlife conservation point of view.

TOWARDS CONSERVATION OF THE DINGO

It is surely time for the dingo to be recognised as a native animal and removed from the various state noxious animal and vermin lists. This process has begun in the Northern Territory where the dingo has been taken off the vermin list and put on the unprotected list, except in national parks and equivalent reserves where it is fully protected. Only in the Australian Capital Territory is the dingo on the protected animals list. All the states should follow this example and the Northern Territory should take its courageous step a little further by also putting the dingo on the protected list outside wildlife reserves. The history of wildlife conservation in Australia is characterised by the gradual addition of once-despised species to the protected animal lists.

There must be provision for farmers to control dingoes that are killing livestock. This has been done in the case of other protected species that can be pests at certain times or under particular circumstances and it would be easy to devise similar provisions that are appropriate for the dingo. For example, reptiles are protected animals but there is provision for people to kill venomous snakes if they pose a threat to human safety. A tiger snake in the laundry can still be despatched but one that is minding its own business in the swamp should be left alone. Similar provisions could easily be negotiated for dingoes that run on private agricultural land.

Protection would, however, make it harder to get at dingoes in national parks and reserves. Rather than the onus being on the authorities that manage such areas to get rid of dingoes because they are officially declared vermin, large national parks would become legitimate places for the dingo to run. This in turn would place more responsibility on the landowners adjoining those areas to protect their sheep.

MANAGEMENT PLANS FOR THE DINGO

Management plans are developed for single species when they have particular conservation requirements that conflict with other uses of the land. One reason for conflict between farmers and wildlife conservation authorities is that there is no clearly articulated management policy for dingoes. A system of management that takes into account the needs of the species of wildlife and the concerns of the people it affects is one of the aims of a wildlife management plan. For example, there are now state kangaroo management plans as well as an overall federal government policy. Only Victoria has a wild dog control plan that could become the basis for a conservation-orientated management plan for the dingo.[4]

A DINGO STUD BOOK

An important step in the process of conserving the dingo is for complete breeding records to be kept on all dingoes kept in zoos. This will amount to a dingo stud book that contains pedigrees of dingoes of known origin and parentage. This may not seem so vital now but imagine how important it will be after another 200 years when the pure dingo may well be quite rare over most of Australia.

The dingo stud book should be limited to government zoos and accredited private zoos and wildlife parks. This limitation is necessary because some groups that promote the cause of the dingo also keep them as pets and apply selection pressure on standards that may be desirable for domestic dogs but have no relevance whatsoever to wild dingoes.

Just as it is possible to envisage a colony of thylacines being pampered in the Tasmanian bush today, should a wondrous discovery occur, it is equally easy to foresee the time when pure dingoes are pampered in appropriate places. The time will come when the pure dingo is rare because it has been swamped by feral dogs. There may come a time when it is decided to re-establish them in the wild by introducing surplus zoo stock whose genetic history can be traced through the stud book. By then science and technology may have made it possible to keep dingoes and sheep apart and everyone will rejoice to see the dingoes ranging free in a national park or reserve. A closed stud book is essential to maintain a colony of pure dingoes for as long as is necessary.

IN CONCLUSION

There is no better time to accept the dingo as a native of Australia. The dingo started out as a quiet observer but soon came to represent everything that was dark and dangerous on the continent. Things have changed so quickly that there is now a real possibility that the pure dingo will gradually disappear. It cannot happen as early as the imminent extinction of other species but this provides the opportunities to come to a compromise with this elegant animal. If we do not make peace there is the danger of losing the dingo by failing to accept that not everything in Australia was designed only for human benefit.

References

CHAPTER ONE (no references)

CHAPTER TWO

1. Stains, H. J., "Distribution and taxonomy of the canidae", in Fox, M. W. (ed.), *The Wild Canids: Their Systematics, Behavioral Ecology and Evolution*, Van Nostrand Reinhold Company, New York, 1975, pp. 3–26.

2. Cox, C. B., Healey, I. N. & Moore, P. D., *Biogeography: an Ecological and Evolutionary Approach*, Blackwell Scientific Publications, London, 1973, pp. 109–28.

3. Dampier, W., in Masefield, J. (ed.), *The Voyages of Captain William Dampier,* E. Grant Williams, London, undated, vol.1, p. 452.

4. Dampier, W., *A Voyage to New Holland, in the Year 1699,* London, undated, vol. 3, pp. 86–106.

5. White, J., *Journal of a Voyageur to New South Wales with Sixty-five Plates of Non Descript Animals, Birds, Serpents, Curious Cones of Trees and Other Natural Productions,* London, 1790.

6. Iredale, T. & Whitely, G. P., "A Checklist of the Mammals Recorded for Australia", *Australian Museum memoir* 6, 1934.

7. Ride, W. D. L., "A List of Mammals Described for Australia Between 1933 and 1963 (Comprising Newly Proposed Names and Additions to the Australian Faunal List)", *Supplement to Australian Mammal Society Bulletin* 7, 1964.

8. Gould, J., *The Mammals of Australia*, Macmillan, Melbourne, 1983, pp. 402–5.

9. Horton, D. R., "Red Kangaroos: Last of the Australian Megafauna", in Martin, P. S. & Klein, G. R., *Quaternary Extinctions: a Prehistoric Revolution*, The University of Arizona Press, —— pp. 639–80.

10. McCoy, F., "On the Ancient and Recent Natural History of Victoria" (Essays for the Melbourne Exhibition), *Geological Survey of Victoria*, 1861.

11. McCoy, F., "The Dingo, Prodomus of the Palaeontology of Victoria", *Geological Survey of Victoria* 7, 1882, pp. 7–10.

12. Krefft, G., "Fossil Remains of Mammals, Birds and Reptiles from the Caves of Wellington Valley," *Universal Exhibition* 1, 1861.

13. Darwin, C., *The Variation of Animals and Plants under Domestication*, 2nd edn, John Murray, London, 1875.

14. Wallace, A. R., "The Australian Aborigines", in *Stanfords Compendium of Geography and Travel,* 1893.

15. Wood Jones, F., "The Status of the Dingo", *Transactions and Proceedings, Royal Society of South Australia,* 21 December 1921, pp. 254–63.

16. Mulvaney, D. J., *The Prehistory of Australia*, Penguin, Melbourne, 1975.

17. Gill, E., "Distribution of the Tasmanian Devil, the Tasmanian Wolf and the Dingo in S. E. Australia in Quaternary Time", *The Victorian Naturalist* 70, September 1953, pp. 86–90.

18. Mahoney, J., "The Taxonomic Status of *Dayurus affinus* McCoy [1865] (Dasyuridae) and *Hypsiprymnus trisulcatus* McCoy [1865] (Macropodidae), Two Marsupials from a Holocene Cave Deposit near Gisborne, Victoria", *Proceedings Royal Society of Victoria* 77, 1964, pp. 532–33.

19. Gill, E. & Sinnott, P. J., "Age of Canine Teeth Associated with Giant Extinct Marsupials at Wellington Caves, New South Wales", *Mankind* 9, 1973, pp. 125–6.

20. Thomson, A. R., in *Guide to Australian Remains Exhibited by the Trustees of the Australian Museum,* Australian Museum, Sydney, 1870.

21. Thomson, A. R., in "Exploration of the Caves and Rivers of New South Wales", *Votes and Proceedings,* Legislative Assembly of NSW, Session 1882.

22. Gill, E. D., "Antiquity and Changing Environment of the Australian Aborigines", in Pilling, A. R. & Waterman, R. A., *Diprotodon to Detribalization,* Michigan State University Press, 1970.

23. Gollan, K., "The Australian Dingo: in the Shadow of Man", in Archer, M. & Clayton, G. (eds), *Vertebrate Zoogeography and Evolution in Australia,* Hesperian Press, Carlisle, Western Australia, 1984, pp. 921–7.

24. Macintosh, N. W. G., "A 3000 Years Old Dingo from Shelter 6", *Proceedings Royal Society of Victoria* 77, pp. 498–507.

25. Flood, J., *Archeology of the Dreamtime,* Collins, Sydney, 1983, pp. 186–99.

26. Archer, M., "The Status of Australian Dasyurids, Thylacinids, and Myrmecobiids", in Archer, M. & Clayton, G. (eds), *Vertebrate Zoogeography and Evolution in Australia,* Hesperian Press, Carlisle, Western Australia, 1983, pp. 1015–21.

27. Hope, J., "The Australian quaternary", in Archer, M. & Clayton, G. (eds), ibid., pp. 69–81.

28. Miklouho-Maclay, N. de, "On the Circumvolutions of the Cerebrum of *Canis dingo*", *Poceedings Linnaen Society of New South Wales,* 6, 3, 1881, pp. 624–7.

29. Gollan, K., Prehistoric Dingo, Ph.D. thesis, Australian National University, Canberra, 1982.

30. Jennings, J. N., "Some Attributes of Torres Strait", in Walker, D. (ed), *Bridge and Barrier: the Natural and Cultural History of Torres Strait,* Research School of Pacific Studies, Australian National University, Canberra, Publication BG/3, 1972, pp. 29–38.

31. Rolls, E., *They All Ran Wild,* Angus & Robertson, Sydney, 1969.

32. Bokonyi, S., "Vlasac: an Early Site of Dog Domestication", in Clason, A. T. (ed), *Archeozoological Studies,* North Holland / American Elsevier, 1975, pp. 167–78.

33. Epstein, H., *The Origin of the Domestic Animals of Africa* 1, Africana Publishing Corporation, 1971.

34. Clutton-Brock, J., "Dog", in Mason, I. L. (ed), *Evolution of Domesticated Animals,* Longman, London, 1984, pp. 198–211.

35. Corbett, L. K., "Morphological Comparisons of Australian and Thai Dingoes: a Reappraisal of Dingo Status, Distribution and Ancestry", *Proceedings Ecological Society of Australia* 13, 1985, pp. 277–91.

36. Gollan, K., "Prehistoric Dogs in Australia: an Indian Origin?" *Proceedings 10th ICAES Conference, Poona,* Oxford University Press, 1979.

37. Bellwood, P., *Prehistory of the Indo-Malaysian Archipelago,* Academic Press, Sydney, 1985.

CHAPTER THREE

1. Manwell, C. & Baker, A. C. M., "Domestication of the Dog: Hunter, Food, Bed-warmer, or Emotional Object?", *Z. Tierzuchtg. Zuchtgsbiol.* 101, 1984, pp. 241–56.

2. Meggit, M. J., "The Association Between Australian Aborigines and Dingoes", *Man, Culture, and Animals in Human Ecological Adjustments* Publication 78, American Association for the Advancement of Science, Washington, D.C., 1965, pp. 7–26.

3. Hayden, B., "Dingoes: Pets or Producers?" *Mankind* 10, 1975, pp. 11–15.

4. Giles, E., *Australia Twice Traversed* Vol. 1, Doubleday, Australia, 1986.

5. Basedow, H., *The Australian Aboriginal*, F. W. Preece, Adelaide, 1925.

6. Hamilton, A., "Aboriginal Man's Best Friend?", *Mankind* 8, 1972, pp. 287–95.

7. Kolig, E., "Aboriginal Man's Best Foe?", Notes and Comment, *Mankind* 9, 1973, pp. 122–3.

8. Kolig, E., "Aboriginal Dogmatics": Canines in Theory, Myth and Dogma, *Bijdragen Totdetaal Land en Volkenkunde*, Vol. 134, No.1, 1978, pp. 84–115.

9. In *Every Saturday* 9 October 1906. (Newspaper clipping held in Mitchell Library, Sydney.)

10. Bueler, L., *Wild Dogs of the World*, Constable, London, 1974, pp. 99–107.

11. Gollan, K., Prehistoric Dingo, Ph.D thesis, Australian National University, Canberra, 1982.

12. Tindale, N. B., *Aboriginal Tribes of Australia*, Australian National University Press, Canberra, 1974.

13. Krefft, G., Esq., "On the Vertebrated Animals of the Lower Murray and Darling, their Habits, Economy, and Geographical Distribution", *Transactions of the Philosophical Society of New South Wales 1862–1865*, 1866, pp. 2–3.

14. Durack, M., *Sons in the Saddle*, Constable, London, 1983, p. 77.

15. Meggit, M., "Djanbar among the Walbiri, Central Australia", *Anthropos* 50, 1955, pp. 375–403.

16. Thompson, D. F., "Yellow Dog Dingo", *Walkabout,* 1 May 1955, pp. 16–18.

17. Harney, W. E., "The dingo", *Walkabout*, 1 July 1951, pp. 36–7.

18. Clarke, G., "Australian Stone Age", *Liber Iosepho Kostrzewski*, 1968, pp. 17–18.

19. Ryan, J. S., "Plotting an Isogloss — the Location and Types of Aboriginal names for Native Dog in New South Wales", *Oceania* 35, 1964, pp. 111–23.

20. Fowell, N., "The *Sirius* Letters", *Sydney Morning Herald*, 29 July 1987, p. 6.

21. Trezise, P., "Shadow of the Dingo", *Habitat* 5, 1978, pp. 25–6.

22. Jones, R., "Tasmanian Aborigines and Dogs", *Mankind* 7, 1970, pp. 256–71.

23. White, I. M., "Hunting Dogs at Yalata", *Mankind* 8, 1972, pp. 201–5.

CHAPTER FOUR

1. Del Prado, D., "Relation of Torres' Voyages through the Strait 1606", in Stevens, N. H., *New Light on the Discovery of Australia*, Hakluyt Society.

2. Heeres, J. E., *The Part Borne by the Dutch in the Discovery of Australia 1606–1765*, Leiden, Brill, 1899.

3. Robert, W. C. H., *The Explorations, 1696–1697 of Australia by Willem De Vlamingh*, Philo Press, Amsterdam, 1972.

4. Commodore Byron, Captains Wallis, Carteret & Cook, *New Discoveries Concerning the World and its Inhabitants*, J. Johnson, London, 1788.

5. Worgan, G. B., *Journal of a First Fleet Surgeon*, Library Council of New South Wales and Library of Australian History, Sydney, 1978.

6. Phillip, A., *The Voyage of Governor Phillip to Botany Bay; with an Account of the Establishment of the Colonies of Port Jackson and Norfolk Island; Compiled from Authentic Papers, which have been Obtained from the Several Departments, to which are added the Journals of Lieuts Shortland, Watt, Ball, and Capt. Marshall; with an Account of their discoveries*, London, 1798.

7. White, J., *Journal of a Voyageur to New South Wales with Sixty-five Plates of Non descript Animals, Birds, Serpents, Curious Cones of Trees and Other Natural Productions*, London, 1790.

8. Rolls, E., *They All Ran Wild*, Angus & Robertson, Sydney, 1969.

9. Bennett, E. T., *The Gardens and Menagerie of the Zoological Society Delineated. Quadrupeds Vol.1*, Chiswick, 1830.

10. Garran, J. C., and White, L., *Merinos, Myths and Macarthurs*, Australian National University Press, Canberra, 1985.

11. Barton, G. B., *History of New South Wales from the Records Vol. 1: Governor Phillip 1783–1789*, Government Printer, Sydney, 1889. Facsimile reprint by Hale and Iremonger, Sydney, 1980, p. 551.

12. Kaleski, R., *Australian Barkers and Biters*, Bookstall Series, 1914.

13. Kiddle, M., *Men of Yesterday: a Social History of the Western District of Victoria, 1834–1890*, Melbourne University Press, Melbourne, 1980.

14. Christie, M. F., *Aborigines in Colonial Victoria 1835–86*, Sydney University Press, Sydney, 1979.

15. Boldrewood, R., *Old Melbourne Memories*, Macmillan, London, 1896.

16. Jeans, D. N., *An Historical Geography of New South Wales to 1901*, Reed Education, Sydney, 1982.

17. Forster, A., *South Australia*, Sampson, Low, Son and Marston, London, 1866.

18. Krefft, G., *The Mammals of Australia*, Lansdowne, Melbourne, 1979.

19. Finch-Hatton, H., *Advance Australia: an Account of Eight Years' Work, Wandering, and Amusement in Queensland, New South Wales and Victoria*, Allen, London, 1885.

20. Aflalo, F. G., *A Sketch of the Natural History of Australia: With Some Notes on Sport*, Macmillan, London, 1896.

21. Beilby, W., *The Dog in Australia*, George Robertson & Co., 1897.

22. Kennel Control Council, Victoria, *Dogs of Australia*, Humphrey & Formula Press, Melbourne, 1974.

23. Dalby Davison, F., *Dusty*, Angus & Robertson, Sydney, 1983.

24. *An Act for Abating the Nuisance Occasioned by the Great Number of Dogs which are Loose in the Streets of the Towns of Sydney Parramatta Liverpool and Windsor in the Colony of New South Wales*, 14 April 1830, Public Statutes of New South Wales, 5 Geo.IV to 8 Will. IV, 1824–1837.

25. *An Act for Abating the Nuisance Occasioned by Dogs in the Streets of Certain Towns and on Highways in New South Wales*, 25 August 1835, Public Statutes of New South Wales, 5 Geo. IV to 8 Will. IV, 1824–1837.

26. *An Act to Facilitate and Encourage the Destruction of Native Dogs*, 28 December 1852, Public Statutes of New South Wales, 16 Vict. to 25 Vict., 1852–1862.

27. *An Act to Amend and Extend the Act Commonly Known as the "Dog Act"*, 22 July 1875, Public Library of New South Wales, 38 Vict. to 42 Vict., 1875–1879.

28. *An Act to Amend the Act Sixteenth Victoria Forty-four Known as the "Native Dogs Destruction Act"*, 11 August 1875, Statutes of New South Wales (Public and Private), Public Library of New South Wales, 38 Vict. to 42 Vict., 1875–1879.

29. *An Act to Consolidate the Acts for the Protection of Pastures and Live Stock from the Depredations of Noxious Animals*, 27 July 1898.

30. Kipling, Rudyard, "The Sing Song of Old Man Kangaroo", in *Just So Stories for Little Children*, Charles Scribner's Sons, New York, 1910.

31. Twain, Mark, in Maloney, E. W. (ed), *The Literary Dog*, Berkley Windover Books, New York, 1978.

32. Williams, Max, *Dingo: My Life on the Run*, Fontana/Collins, Melbourne, 1980.

33. Hewett, D., *The Man from Mukinupin*, Currency Press, Sydney, 1979.

34. Frail, R., "The Howl as a Weapon of Debate", *Sydney Morning Herald*, 12 April 1986, p.3.

35. *Dingo*, Stereo Fm Pty Ltd, Sydney, 1983.

36. Shepherd, N. C., "Predation of Red Kangaroos, *Macropus rufus*, by the Dingo, *Canis familiaris dingo* (Blumenbach), in North-western New South Wales", *Australian Wildlife Research* 8, 1981, pp. 255–62.

CHAPTER FIVE

1. Strahan, R. (ed), *Complete Book of Australian Mammals*, Angus & Robertson, Sydney, 1983, p. 483.

2. Corbett, L. K., Contributions to the Biology of Dingoes (Carnivora: Canidae) in Victoria, Master of Science Thesis, Department of Zoology, Monash University, Melbourne, 1974.

3. Green, B. & Catling, P., "The Biology of the Dingo", in Messel, H. & Butler, S. T. (eds), *Australian Animals and their Environment*, Shakespeare Head Press, Sydney, 1977, pp. 51–60.

4. Newsome, A. E., Corbett, L. K., Best, L. W. & Green, B., "The Dingo", *Australian Meat Research Council Review* 14, 1973, pp. 1–11.

5. Newsome, A. E. & Corbett, L. K., "The Identity of the Dingo 111. The Incidence of Dingoes, Dogs and Hybrids and their Coat Colours in Remote and Settled Regions of Australia", *Australian Journal of Zoology* 33, 1985, pp. 363–75.

6. Catling, P. C., CSIRO Division of Wildlife and Rangelands Research, personal communication to the author, 1983.

7. Mitchell, J., Merrell, P. & Allen, L., *Vertebrate Pests of Queensland*, Stock Routes and Rural Lands Protection Board, Department of Lands, Queensland, 1982.

8. Macintosh, N. W. G., "The Origin of the Dingo", in Fox, M. M. (ed), *The Wild Canids*, Van Nostrand Reinhold, New York, 1975, pp. 87–106.

9. Barker, B. C. W. & Macintosh, A., "The Dingo: a Review", *Anthropology in Oceania*, XIV, 1, April 1979, pp. 27–53.

10. Clutton-Brock, J., "Dog", in Mason, I. L. (ed), *Evolution of Domesticated Animals*, Longman, 1984, pp. 198–211.

11. Shield, J., "Acclimation and Energy Metabolism of the Dingo, *Canis dingo* and the Coyote, *Canis latrans*", *London Journal of Zoology* 168, 1972, pp. 483–501.

12. Gollan, K., Prehistoric Dingo, Phd. thesis, Australian National University, Canberra, 1982.

13. Thomson, P. C., Agriculture Protection Board Western Australia, personal communication to the author, 1987.

14. Catling, P. C., "Seasonal Variation in Plasma Testosterone and the Testes in Captive Male Dingoes, *Canis familiaris dingo*", *Australian Journal of Zoology* 27,1979, pp. 939–44.

15. Corbett, L. & Newsome, A., "Dingo Society and its Maintenance: a Preliminary Analysis", in Fox, M. W. (ed), *The Wild Candis*, Van Nostrand Reinhold, New York, 1975, pp. 369–79.

16. Robertshaw, J., National Parks and Wildlife Service of New South Wales, personal communication to the author, 1987.

17. Harden, B., "A Look at the Dingo", *Australian Natural History* 20, 6, 1981, pp. 191–4.

CHAPTER SIX

1. Corbett, L. K., Contributions to the biology of dingoes (*Carnivora:* Canidae) in Victoria, Master of Science Thesis, Department of Zoology, Monash University, Melbourne, 1974.

2. Newsome, A. E., Corbett, L. K., Catling, P. C. & Burt, R. J., "The Stomach Contents of Trapped Dingoes and the Catching of Non-target Wildlife in Dingo Traps in South-eastern Australia", *Australian Wildlife Research* 10, 1983, pp. 477–86.

3. Corbett, L., "Dingo Diet in Relation to Prey Availability in Arid, Sub-monsoonal and Tropical Habitats of the Northern Territory", paper delivered to Australian Vertebrate Pest Control Conference, Dubbo, New South Wales, July 1983.

4. Robertshaw, J., The analysis of Dingo (*Canis familiaris dingo* Blumenbach) Scats from a New England Escarpment region of North-eastern New South Wales, Hons. Thesis, University of New England, Armidale, November 1976.

5. Robertshaw, J. R. & Harden, R. H., "Ecology of the Dingo in North-eastern New South Wales II. Diet", *Australian Wildlife Research* 12, 1985, pp. 39–50.

6. Robertshaw, J. D. & Harden, R. H., "Ecology of the Dingo in North-eastern New South Wales III. Analysis of Macropod Bone Fragments in Dingo Scats", *Australian Wildlife Research* (in press).

7. Robertshaw, J. D., & Harden, R. H., "Ecology of the Dingo in North-eastern New South Wales IV. Prey Selection by Dingoes and its Effects on the Major Prey Species, the Swamp Wallaby *Wallabia bicolor* (Desmarest)", *Australian Wildlife Research* 13, 1986, pp. 141–63.

8. Newsome, A. E. & Catling, P. C., "The Feeding Ecology of the Dingo II. Dietary and Numerical Relationships with Fluctuating Prey Populations in South-eastern Australia", *Australian Journal of Ecology* 8, 1983, pp. 345–66.

9. Triggs, B., Brunner, H. & Cullen, J. M., "The Food of Fox, Dog and Cat in Croajingolong National Park, South-eastern Victoria", *Australian Wildlife Research* 11, 1984, pp. 491–9.

10. Whitehouse, S. J. O., "The Diet of the Dingo in Western Australia", *Australian Wildlife Research* 4, 1977, pp. 145–50.

11. Green, B. & Catling, P., "The Biology of the Dingo" in Messel, H. & Butler, S. T. (eds), *Australian Animals and their Environment*, Shakespeare Head Press, Sydney, 1977, pp. 51–60.

12. Zimen, E., *The Wolf: His Place in the Natural World*, Souvenir Press, London, 1981.

13. Newsome, A. E., "An Ecological Comparison of the Two Arid Zone Kangaroos of Australia, and their Anomolous Prosperity since the Introduction of Ruminant Stock to their Environment", *The Quarterly Review of Biology* 50, 1975, pp. 389–424.

14. Newsome, A. E. & Corbett, L. K., "Outbreaks of Rodents in Semi-arid and Arid Australia: Causes, Preventions, and Evolutionay Considerations", in Prakash, I. & Ghosh, P. K. (eds), *Rodents in Desert Environments*, Junk, The Hague, 1975, pp. 117 et seq.

15. McBride, M. P., "Kangaroo Harvesting and Conservation", in *Kangaroo Management: Proceedings Public Forum Adelaide, 28 June 1983*, Department of Environment and Planning, South Australia, 1983.

16. Best, L. M., "Kangaroo Management in South Australia", in *Kangaroo Management: Proceedings Public Forum Adelaide, 28 June 1983*, Department of Environment and Planning, South Australia, 1983.

17. Caughley, G., Grigg, G. C., Caughley, J. & Hill, J. E., "Does Dingo Predation Control the Densities of Kangaroos and Emus?", *Australian Wildlife Research* 7, 1980, pp. 1–2.

18. Woodall, P. F., "Distribution and Population Dynamics of Dingoes (*Canis familiaris*) and Feral Pigs (*Sus scrofa*) in Queensland, 1945–1976", *Journal of Applied Ecology* 20, 1983, pp. 85–95.

19. Shepherd, N. C., "Predation of Red Kangaroos, *Macropus rufus*, by the Dingo, *Canis familiaris dingo* (Blumenbach), in North-western New South Wales", *Australian Wildlife Research* 8, 1981, pp. 225–62.

20. Oliver, A. J., *Dingo Research*, Agriculture Protection Board of Western Australia, April 1980.

21. Thomson, P. C., "Dingoes and Sheep in Pastoral Areas", *Journal of Agriculture — Western Australia* 25, 1, 1984, pp. 27–31.

CHAPTER SEVEN

1. Fox, M. W., "Evolution of Social Behaviour in Canids", in Fox, M. W. (ed), *The Wild Canids: their Systematics, Behavioural Ecology and Evolution*, Van Nostrand Reinhold, New York, 1975, pp. 429–60.

2. Harden, R. H., "The Ecology of the Dingo in North-eastern New South Wales 1. Movements and Home Range", *Australian Wildlife Research* 12, 1985, pp. 25–37.

3. Whitehouse, S., Dingo Movements in Rangeland Areas of Western Australia, Proceedings first International Rangelands Congress 1978, pp. 456–8.

4. Thomson, P. C.; Agriculture Protection Board of Western Australia, personal communication to the author, 1981 and 1987.

5. Mitchell, J., Merrell, P. & Allen, L., *Vertebrate Pests of Queensland*, Stock Routes and Rural Lands Protection Board, Department of Lands, Queensland, 1982.

6. Newsome, A. E., Corbett, L. K., Best, L. W. & Green, B., "The Dingo", *Australian Meat Research Council Review* 14, 1973, pp. 1–11.

7. Catling, P. C., CSIRO Division of Wildlife and Rangelands Research, personal communication to the author, 1981.

8. Thomson, P. C., "The Use of Buffer Zones in Dingo Control", *Western Australian Journal of Agriculture* 25, 1, 1984, pp. 32–3.

9. Whitehouse, S. J. O., "Movements of Dingoes in Western Australia", *Journal of Wildlife Management* 41, 3, 1977, pp. 575–6.

10. Bacon, J. S., *The Australian Dingo: the King of the Bush,* self published, undated, copy held in CSIRO Division of Wildlife and Rangelands Research, Canberra.

11. Major, B. V., *Dingo Control in Australia: a Review of Past Action and Future Possibilities*, Council for Scientific and Industrial Research, Report no. T.4., Melbourne, 1947.

12. Corbett, L. & Newsome, A., "Dingo Society and its Maintenance: a Preliminary Analysis", in Fox, M. W. (ed), *The Wild Canids: their Systematics, Behavioral Ecology and Evolution*, Van Nostrand Reinhold, New York, 1975, pp. 369–79.

13. Robertshaw, J., National Parks and Wildlife Service of New South Wales, personal communication to the author, 1987.

CHAPTER EIGHT

1. Etheridge, R., "The Warrigal or Dingo, Introduced or Indigenous?", *Mem. Geological Survey, N.S.W. Ethnol. Ser.* 2, 1916, pp. 44–54.

2. Mitchell, J., Merrell, P. & Allen, L., *Vertebrate Pests of Queensland*, Stock Routes and Rural Lands Protection Board, Department of Lands, Queensland, 1982.

3. Burley, J. R. W., Creeper, D. A. & Moulds, G. A., *Damage to Livestock Caused by Domestic Dogs in Adelaide's Urban Fringe*, Technical report no. 24, Department of Agriculture, South Australia, 1983.

4. Ordinance Officer, Bega Valley Shire Council, personal communication to the author, 1984.

5. Lunney, D. & Barker, J., "Mammals of the Coastal Forests near Bega, New South Wales 1. Survey", *Australian Zoologist* 23, 1986, pp. 19–28.

6. Corbett, L. K., Contributions to the Biology of Dingoes (Carnivora: Canidae) in Victoria, Master of Science thesis, Department of Zoology, Monash University, Melbourne, 1974.

7. Newsome, A. E. & Corbett, L. K., "The Identity of the Dingo III. The Incidence of Dingoes, Dogs, and Hybrids and their Coat Colours in Remote and Settled Regions of Australia", *Australian Journal of Zoology* 33, 1985, pp. 363–75.

8. Newsome, A. E. & Corbett, L., "The Identity of the Dingo II. Hybridization with Domestic Dogs in Captivity and in the Wild", *Australian Journal of Zoology* 30, 1982, pp. 369–74.

9. Cole, S. R., Baverstock, P. R. & Green, B., "Lack of Genetic Differentiation between Dogs and Dingoes at a Further 16 Loci", *Australian Journal of Experimental Biology and Medical Science* 55, 1977, pp. 229–32.

10. Macintosh, N. W. G., "The Origin of the Dingo", in Fox, M. W. (ed), *The Wild Canids*, Van Nostrand Reinhold, New York, 1975, pp. 87–106.

11. Barker, B. C. W. & Macintosh, A., "The Dingo: a Review", *Anthropology in Oceania* XIV, 1 April 1979, pp. 27–53.

12. Newsome, A. E., Corbett, L. K. & Carpenter, S., "The Identity of the Dingo I. Morphological Discriminants of Dingo and Dog Skulls", *Australian Journal of Zoology* 28, 1980, pp. 615–25.

13. Newsome, A. E., Corbett, L. K., Best, L. W. & Green, B., "The dingo", *Australian Meat Research Council Review* 14, 1973, pp. 1–11.

14. McIlroy, J. C., Cooper, R. J., Gifford, E. J., Green, B. F. & Newgrain, K. W., "The Effect on Wild Dogs, *Canis f. familiaris*, of 1080-Poisoning Campaigns in Kosciusko National Park, N.S.W.", *Australian Wildlife Research* 13, 4, 1986, pp. 535–44.

15. Lorenz, K., foreword in Fox, M. W. (ed), *The Wild Canids*, Van Nostrand Reinhold, New York, 1975.

CHAPTER NINE

1. Newsome, A. E. & Corbett, L. K., "The Dingo", *Australian Meat Research Council Review* 14, 1973, pp. 1–11.

2. Corbett, L. K., Contributions to the Biology of Dingoes (Carnivora: Canidae) in Victoria, Master of Science thesis, Department of Zoology, Monash University, Melbourne, 1974.

3. Sabine, M., Department of Veterinary Pathology, University of Sydney, personal communication to the author, 1986.

4. Dunsmore, J. D. & Burt R. J., "*Filaroides osleri* in Dingoes in South-eastern Australia", *Australian Veterinary Journal* 48, October 1972, pp. 548–51.

5. Kumaratilake, L. M. & Thompson, R. C. A., "Hydatidosis/Echinococcosis in Australia", *Helminthological Abstracts — series A: Animal and Human Helminthology* 51, 6, June 1982, Commonwealth Institute of Parasitology, pp. 233–51.

6. Thompson, R. C. A. & Kumaratilake, L. M., "Comparative Development of Australian Strains of *Echinococcus granulosus* in Dingoes (*Canis familiaris dingo*) and Domestic Dogs (*C. f. familiaris*), with Further Evidence for the Origin of the Australian Sylvatic Strain", *International Journal for Parasitology* 15, 5, 1985, pp. 535–42.

7. Harvey Johnson, T., "The Endoparasites of the Dingo, *Canis dingo*, Blum", *Proceedings Royal Society of Queensland XXVII*, 1,1915, pp. 96–100.

8. Durie, P. H. & Riek, R. F., "The Role of the Dingo and Wallaby in the Infestation of Cattle with Hydatids (*Echinococcus granulosis (Batsch. 1786) Rudolph, 1805*) in Queensland", *Australian Veterinary Journal*, October 1952, pp. 249–54.

9. Coman, B. J., "A Sylvatic Cycle for the Hydatid Tapeworm (*Echinococcus granulosis*) in Remote Areas of Eastern Victoria", *Australian Veterinary Journal* 48, October 1972, pp. 552–3.

10. Coman, B. J., "Helminth Parasites of the Dingo and Feral Dog in Victoria with Some Notes on the Diet of the Host", *Australian Veterinary Journal* 48, August 1972, pp. 456–61.

11. Kumaratilake, L. M. & Thompson, R. C. A., "Morphological Characterisation of Australian strains of *Echinococcus granulosis*", *International Journal of Parasitology* 14, 5, 1984, pp. 467–77.

12. Banks, D., "Bovine Hydatidosis", *Tropical Veterinary Medicine: Research and Graduate*

Studies Report, James Cook University of North Queensland, Townsville, 1983, pp. 19–20.

13. Baldcock, F. C., Thompson, R. C. A., Kumaratilake, L. M. & Shield, J., "*Echinococcus granulosis* in Farm Dogs and Dingoes in South-eastern Queensland", *Australian Veterinary Journal* 62, 10, October 1985, pp. 335–7.

14. Thompson, R. C. A., "Evidence that the Australian sylvatic strain of *Echinococcus granulosis* is infective to humans", *The Medical Journal of Australia* 146, 6 April 1987, pp. 396–7.

15. Herd, R. P. & Coman, B. J., "Transmission of *Echinococcus granulosis granulosis* from Kangaroos to Domestic Dogs", *Australian Veterinary Journal* 51, December 1975, p. 591.

16. *Wildlife and Exotic Diseases*, a joint working party report to the Vertebrate Pests Committee and Animal Health Committee of the Standing Committee of Agriculture, Department of Primary Industry, Canberra, May 1984.

17. Australian Bureau of Animal Health, *Report on Vertebrate Pests and Exotic Animal Diseases*, Department of Primary Industry, Canberra, June 1980.

18. World Health Organization Expert Committee on Rabies, *Seventh Report*, WHO Technical report series 709, Geneva, 1984.

19. Elsevior Publications, *Parasitology Today*, 3, 9, 1987, p. 261.

CHAPTER TEN

1. Rolls, E., *They All Ran Wild*, Angus & Robertson, Sydney, 1984.

2. Spencer, H. C., A History of the Border Fences with South Australia and Queensland, Western Lands Commissioner, 1957–58, in an unpublished paper, 1962.

3. Gerritsen, J., *Tibooburra: Corner Country*, Tibooburra Press, Tibooburra, 1981.

4. Condon, R. W., *Report of the Chairman of the Wild Dog Destruction Board: For the Year Ended 31st December, 1974*, Government Printer, New South Wales, 1976.

5. Grant, D., History of Barrier Fences and Recent Government Decisions, Chairman. Rural Lands and Stock Routes Protection Board, Queensland, unpublished paper, 1985.

6. Royal Commission Appointed to Inquire into Certain Matters Relating to Rabbit, Dingo, and Stock Route Administration, *Report*, Government Printer, Queensland, 1930.

7. Collection of correspondence held by Gerritsen, J., formerly Ranger in Charge, Sturt National Park.

8. Wright, S., *The Way of the Dingo*, Angus & Robertson, Sydney, 1968.

9. Wilkinson, F., "In the Track of the Dingo: Along the Vermin-proof Fence", *The Observer*, 6 June 1925, p. 18.

10. Madden, J. F., "First Appointment", *Veterinary Inspector* 1967, pp. 68–74.

11. Kennewell, M., in family history related to Gerritson, J., formerly Ranger in Charge, Sturt National Park.

12. Pastoralists Association of West Darling, *Circular to Landholders Adjoining Border Fences*, 7 November 1955.

13. Korn, T., Special Livestock Officer (Vertebrate Pests), Department of Agriculture New South Wales, personal communication to the author, 1986.

14. NSW Parliament 1983–84, *Second Report of the Joint Select Committee of the Legislative Council and the Legislative Assembly to Inquire into the Western Division of New South Wales (First Term of Reference)*, Government Printer, 1984.

15. NSW Parliament 1983–84, *Third Report of the Joint Select Committee of the Legislative Council and the Legislative Assembly to Inquire into the Western Division of New South Wales (Second Term of Reference with the Proceedings of the Committee)*, Government Printer, 1984.

16. Caughley, G., Grigg, G. C., Caughley, J. & Hill, J. E., "Does Dingo Predation Control the Densities of Kangaroos and Emus?", *Australian Wildlife Research* 7, 1980, pp. 1–12.

CHAPTER ELEVEN

1. *Annual Report on the Operations of the Stock Routes and Rural Lands Protection Acts, 1944 to 1951 and the Barrier Fences Act of 1954 for the year 1958–59*, Government Printer, Queensland, 1959.

2. Royal Commission Appointed to Inquire into Certain Matters Relating to Rabbit, Dingo, and Stock Route Administration, *Report*, Government Printer, Queensland, 1930.

3. Committee of Inquiry into Animal and Vegetable Pests, *Report*, Queensland, 1976.

4. Cameron, W., "The Menace of the Wild Dog", *Australian Shorthorn*, September 1957.

5. Capper, W., "Destruction and Control of Dingoes Along the Dingo Barrier Fence in Queensland", *Wool Technology and Sheep Breeding*, December 1959.

6. Stock Routes and Rural Lands Protection Board, *A Proposal for the Maintenance of the Dingo Barrier Fence in Southern Queensland*, Queensland, August 1981.

7. Roy. A., "3000 km Fence Can't Keep Dingoes out", *The Weekend Australian*, 28–29 September 1985, p.1.

CHAPTER TWELVE

1. Newland, N. P., *Vermin Control in South Australia*, Vermin Control Branch, Department of Lands, South Australia, 1971.

2. Everett, R. A., *The South Australian Dog Fence Scene*, South Australian Dog Fence Board, November 1983.

3. Dog Fence Board, Brief Prepared for Inspection of Dog Fence by the Hon. P. B. Arnold M.P. Minister for Lands: an Historical Review and Assessment of the S.A. Dog Fence, undated report.

4. Kelly, B. ("The Modest Farmer"), "Dogged by the Dingo Fence", *Bulletin*, 3 May, 1978, p. 124.

CHAPTER THIRTEEN

1. Thompson, P. C., "Dingoes and Sheep in Pastoral Areas", *Journal of Agriculture — Western Australia* 25, 1, 1984, pp. 27–31.

2. Wright, P. A. et al., *Dingoes in New England*, Community Development Pamphlet No. 7, Department of University Extension, University of New England, Armidale, 1963.

3. Fleming, P., Department of Agriculture New South Wales, Research & Advisory Station, Glen Innes, personal communication to the author, 1987.

4. Burgess, R., Secretary, Southern Tablelands Wild Dog Destruction Board, in a submission to the Minister for Agriculture, May 1983.

5. Hone, J., Waithman, J., Robards, G. E. & Saunders, G. R., "Impact of Wild Mammals and Birds on Agriculture in New South Wales", *Journal of the Australian Institute of Agricultural Science*, 1981, pp. 191–9.

6. Begg, R. & Davey, G., *Victorian Wild Dog Control Plan*, Conservation Forests and Lands, Victoria, Verminpac 12 April 1987, p. 10.

7. Lankine, G. & Donaldson, L. E., "Animal Behaviour and Calf Mortality in a North Queensland Breeding Herd", *Proceedings Australian Society of Animal Production* 7, 1968, pp. 138–43.

8. Donohue, J. T., *A Proposal for the Future Maintenance of the Dingo Barrier Fence in Southern Queensland*, Stock Routes and Rural Lands Protection Board, 1981.

9. Saunders, G., Korn, T. & Giles, J., *A Review of Wild Dog Control in Eastern New South Wales*, Department of Agriculture, New South Wales, 1986.

CHAPTER FOURTEEN

1. Harden, R. H., A Review of the Biology and Management of the Dingo in Australia, unpublished report, National Parks and Wildlife Service of New South Wales, 1980.

2. Newsome, A. E., Corbett, L. K. & Stephens, D. R., *Assessment of an Aerial Baiting Campaign against Dingoes in Central Australia*, Division of Wildlife Research Technical Paper No. 24, CSIRO, 1972.

3. Best, L. W., Corbett, L. K., Stephens, D. R. & Newsome, A. E., *Baiting Trials for Dingoes in Central Australia, with Poison "1080", Encapsulated Strychnine and Strychnine Suspended in Methyl Cellulose*, Division of Wildlife Research Technical Paper No. 30, CSIRO, 1974.

4. Rolls, E., *They All Ran Wild*, Angus & Robertson, Sydney, 1984, p. 455.

5. McIlroy, J. C., "The Sensitivity of Australian Animals to 1080 Poison 11. Marsupial and Eutherian Carnivores", *Australian Wildlife Research* 8, 1981, pp. 385–99.

6. McIroy, J. C., "The Sensitivity of Australian Carnivorous Mammals to 1080 Poison", in Archer, M. (ed), *Carnivorous Marsupials*, Royal Zoological Society of New South Wales, Sydney, 1982, pp. 267–71.

7. Begg, R. & Davey, G., *Victorian Wild Dog Control Plan*, Conservation Forests and Lands, Victoria, Verminpac 12, 1987, p. 10.

8. Thomson, P. C., "The Effectiveness of Aerial Baiting for the Control of Dingoes in North-western Australia", *Australian Wildlife Research* 13, 1986, pp. 165–76.

9. Thomson, P. C., "The Use of Buffer Zones in Dingo Control", *Journal of Agriculture — Western Australia* 25, 1, 1984, pp. 32–3.

10. McIlory, J. C., Cooper, R. J., Gifford, Green, B. F. & Newgrain, K. W., "The Effect on Wild Dogs, *Canis f. familiaris*, of 1080-Poisoning Campaigns in Kosciusko National Park, N.S.W.", *Australian Wildlife Research* 13, 1986, pp. 535–44.

11. Brown, A., "Alternative Traps for Dog Control", *Newsletter*, South East Region Feral Animal Control Task Force, Cooma, NSW, Feb-March 1987, pp. 18–21.

12. Korn, T., Special Livestock Officer (Vertebrate Pests), Department of Agriculture New South Wales, personal communication to the author, 1987.

13. Allen, L., Stock Routes and Rural Lands Protection Board, Queensland, personal communication to the author, 1987.

14. Stain, N., "The Kangaroo as a Moral Consideration", in *Kangaroo Management*, (proceedings of a public forum, Adelaide June 28, 1983), National Parks and Wildlife Service of South Australia, 1983.

15. Newsome, A. E., Corbett, L. K., Catling, P. C. & Burt, R. J., "The Feeding Ecology of the Dingo 1. Stomach Contents from Trapping in South-eastern Australia, and the Non-target Wildlife Also Caught in Dingo Traps", *Australian Wildlife Research* 10, 1983, pp. 477–86.

16. Gustavson, C. R., Gustavson, J. C. & Halzer, G. A., "Thiabendazole Baded Taste Aversions in Dingoes (*Canis familiaris dingo*) and New Guinea Wild Dogs (*Canis familiaris hallstromi*)", *Applied Animal Ethology* 10, 1983, pp. 385–8.

17. Gustavson, C. R., Jowsey, J. R. & Milligan, D. N., "A 3-year Evaluation of Taste Aversion Coyote Control in Saskatchewan", *Journal of Rangeland Management* 35, 1, 1982, pp. 57–9.

18. Bourne, J. & Dorrance, M., "A Field Test of Lithium Chloride Aversion to Reduce Coyote Predation on Domestic Sheep", *Journal of Wildlife Management* 46, 1, 1982, pp. 235–9.

19. Burns, R. J., "Coyote Predation Aversion with Lithium Chloride: Management Implications and Comments", *Wildlife Society Bulletin* 11, 2, 1983, pp. 128–33.

20. Herbst, R. L., *Predator Damage in the West: a Study of Coyote Management Alternatives*, United States Fish and Wildlife Service, Department of Interior, 1978.

21. Coppinger, R., Lorenz, J., Glendinning, J. & Pinardi, P., "Attentiveness of Guarding Dogs for Reducing Predation on Domestic Sheep", *Journal of Rangeland Management* 36, 3, 1983, pp. 275–9.

22. Newsome, A. E., Corbett, L. K., Best, L. W. & Green, B., "The Dingo", *Australian Meat Research Council Review* 14, 1973, pp. 1–11.

23. Thomson, P. C., Agriculture Protection Board, Western Australia, personal communication to the author, 1987.

CHAPTER FIFTEEN

1. Chipp, D., "The Vanishing Dingo", *Habitat* 11, 1, 1983, p. 35.

2. Riley, G. A. & McBride, R. T., "A Survey of the Red Wolf (*Canis rufus*)", in Fox, M. W. (ed), *The Wild Canids*, Van Nostrand Reinhold, New York, 1975, pp. 263–77.

3. Shaw, J. H., "Some Contributions to the Ecology and Systematic Position of the Red Wolf: an Interim Report", in Fox, M. W., ibid, pp. 278–9.

4. Begg, R. & Davey, G., *Victorian Wild Dog Control Plan*, Conservation Forests and Lands, Victoria, Verminpac 12, 1987, p. 10.

Index

A

B

C

D

E

F

N

O

P

Q

R

Z